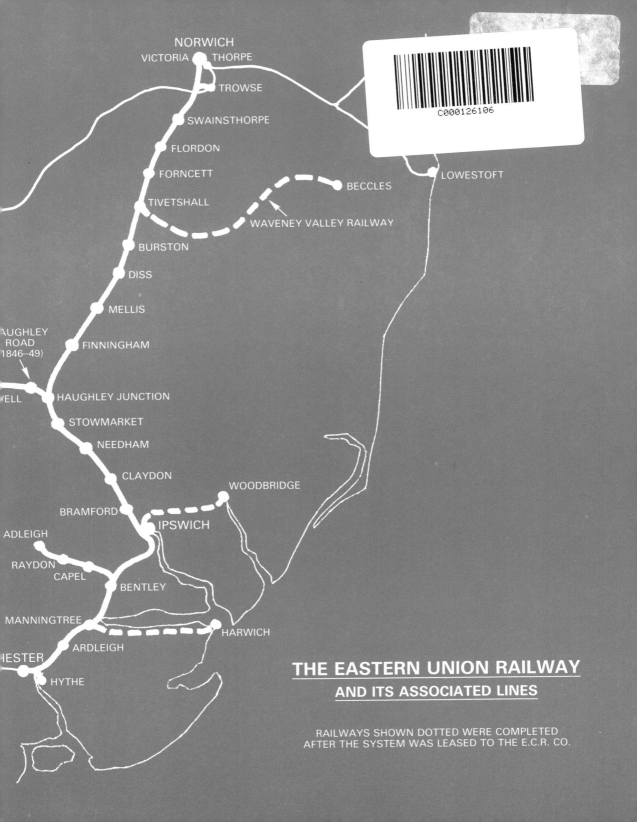

NORWICH
VICTORIA — THORPE

TROWSE

SWAINSTHORPE

FLORDON

FORNCETT

TIVETSHALL

BECCLES

WAVENEY VALLEY RAILWAY

LOWESTOFT

BURSTON

DISS

MELLIS

AUGHLEY
ROAD
(1846—49)

FINNINGHAM

WELL

HAUGHLEY JUNCTION

STOWMARKET

NEEDHAM

CLAYDON

WOODBRIDGE

BRAMFORD

IPSWICH

ADLEIGH

RAYDON

CAPEL

BENTLEY

MANNINGTREE

HARWICH

ARDLEIGH

HESTER

HYTHE

THE EASTERN UNION RAILWAY
AND ITS ASSOCIATED LINES

RAILWAYS SHOWN DOTTED WERE COMPLETED
AFTER THE SYSTEM WAS LEASED TO THE E.C.R. CO.

EAST ANGLIA'S

FIRST RAILWAYS

Overleaf: *Materials for the building of the Eastern Union were landed in 1844 at Cattawade, where the Stour was to be crossed by timber bridges. In 1904 these were replaced by iron structures, here being crossed by B12 No 61523 on an up passenger train about 1950.* H. N. James

East Anglia's
FIRST RAILWAYS

Peter Bruff and the Eastern Union Railway

HUGH MOFFAT

TERENCE DALTON LIMITED
LAVENHAM, SUFFOLK 1987

Published by
TERENCE DALTON LIMITED

ISBN 0 86138 038 X

Text photoset in 10/11 pt Baskerville

Printed in Great Britain at
The Lavenham Press Limited, Lavenham, Suffolk

Contents

Preface and Acknowledgements

BOOKS about "The Heroic Age" of Britain's railways — that is to say, the period before about 1850 — rarely seem to mention East Anglia. Its railways were not among the very first in the country, and they did not link major centres of population or production. Railway historians tend to dismiss the region as being flat and uninteresting, and therefore devoid of those major civil engineering works which are an essential part of early railway history.

I hope that this book will help to redress the balance. It is about one small East Anglian railway, the Eastern Union, which had an independent life of less than twenty years.

It had no great tunnels like Box or Woodhead, but it had the most sharply curved one at that time, driven through a little hill so wet that it reminded the engineer in charge of his time in Brunel's tunnel under the Thames. Its line crossed a swamp, not as extensive as Chat Moss but twice as deep.

It was probably the first railway in Britain to experiment with fish-plates for joining each rail to the next and to try a communication cord.

The area the railway served was predominantly agricultural, yet within it one company made parts of its permanent way and another built much of its rolling stock.

The book was originally intended to be my contribution towards a biography of the engineer, Peter Bruff, and although the narrative has since been extended in other directions he remains the principal personality.

Purists, particularly those from north of the Waveney, will no doubt complain that I have not dealt fully with the first railway in the region to carry public traffic, the Yarmouth and Norwich. This is true, but the Eastern Union was the first truly East Anglian "Inter City" line, linking the ancient capitals of the region, Norwich, Ipswich and Bury St Edmunds. The long and continuous involvement of the Cobbold family had no counterpart in Norfolk.

The Eastern Counties Railway only entered East Anglia by the back door, so to speak, and as we shall see, the local directors were quickly ousted from their places.

I have included some account of East Anglian railways which were never built, from the spurious Norfolk, Suffolk and Essex Rail-Road of the mid 1820s to those which featured in the "Railway Mania" of twenty years later. These, and references to characters as diverse as Captain Bligh and Willy Lott, I came upon by chance. I thought they were interesting, and I include them without apology.

In writing the book, I have been helped by a great many people. First of all, my thanks are due to the staffs of the public libraries at Norwich, Colchester, Bury St Edmunds, Woodbridge, and especially Ipswich — for the latter housed much of the material I used in the early days, before it was removed to the Ipswich branch of the Suffolk Record Office. I followed it there, and found much more besides.

I am grateful to the staffs of the county record offices of Suffolk, Norfolk and Essex; British Rail's Historical Records Department (in the days when it was in Porchester Road, W2); the Public Record Office, Kew; The House of Lords Record Office; the Science Museum, South Kensington; the National Railway Museum, York; and the Patent Office.

I wish to thank my former employers, Ipswich Borough Council, for allowing me to abstract details from leases of their land; the Institution of Civil Engineers, for permission to quote from their Minutes of Proceedings; and Mr W.A. Morris, the Institution's Archivist, for information about Robert Richardson.

The book would have lacked some details without the help of Mr W.M. Lewis, then Divisional Civil Engineer at Norwich, in allowing me to walk along the railway at Stowmarket and Playford; and of Mr A.J. Lickfold, of British Rail's London and Anglia Press Department.

I am grateful to ex-Chief Inspector Angus Andrews, of the Suffolk Constabulary, for information about the policeman George Cole; to Mr A.G. Dunford, of Ipswich, for details of the history of his office building and of Peter Bruff; to Mr A.B. Henwood, formerly District Civil Engineer at Ipswich, for details of the tunnel, and of tunnelling long before his time; to Mr Geoff Cutting, Station Manager at Bury St Edmunds, for resolving the rumour that there was an ancient Rule Book in the signalbox at Elmswell, and to Mrs E.W. Robinson, of Woolpit, for lending me this treasure, which had belonged to her late husband.

I am particularly grateful to Mr Fred Bridges, of Ipswich, Mr Alastair Robertson, of Bury St Edmunds, and Mr Jerzy Swieszkowski, of Chignall St James, who have all freely helped me from their own research. Nor must I forget Mr Geoff Cordy, of Felixstowe, for his help with the illustrations, especially in producing prints from my colour slides.

I have received much help and encouragement from fellow-members of the Ipswich and District Historical Transport Society, particularly from Mr Fred Rogers, who lent me his E.U.R. rail chairs to photograph; from Mr S.A. Strange, who invited me to a meeting of the Permanent Way Institute where I met many railway engineers (whose names, alas, I have forgotten), and from Mr Alan Woodard, who first called my attention to the great borrow pit at Stowmarket.

I knocked on the doors of complete strangers; and Mr and Mrs A. Carter, of Tharston, allowed me to photograph the plaque above their door, while Mrs L. Cooper, of Thurston, let me photograph Jannings' Bridge from her property. I thank them all.

Others who have helped me come to mind (or perhaps not), but space is short. I am grateful to everyone.

Lastly, but certainly not least, I owe a special debt to Hervey Benham (who started me off on all this), Frank Hussey, Ken Leighton, Bob Malster (now with Terence Dalton), Peter Northeast, Bob Pratt and the late Harry Wilton. Space does not permit details of what each has done to help me over many years, but between them they have provided specialised knowledge in many fields; supplied me with many vital details, either from their own research or carefully abstracted from their own libraries; opened doors for me which might otherwise have remained closed; given me material and lent me books — even bound files of old newspapers. They have all given me hours of stimulating conversation.

I alone am responsible for the errors which this book probably contains. I hope I have avoided some of the more obvious ones by confining myself to a limited period and to a region where I have always lived.

Hugh Moffat,
Clopton,
Suffolk.

March, 1986.

Note on Sources

Wherever possible I have used contemporary, if not original, sources.

Most of the material was culled from files of old local newspapers, particularly those of the *Ipswich Journal*. The railway company was always based in the town; the paper supported it from its conception, and closely followed its fortunes. Coverage of the general meetings usually included the directors' reports verbatim, and often capital accounts and the engineer's reports as well. As journalists probably often attended these meetings, the words of individual shareholders were sometimes recorded, which of course they were not in the company's own minutes.

Similarly, the Colchester *Essex Standard* gave excellent coverage to the general meetings of the Eastern Counties Railway

Company, certainly in days when its readers must have been wondering when the railway would reach them.

The *Ipswich Journal* frequently copied news from the papers at Bury St Edmunds, Colchester and Norwich, so that recourse to them has often only been necessary for material of purely local relevance. Fortunately these other papers, and the Ipswich *Suffolk Chronicle*, were often more interested in outdoor events.

The newspapers contain the railway companies' official notices and advertisements, besides a wealth of other material, all recorded and printed with a precision reflecting the slower pace of life at that time.

For the more intimate details of the railway companies' affairs, I have used the original minute books of directors' meetings, which are now in the Public Record Office, under reference RAIL 186, RAIL 187 and RAIL 326, for the E.C.R., E.U.R. and I.&B.R. respectively.

The amazing correspondence between the swindler John Wilks and the Bury solicitor, Henry Borton, is among the latter's papers in the Ipswich branch of the Suffolk Record Office, together with the Parliamentary plans of Suffolk railways, whether subsequently built or not. Similar collections of plans are held in other county record offices. Bruff's letter book is also in the Record Office at Ipswich.

Other original sources are referred to in the text. It has not been practicable to give many references, but the type of source will usually be obvious.

The details of the steamer *Railway* which appear in Appendix six were taken from *Railway and Other Steamers,* by Duckworth and Langmuir (1968). All details of the other ships are from the official Customs House Register for the Port of Ipswich, now in the Ipswich branch of the Suffolk Record Office.

In the course of my research, it was not long before I became aware of discrepancies between contemporary accounts (and what I found in the field) and more recently published works. The booklet produced by the L.N.E.R. was possibly written in haste to meet a centenary deadline, but it contains a number of statements which I can only regard as fiction. Its sins were compounded in a well-known book on the Great Eastern Railway, and consequently many later authors have been misled.

The scale plans on pages 64, 132 and 134 have been re-drawn by the author from originals in the Ipswich Branch of the Suffolk Record Office, by kind permission of the County Archivist, Miss Amanda Arrowsmith.

The line diagrams of locomotives have been reproduced from *The Locomotive Magazine*: the 0-4-0 goods engine appeared in vol VI (1901), and the others in vol XI (1905). The engravings of earthworks, etc, have been reproduced from *Our Iron Roads,* by F. S. Williams, published in 1852.

The Rail-Road Bubble 1

THE STORY of railways in East Anglia probably began on Christmas Eve, 1824, when a traveller who had just arrived from London called at the office of Messrs Borton and Son, a well-known firm of solicitors in Bury St Edmunds. Finding none of the principals in, he went away to the *Bell Inn* in the town and wrote a letter:

> Mr Smith presents his respectful compliments to Mr Borton, is sorry he is so unfortunate as to find Mr. B. from home — but as Mr Smith's visit to Bury is *expressly* to see Mr Borton in the part of Mr Wilks, perhaps Mr B. will be kind enough to allow Mr Smith an interview some time in the course of tomorrow . . .

Whether or not Mr Borton consented to allow this intrusion into his celebration of Christmas I do not know, but certainly within a day or two he was reading a tersely-written letter which Smith had brought with him:

> My Dear Sir,
>   Have the goodness to attend very seriously to the business about which my factotum Mr Smith attends upon you and be pleased to give it your favourable consideration. I hope that by the arrangement you will be benefitted. 1st, in the way of shares & 2nd in the way of being Solicitor for Suffolk & 3rd in the way of benefitting your county and town.
>
> I am, my dear Sir,
Yours faithfully,
John Wilks Jnr.

"The business" was really the first railway ever proposed for East Anglia; turning from the letter, Mr Borton read the prospectus of the Norfolk and Suffolk Rail-Road Company. The proposed rail-road was to run from London to Norwich by way of Chelmsford, Colchester and Ipswich. From Colchester there was to be a branch to Harwich, and another was to link Bury St Edmunds to Ipswich. At Norwich the main line would divide, one branch terminating at Yarmouth and the other at King's Lynn. The total estimated cost was £980,000 and the proposed capital of the company was to be £1,000,000, for which subscriptions were invited in £100 shares.

The prospectus went on to paint a glowing picture of the trade between the metropolis and the towns along the proposed route; there would be considerable passenger traffic, and due to the general flatness of the region the cost of construction would not be great. There were to be twelve London directors and a similar number from the provinces, but none was named. Applications "for the remaining Shares" were to be sent to a certain firm of City

Opposite page: *The site of the original Eastern Union station at Ipswich, seen from above the mouth of the tunnel constructed for the Ipswich and Bury St Edmunds Railway in 1845–46.*   H. N. James

An advertisement inserted in East Anglian newspapers on behalf of the Norfolk and Suffolk Rail-Road.

bankers, or to Messrs Wilks and Verbeke, Solicitors, of 36, New Broad Street, London — of which practice John Wilks, junior, was a partner.

If Mr Borton had any reservations about the project, they were dispelled when his visitor showed him a prospectus of the Kentish Railway Company, for which Wilks and Verbeke were also acting as solicitors. Here there was a goodly string of impressive names on the provisional committee, with a number of titles and Members of Parliament among them, and the engineer was none other than Thomas Telford.

On 28th December, Wilks wrote to Smith:

Give my best regards to Mr Borton and tell him that I am very much obliged to him for his very kind and obliging letter and that I anticipate much advantage from his co-operation . . .

He continued with a stream of instructions for Smith to get Borton to advertise the scheme, both in the press and among his friends, to appoint bankers to receive deposits,

and if you want Prospectuses and forms of Tenders employ Mr Borton's printer at Bury to print as you want so as to make the measure popular with the Townspeople.

Above all, he was to

Request Mr Borton to procure the names and addresses of six Gentlemen who will be Directors for Suffolk, and forward their names to me — Each Director's qualification is only ten Shares.

Smith was told to stay on in Bury to assist Borton, which he did until New Year's Day, so impressing the Bury solicitor that upon his return to London he was able to confer with Wilks while dining off a fine hare which Borton had sent as a present.

The Bury newspapers at first greeted the proposed line with cautious optimism but, on 5th January, the *Bury and Norwich Post* published a letter from "A Norfolk Man" which highlighted the defect of the whole scheme, namely, that all the towns lying on the route already had sea and river communications with London and with each other. What was wanted in East Anglia were better transport facilities between the ports and the inland districts; but no railway, even so, could succeed unless there was a heavy mineral traffic. There was editorial comment in the same vein. Meetings should have been convened in the various towns to explain and discuss the scheme — "The call for 'tenders and deposits' might then have been made with propriety . . ."

Wilks was furious and wrote at once to Borton:

The Bury paper you sent is confoundedly stupid. Can you not silence the fellow for a fortnight till he sees the thing complete . . . Pray push about and get all the shares taken and all the money you can, also have the goodness to get a Board of Directors for Suffolk; say six, as soon as possible. All is going on well at Norfolk and in London.

Borton, however, could only reply that he was finding a general suspicion and reluctance to invest, due partly to lack of information about the promoters. He wrote:

Ours is one of the most difficult counties to manage — and as to our Borough, I have found in some cases personal rudeness upon the subject. In fact, I believe that the most determined opposition is already contemplated by the county in general.

Wilks, however, was not to be deterred; he was determined to have some Suffolk names to bandy about, and then, perhaps, the money would come in. He replied:

As there is great difficulty respecting Directors for Suffolk, you will be so good as to send round and obtain respectable names of persons who will act as Honorary Vice-Presidents and who need not, unless they like, become Shareholders . . .

But only a handful of shares was taken up, and Borton could find no-one who would consent to allow even his name to be used in connection with the scheme.

A revised prospectus was issued on 19th January, with "Essex" included in the company's title and an impressive list of directors, including six from Norfolk and one each from Suffolk and Essex. A meeting in London resolved to pursue the project and that the engineer should proceed with the survey of the route. This engineer was Henry Palmer, who had taken a leading part in the formation of the Institution of Civil Engineers and was later to make a name for himself as a dock engineer.[1]

In November, 1825, the Rail-Road Company advertised that they intended to introduce a Bill into Parliament for a truncated scheme, a "Railway or Tramroad" from Whitechapel to Ipswich only. The notice was signed by Henry Verbeke, Wilks' partner.

Henry Palmer's proposed route for the Norfolk, Suffolk and Essex Rail-Road compared with the E.C.R. and E.U.R. lines actually built between 1837 and 1846.

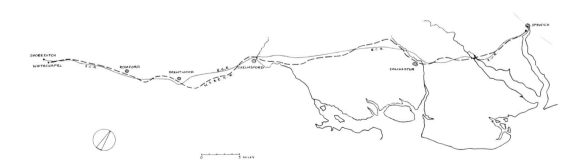

As a railway company was intended to provide a public utility, and would have to be given powers to purchase land compulsorily if it was to do so, it was necessary for it to be incorporated by an Act of Parliament. In accordance with the Standing Orders of Parliament, plans of the proposed line were deposited with the Clerks of the Peace of the counties through which it was intended to pass; these beautifully drawn and coloured documents are still to be seen in the county record offices for Suffolk and Essex. The line was to follow fairly closely the route actually taken by the Eastern Counties and Eastern Union railways in the course of the next two decades.

Little more seems to have transpired until a shareholders' meeting was held in London on 24th August, 1826; it was presided over by a certain William Clark, who, although not a member of the provisional board of directors, apparently knew what had been happening. He quickly revealed a sorry story.

Of the 10,000 shares, only 3,346 had been subscribed for, a deposit of one pound being paid on each. Although the project was not originally his idea, the direction of the company's affairs had soon been assumed by John Wilks, junior, who, in spite of the fact that it soon became obvious that the railway would be opposed by every landowner along its route, embarked upon the next steps in the most irresponsible manner.

He had appointed "all the usual officers with liberal salaries" and had incurred the heavy expenses of a survey of the land to be traversed. Clark said that some of the directors were very respectable but "there were a few of a very different description". Accounts prepared by Wilks showed that fees of £1,000 had been paid to the engineer, and expenses of £573 were owing. Solicitors' fees of £771 included items like five guineas a day for a clerk to fold letters!

Clark went on to say that when the directors first saw these accounts they had, to their credit, all refused their fees and returned the statement to Wilks for revision. No other accounts were available, but there could be no doubt that the company was bankrupt; and the speaker concluded his remarks with "certain severe observations upon Mr Wilks' conduct". Needless to say, the latter was not present at the meeting.

Henry Palmer rose and said that he had, in fact, received only £750 but as this would cover his out-of-pocket expenses he would not press for further payment. After much angry discussion had taken place, a committee of seven shareholders was appointed to investigate the company's affairs.

Less than a fortnight previously, Clark had addressed a similar meeting of the Cornwall and Devon Mining Company, which had lost a large part of its assets through the shady dealings of the same Mr Wilks. Before the committee of seven could report back, if indeed it ever did, much more burst into the light of day.

Four armed men seized Wilks' house and office in New Broad Street, making "preparations of a most formidable nature" to defend the place; they had been sent by Henry Verbeke, his partner. Wilks appealed to the Lord Mayor and the parties argued it out in court until they were all bound over to keep the peace and dismissed.

In June, 1826, Wilks had been elected a Member of Parliament for Sudbury, Suffolk, after a campaign of remarkable extravagance even for those days. A lavish dinner for several hundred schoolchildren had earned him the nickname of "Plumpudding"; but once he had gained his seat his supporters were unable to get him to meet the debts they had incurred on his behalf. They sought to have the election annulled, but in vain.

"Bubble" Wilks, as he was also known, was only once brought before a court — to be charged with forgery, in connection with his British Annuity Company — but the prosecutor failed to appear. Probably too many well-known names were concerned; Sir Stamford Raffles was a vice-chairman of the Norfolk, Suffolk and Essex Rail-Road Company, and the chairman of the Cornwall Mining Company was no less a figure than Lord Palmerston. Wilks continued his extraordinary career until 17th January, 1846, when, according to the *Suffolk Chronicle*, "This notorious individual paid the debt of nature (the only liability he ever settled) . . ." The *Dictionary of National Biography* commemorates him as "swindler".

Long before the bubble of the Norfolk, Suffolk and Essex Rail-Road burst, people in Ipswich were thinking that their town, too, would benefit more by a railway which connected the port facilities with the interior of the county. Such a line would be much cheaper and therefore within the scope of local capital and would supplement, and not compete with, established navigation interests. There was already a considerable barge traffic up the canalised River Gipping to Stowmarket, so they looked in other directions.

On 11th February, 1825, a provisional committee of local businessmen and others issued a prospectus for a line to run northwards from Ipswich to Diss via Eye. The estimated cost was £100,000 and it was proposed to work the line with "loco-motive steam engines". On the 22nd of that month, a public meeting to consider the project was called in Ipswich Shire Hall, at which the chair was taken by the Reverend Dr John Chevallier,[2] principal landowner and rector of the tiny parish of Aspall, near which the line was proposed to run.

The proposals were outlined by a banker named Dykes Alexander and questions were answered by the engineer, William Cubitt, who at that time was engineer to the Ipswich Gas Company and a partner in the agricultural implement manufacturing firm of Ransome & Sons; he was already becoming known in wider fields and was later to be engineer of the South Eastern Railway. He

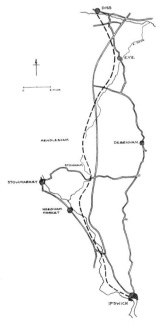

The probable course of the proposed Ipswich and Suffolk Railway, 1826. Cubitt had previously surveyed the route for a canal, and it seems likely that this would have followed the river valleys as shown. The summit of the railway was to be at Mendlesham.

explained how he had recently visited the Stockton and Darlington Railway, then under construction; the Suffolk line would have much less severe gradients than the one in County Durham and stationary engine haulage would therefore be unnecessary. He recommended that the line should be double for the first ten miles or so, as far as Stonham, and single for the remaining fifteen miles to Diss.

Cubitt's references to the use of high-pressure steam engines caused some alarm and someone asked if it would not be possible to use low-pressure ones instead. He replied that there would be no danger and we can only guess what he must have thought when another of the Alexanders jumped up to say that explosions were rare, as boilers were then made of wrought instead of cast iron; when they did occur, he said, "the iron rent or tore open, without occasioning the same mischief". On this reassuring note, a committee was appointed to get the scheme moving and it was resolved to introduce a Bill into Parliament to incorporate the "Ipswich and Suffolk Rail-way Company" with a capital of £200,000.

However, the people of Suffolk were never to be exposed to even the slightest risk of the company's boilers rending open, as nothing more seems to have been heard of the project; the county thereby lost the chance to have what would have been one of the first locomotive-operated public railways. It is extremely doubtful that it could have prospered; unlike the Stockton and Darlington it could have had little mineral traffic and unlike the Canterbury and Whitstable it would not have had its most populous terminal at its inland end.

The next proposals for a railway in Suffolk originated in 1833 in Lavenham, that delightful village in the heart of Suffolk, where some of the local landowners thought that improved communications to the coast would relieve unemployment and lower prices in the district. They consulted James Walker, a well-known engineer of the day, and he recommended a railway from Bury St Edmunds to Ipswich, with short branches to Lavenham and Hadleigh.

The scheme, like many others, came to nothing, but among the members of a steering committee formed in Ipswich were two who were destined to play an important part in bringing railways to East Anglia. One was Dr Chevallier's brother-in-law, John Cobbold (1774–1860), a brewer and shipowner from a family still well known in Suffolk. His father had once employed a servant girl named Margaret Catchpole, and his younger half-brother, Richard Cobbold (1797–1877), wrote the book — part fact, part fiction — about her romance with the smuggler Will Laud which is one of the minor classics of English literature. The other was John's son, John Chevallier Cobbold (1797–1882), a solicitor who was later to become chairman of the Eastern Union Railway.

John Cobbold (1774–1860), one of the first directors of the Eastern Counties Railway.

J. C. Cobbold and the Eastern Counties Railway 2

IN 1834, by which time the success of the Liverpool and Manchester Railway was seen to be assured, schemes for trunk lines in many different parts of the country were being brought forward. Two rival lines were proposed to connect London and York — Nicholas Cundy's Grand Northern and Eastern Railway and the Great Northern Railway, surveyed by one Joseph Gibbs, and not to be confused with the railway of that name which was actually built after 1846. Both these early lines were to pass through Cambridge and both were to have a branch to Norwich.

A third scheme, which was to serve only East Anglia, was that of the Grand Eastern Counties Railway — somewhat reminiscent of Wilks' Rail-Road — for a line from London to Yarmouth by way of Ipswich and Norwich. The prospectus was first issued in 1834 but progress was slow for the first year or so. Agricultural East Anglia was in a depressed state and the idea of a railway in such a sparsely populated region was received with some scepticism.

In November, 1835, Henry Bosanquet, the chairman of the provisional committee, with two other promoters, toured the area, calling meetings in various towns and organising the formation of local committees to further the project. Prominent among Suffolk supporters were Dr Chevallier and the two Cobbolds. John Chevallier Cobbold was also one of the solicitors acting for the provisional committee of directors.

The prospectus issued at that time painted a glowing picture of a line passing through a rich agricultural area from which London drew the greater part of its food supplies. It was also an area which would not involve major engineering works for the railway; no tunnels would be required, "nor even an embankment of more than 30 feet high and the greatest rise in any part of the line will not exceed 1 in 400 feet".

However, when the engineer, John Braithwaite — better remembered perhaps as one of the builders of the locomotive *Novelty* for the famous Rainhill trials — had completed his plans he proposed that the line should cross the valley of the Stour, on the Essex–Suffolk border, by means of a viaduct 70 feet high. This would have had about a hundred arches, each of 40 feet span, giving a total length of over three-quarters of a mile; the Gipping valley at Ipswich was to be traversed on a structure not much lower. To keep the earthworks within reasonable limits there were to be two one-mile inclines of 1 in 102 at Brentwood, where he proposed that ascending trains should be assisted by powerful banking engines.

The first edition (1838) of the 1" Ordnance Survey maps of East Anglia showed the route of the Eastern Counties Railway; although sanctioned by Parliament, it was never constructed north of Colchester. Braithwaite's great viaduct across the Stour would have been at Flatford.

Suffolk Record Office

*John Braithwaite
(1797–1870) at the time
of the Rainhill Trials in
1829.*   Science Museum

Northwards from Colchester, Braithwaite's proposed route was to be almost straight from the later Parson's Heath signal box, between Colchester and Ardleigh, to Ipswich. Beyond Ipswich, the line was to swing to the east of the turnpike road to Norwich, passing about two miles west of Debenham, and so down to Scole, on the eastern side of the turnpike, curving away through Trowse to run in an almost straight line to Yarmouth. The last four miles or so would have corresponded almost exactly with the alignment adopted nearly fifty years later for the railway from Acle to Yarmouth.

The Parliamentary battle was joined in 1836, the Eastern Counties Bill (the "Grand" was very soon dropped) being introduced into the Commons on 19th February. There was opposition not only from landowners but from the Great Northern and the Northern and Eastern Railways — the latter also minus its "Grand" and re-surveyed by James Walker.

The Great Northern Bill was defeated at its second reading, while the Northern and Eastern and the E.C.R. both secured Acts dated 4th July, 1836, although the former's powers were limited to the construction of a line from London to Cambridge. The E.C.R., from London to Yarmouth, was to be 126 miles long, and was at that time the longest railway which had been sanctioned in a single Act of Parliament.

To extend railway coverage of Suffolk, the Cobbolds had revived Walker's scheme for a line from Ipswich to Bury St Edmunds in April, 1836. The route was re-surveyed by Braithwaite, who proposed to have a junction with the E.C.R. at Belstead, a few miles south of Ipswich. There was also to be a tunnel, over a mile long, near Bradfield St George, about five miles from Bury. (If all Braithwaite's proposals had been carried out, Suffolk would have had some major railway works indeed!)

The provisional committee of directors for this Bury Railway Company included Henry Bosanquet, Dr Chevallier and the elder John Cobbold — all to be directors of the E.C.R. — while J.C. Cobbold was one of the solicitors acting for them. It is perhaps interesting to note that the others were Bortons of Bury St Edmunds (Wilks had evidently not put them off railways) and a London firm with offices in Liverpool Street, an address at that time with no railway significance whatsoever.

The promoters advertised their intention of introducing a Bill into Parliament, but nothing more was ever heard of the scheme; presumably again insufficient subscribers came forward.

The construction of the Eastern Counties Railway began in the spring of 1837, at the London end of the line. The company had intended to carry on the work at both ends of the proposed route simultaneously, but incomplete negotiations for land postponed the start in Norfolk until difficulties encountered near London precluded it altogether.

The viaduct over the River Lea, from an 1847 booklet, Pleasure Excursions, *by "Felix Summerley", the* nom de plume *of Henry Cole, later the organising secretary of the 1851 Great Exhibition.*

Costs soon greatly exceeded the estimates, particularly in the purchase of land and in compensation to owners and tenants for damage and disturbance. Difficult site conditions were found in forming the embankment across the Lea Marshes near Stratford.

By the end of 1838 work was in hand only between Mile End and Brentwood. The shareholders were becoming more and more reluctant to pay the calls, or instalments, on their shares; and just over half the capital had been called.

Only a minority of these shareholders lived in the area which the railway was to serve. When the company's Bill was at the Committee stage in Parliament, it was stated that 18,917 of the 64,000 shares had been taken up by people living in the locality; but at the first general meeting of the company on 26th September, 1836, the directors reported that "little more than one twelfth of the whole" had been subscribed in the East of England. A large body of the proprietors lived in the industrial Midlands and the North, particularly in Liverpool.

The original Board of Directors consisted of twenty-two members, named in the company's Act of Incorporation. Within a short time one had died and another had resigned, and Liverpool men were co-opted into their places. Of the remaining twenty, nine, including the chairman, Henry Bosanquet, were Londoners; five were from Essex, three from Suffolk and three, including the vice-chairman, Colonel Sir Robert Harvey, had addresses in Norfolk. Two of the Suffolk directors were Dr Chevallier and the elder John Cobbold.

The Act also laid down that four of the directors should retire and their successors should be elected at a general meeting of the company to be held in February, 1838. A year later six directors were to retire, and six every year thereafter until the last member of the original board retired in 1841. Any retiring director might stand for re-election; and those who were to retire each time were "to be determined by ballot among themselves", but the manner of balloting was not laid down.

In 1838, the first four upon whom the choice fell were the vice-chairman, a Suffolk director named Fowler, a London

EASTERN COUNTIES
RAILWAY COMPANY.

NOTICE is hereby given, that the Directors have this day resolved to make a second call of £1 per Share, payable on or before the 16th of October next; and that the several Proprietors of Shares in the Capital Stock of the Company are required to pay the same, within the time above specified, to any of the following Bankers of the Company:—

London and Westminster Banks, Throgmorton Street, or any of its Branches
Bank of Liverpool .... Liverpool
Liverpool Boro' Bank............ Ditto
Manchester and Liverpool District Bank .... Manchester
National Provincial Bank .... Birmingham
National Provincial Bank .... Bath
National Provincial Bank .... Boston
West of England and South Wales District Bank .... Bristol
Messrs. Fryer, Andrews, and Co. Wimborne
Messrs. Brodie and Co. .... Salisbury
Wilts & Dorset Banking Company Ditto
Messrs. Lemon and Co. .... Brentwood
Messrs. Sparrow and Co. .... Chelmsford
Messrs. Mills, Bawtree, and Co. . Colchester
Messrs. Alexander and Co. ...... Ipswich
Messrs. Bacon, Cobbold, and Co. . Ditto
Messrs. Harveys and Hudsons.... Norwich
East of England Bank........... Great Yarmouth
Western Bank of Scotland ...... Edinboro'
Western Bank of Scotland ...... Glasgow
Royal Bank of Ireland ... . Dublin.

By order of the Board,'
J. C. ROBERTSON, Secretary.
Office, 1, Adelaide Place,
15th Aug. 1837. (3504

An advertisement from the Norwich Mercury *of 19th August, 1837, giving notice of a second call on E.C.R. shares.*

director and one of the newly co-opted Liverpool members of the board. All stood for re-election and all regained their seats except Fowler, who lost his to a man named Theodore Rathbone, a director of the London and Birmingham Railway. The position of the shareholders who lived away from the company's theatre of operations was strengthened by a decision to allow voting by proxy.

Under the original Act of 1836, the company's powers for the compulsory acquisition of land were for two years only; before the time expired all the land required, between the proposed terminus in Shoreditch and a point just beyond Colchester, had been secured. An amending Act dated 27th July, 1838, contained, among other things, an extension of land acquisition powers for a further two years, inserted at the instigation of the Norfolk vice-chairman and intended to be exercised in Suffolk and Norfolk. At the general meeting in August, however, one of the directors said that it was not intended to spend any money beyond Colchester for the time being.

The directors were becoming divided into two groups. On the one hand there were those living in the Eastern Counties, who had appeased hostile landowners through whose estates the line was to pass by promising them large sums by way of compensation. Most were landowners themselves. They were as interested in the benefits which the railway would confer on their home commercial interests as in the dividends to be derived from the company.

On the other hand, there were those who had no direct interest in the area the line would serve; they resented the agreements which had been made with the landowners. They were eager to see the line opened as soon as possible to start earning revenue, but they were not concerned which districts were served, or which were not, so long as there was ample traffic.

At the beginning of 1839 neither group could find much satisfaction in the company's position, and the February election of directors marked another stage in the struggle for control of the policy to be followed. The East Anglian directors had by then lost another of their number — as a clergyman, Dr Chevallier was ineligible to sit on the board of a joint stock company and had resigned.

The *Norwich Mercury* lashed the investors of the county for their apathy:

What then is wanted to enforce the understanding that the line be continued, as originally projected, to Yarmouth? The votes of a sufficient number of shareholders resident on this part of the line. The West and North countrymen are the large holders . . . but alas, there are not a dozen shareholders in Norfolk. Two Norfolk and Suffolk Directors go out this year, and they may be replaced by Lancashire gentlemen. One or two thousand shares, to be taken up for a sum not larger than was expended in bribery at the last Norwich election, would insure us this indispensable communication!

The two to go were John Cobbold and Edward Leathes, later vice-chairman of the East Suffolk Railway Company. The other retiring directors were three from London and one from Essex.

John Chevallier Cobbold could see that the railway would never enter Suffolk, let alone Norfolk, so long as the local directors could be chosen for retirement by their colleagues; and for them to stand for re-election was futile in the face of the massed proxy votes of the North. Therefore at the general meeting in February, 1839, he proposed a byelaw that retiring directors should be chosen by lot instead of by ballot.

In proposing five candidates from Liverpool for the vacancies, a Lancashire director asked the chairman to confirm that those who were retiring had been chosen as laid down in the Act. Bosanquet replied that the board had taken legal advice on the point, whereupon J.C. Cobbold demanded to know exactly what had been said. The chairman said he did not wish to open a legal discussion; they had studied the Act, taken legal advice and selected the directors to retire "without reference to private feelings, and had selected those gentlemen who, from their place of residence, or possessing little information on the subject of railways, were the least calculated to benefit the undertaking".

In fact, when the question had first arisen the directors had asked their solicitors how they should select the ones to go. They had been advised that they could do it in any way they liked, and the selection had actually been by lot. On the next occasion the method was changed and the board had chosen, or elected, those who were "least calculated to benefit the undertaking".

After some discussion it was decided that Cobbold's proposed byelaw was "ultra vires", i.e. beyond their powers, because they could not alter what had been laid down by Parliament. Cobbold was obliged to withdraw his proposal and watch his father, with Leathes and three others, lose their seats to the Lancashire men. A retiring director from London was re-elected. Only three of those on the board came from Essex, two from Norfolk and none from Suffolk.

The Cobbolds, with Dr Chevallier and a few others, seeing that the railway could never be extended into East Anglia by votes in the boardroom, turned to other means to achieve their aim.

First, they applied to the High Court for a writ of mandamus to compel the company to continue the line beyond Colchester, "to perform the whole of the contract which they had entered into with the public". They argued that if the Eastern Counties Railway Bill had been to authorise a line only as far as Colchester it would never have passed; Parliament had approved it because it was to serve the whole of the region.

The company's case was that it was in the best interests of the shareholders, and the general public, to open the line in short lengths. Funds were scarce, and if they spent money on acquiring land in Suffolk and Norfolk no part of the railway could be completed and everything would be lost. The plaintiffs held only 138 of the 64,000 shares in the company and the directors had always acted in accordance with the wishes of the great majority of the shareholders.

A "rule", calling upon the company to show why a mandamus should not be issued, was obtained in the High Court on 10th June, 1839, and the company was given until November to make its return. The return was duly made, repeating the company's arguments, and came before the court on 16th June, 1840. The case was argued again on both sides, and the next day judgment was given for the company. It could hardly have been otherwise.

The directors spoke of these "most extraordinary and unprecedented" proceedings in their report to the half yearly general meeting on 28th August, 1839. J.C. Cobbold explained why he had acted as he did, but he had done nothing, he said, until he had written to the directors on the subject back in April. He had been concerned that the company's right to deviate, within limits, from the alignment authorised by Parliament in Suffolk and Norfolk would expire on 27th July, and nothing had been done to set out the line on the ground. He had claimed that all the remaining land required, right through to Yarmouth, could have been secured for £20,000, but none of the directors had even so much as looked at the ground north of the Stour. If they had shown any sign of wishing to continue the line beyond Colchester, many more shares would have been taken up in Suffolk and Norfolk.

"We never said we would stop at Colchester. We will go on as fast as we can", replied Bosanquet, the chairman, but Cobbold retorted that many shareholders had decided that that was where the line would stop; one had even said to him, "If you want a railroad in Suffolk, you must make it yourselves".

After some further discussion, a vote of confidence in the directors was carried by forty-one votes to nine.

J.C. Cobbold and his friends were still not defeated. Their next move, concocted even as the company prepared its reply to the mandamus, was nothing less than the introduction of a private Bill into Parliament to achieve their ends — "a novelty, and rather audacious", as Cobbold said of it later.

It was indeed. The share capital was to be increased by £800,000, with power to borrow a third of this sum in addition. When the line had been completed from London to Chelmsford, it was to extend no further until an equal length had been built from the Yarmouth end; when the London end of the railway had reached Colchester, it was to be constructed no further until the line from Yarmouth had reached Ipswich.

The sore point of local directors on the board was to be settled once and for all by reducing the total number of directors from twenty-two to seventeen after February, 1841, and of these, five

were to be the mayors of Colchester, Ipswich, Eye, Norwich and
Yarmouth, who would be *ex-officio* members of the board.
Thereafter, four of the other directors were to retire every year
and all retirements were to be decided by writing the names on
pieces of paper, which were to be "thrown promiscuously into a
glass or ballot box", the requisite number of names being drawn
out by the chairman. The final clause of this astonishing Bill
specified that the expense of its passage through Parliament was to
be defrayed by the railway company.

With this Bill about to be introduced into the Commons, and
the company's return to the mandamus still to be considered by the
High Court, it was hardly surprising that the directors' report
presented to the company's general meeting on 27th February,
1840, referred to the "vexatious and discreditable" proceedings
being instituted against them.

J.C. Cobbold was immediately on his feet to move the deletion
of those words from the report, but he could find no seconder. He
said that the Act of 1838 had given the company two years more in
which to acquire land in Suffolk and Norfolk; this time had nearly
expired, and nothing had been done. He proposed that the
company should acquire all the necessary remaining land before its
powers expired, but again no one seconded him. Rathbone, the
vice-chairman (Sir Robert Harvey, the original holder of that
office, had resigned not long before), said it was absurd in view of
the company's financial position.

There was an awkward moment when one of the directors
from Liverpool, a Mr Hodgson, suggested that the reason why
Cobbold was so keen for the company to acquire land was because
he had bought an estate through which the line was to pass. He
hoped to make a handsome profit selling it to the company.

Cobbold hotly denied this, although he admitted that he had
purchased the Crane Hall estate near Ipswich only three weeks
after the railway was authorised by Parliament. He claimed that he
only did so to secure it for the company, and he had offered it to
Braithwaite at cost. The engineer said he remembered Cobbold

*Stratford station, where
the lines to Cambridge and
Colchester then diverged,
and the scene of an
explosion in the E.C.R.
detonator factory, from*
Pleasure Excursions,
1847.

saying that he now owned the land, but he could not recall anything being said about prices.

Cobbold maintained that the conversation had been before he bought the estate; he had been requested to approach the owners about the line passing through before he even knew the land was for sale. He could prove his point as he had a plan, drawn by Braithwaite himself, showing alternative routes.

The chairman intervened to say that no one could doubt Mr Cobbold's integrity, and even Hodgson said that he had thought it only fair to give him an opportunity to deny this story which was going about! Cobbold withdrew his proposal.

The private Amendment Bill to ensure the extension of the railway into East Anglia was duly introduced into the House of Commons by Sir Charles Vere, one of the Members for East Suffolk, who had introduced the original E.C.R. Bill in 1836. Norwich, Ipswich and Yarmouth petitioned in favour of the Bill, and the directors of the company against it, saying that it had been brought in their name but without their consent. Only nine shareholders supported the measure while no fewer than 1,322 were opposed to it. At the Second Reading on 11th May, 1840, the Bill was thrown out by 195 votes to 58.

These proceedings naturally put an additional strain on the company's financial resources. The extraordinary actions and impractical hopes of J.C. Cobbold and his friends contrasted sharply with the views of other shareholders, meeting in Liverpool, who passed a resolution calling upon the directors to warn all the proprietors that unless all calls on shares were met in full the whole railway might yet have to be abandoned. The directors did so, with the result that a call of £2 on each of the 64,000 shares in July, 1840, produced, with arrears, £233,000!

Ten and a half miles of the line, from Mile End to Romford, had opened for passenger traffic on 20th June, 1839. Another seven miles, inwards to the terminus in Shoreditch and outwards to Brentwood, followed on 1st July, 1840. The Eastern Counties Railway was manifestly a long way from Suffolk and Norfolk.

In 1841, Norfolk interests took matters into their own hands and went ahead with an independent railway between Norwich and Yarmouth. The Eastern Counties Railway was finally completed from Brentwood to Colchester and opened for passenger traffic on 29th March, 1843.

Meanwhile, J.C. Cobbold paused to consider the next step in the process of bringing a railway across the Stour into Suffolk. It did not look as though it would ever be the E.C.R., but no one could say that he had not tried.

IN the spring of 1842 a deputation of E.C.R. directors went to inspect the construction of the railway, and on 12th May they reported to their colleagues that they were well satisfied with the general progress of the works

and, with one exception, with their condition. The Stanway Embankment is that to which exception must be taken, as exhibiting work of the most discreditable description to the character of the undertaking, and the deputation is glad to learn from the Engineer that Mr Bruff, the Sub-Engineer of that division, is discharged from the Company's service, and they recommend that he be on no account allowed to remain therein longer than is absolutely necessary.

Who was this Mr Bruff?

In spite of such a beginning in the shadow of disgrace, Peter Schuyler Bruff had a long and successful career. He has been called "the Brunel of the Eastern Counties", for the region has many monuments to his skill. He was perhaps the last engineer in the classic mould of the early Victorian era, a non-specialist who could turn his hand to almost any branch of a wide but young science. As a young man, he was to rub shoulders with such great figures as Brunel and Robert Stephenson; he was not much their junior, but unlike them he survived middle age and lived on almost into our own century, into the era of the internal combustion engine, wireless telegraphy and the steam turbine.

His early years are obscure, and he himself seems not to have been the most reliable source of information concerning them. In census returns he gave his place of birth as Devonport, whereas obituary notices stated that he had been born in Portsmouth. He often underwrote his age. On his grave the year of his birth is recorded as 1811. All that we can be sure of is that he was baptised in the parish church of Portsea (now St Mary's, Portsmouth) on 6th August, 1813, and that he was born on 23rd July, 1812, according to the register there.

One fiction that he clung to throughout his life was that his father had been a Captain in the Royal Navy. In fact, Peter Schuyler Bruff, Senior, was a Master, or navigating warrant officer, and it is inconceivable that he had been a personal friend of Lord Nelson, as later accounts stated. At the end of the Napoleonic War he was engaged in a supervisory capacity on the construction of the great breakwater across Plymouth Sound, and there his young son had his first sight of a major civil engineering project.

In due course young Bruff received his engineering training under Joseph Locke, probably at the time when Locke was working under George Stephenson on the Liverpool and Manchester

Peter Bruff in middle age.
Suffolk Record Office

Railway. It appears that Bruff worked on the surveys for the
Eastern Counties Railway, under Braithwaite, from the beginning;
but he did not enter the company's service until about 1840. He
was then once more paid by Braithwaite, who drew an allowance
from the company for this purpose, just as he himself was to do
later on the Eastern Union.

Incidentally, Braithwaite's chief assistant when the E.C.R.
construction began in 1837 was "Captain John Ericsson", who had

worked with him on the locomotive *Novelty* and was later to design the ironclad *Monitor* in America. He had resigned from his job in 1839, before Bruff appeared.

About 1838 Bruff married Harriet Deborah MacAlpine, an Irish lady some six years his senior. She must have been a remarkable woman, for she survived him to die at the age of 102, having apparently borne him ten sons and two daughters. If a press report of the birth of "a tenth son" is to be believed, three of them, including one of a pair of twins, died in infancy.

In this period he wrote *A Treatise on Engineering Fieldwork*, of which the first volume, on surveying and levelling, appeared in 1838 and ran to two editions. Part of the survey for the E.C.R. at Lexden, near Colchester, was reproduced as an illustration. In contrast to some books at that time, it is remarkable for its commonsense approach to the subject; and it is obvious that the author's practical experience lay behind his words:

> We would strongly recommend all persons engaged in levelling operations, neither to take assistants into the field with them unless absolutely of service, or engage in conversation with anyone while so occupied; or if it is impossible to avoid conversation with land occupiers or others, not to attempt to carry on operations at the same time, as, if so, serious errors will be almost certain to be committed.

At least no one in 1838 would have asked Bruff if he was taking photographs — a universal witticism of later land occupiers and others.

The second volume was to have dealt with the setting out of works, but it seems never to have been published.

In August, 1841, we find Bruff writing to Braithwaite from Colchester:

> . . . you, Sir, must be aware that with the many domestic afflictions which I have experienced and the expenses of a young and increasing family, that the income which I have been in receipt of from you is insufficient for support. While the operations of the Eastern Counties Company were in abeyance I should have willingly received a less salary than I did, satisfied that I could not in the then state of affairs give a sufficient remuneration in services for the money I was paid — but now circumstances are changed, and certain that I might render you services of higher value than I have hitherto done and perhaps without presumption might say am worthy of a greater salary than I now enjoy. I beg, Sir, you will not consider this appeal in the way of a complaint — far from it — for I have yet many things to thank you for, but while your attention is so much taken up with important matters of business I thought it unlikely such a matter would occur to you, even though you considered me fully worthy of an extension of your favours . . .

Perhaps this flowery effort was successful, since Bruff preserved the heavily amended draft of it, a sole survivor from the early part of his life, pasted into a later but still only sparsely filled letter book.

Stanway embankment, the cause of Bruff's dismissal by Braithwaite in 1842.

He was certainly not incompetent. Why then was he dismissed? Why was the deputation of E.C.R. directors so "glad to learn" of his dismissal that they worded their recommendation so strongly? And why did the full board so vehemently resolve:

> That the wish of the Board that the Sub-Engineer Bruff on no account remain in the Company's Service longer than is absolutely necessary for winding up what he is now engaged in be conveyed to the Engineer in Chief.

They were evidently glad to see the back of him. A clue lies in the opening words of a report which Bruff prepared for the Colchester Channel and Paving Commissioners in the following August:

> For the past eight years, while engaged on the plans and works of the Eastern Counties Railway, the state of the port has occupied much of my attention . . .

Too much probably! Bruff was working on a proposed scheme for improving the port facilities at Colchester, with a basin at the Hythe in which vessels would remain afloat at all times and a canal down to Wivenhoe, where there would be a lock into the estuary of the Colne. He was ambitious and determined to make a name for himself, but unfortunately for his aspirations at that time he was being paid a salary to supervise the construction of a length of railway with no very extraordinary works upon it.

Bruff undoubtedly considered himself unfairly treated by the Eastern Counties Company, but by that time he was well on the way to greater things. He had launched his own scheme for extending the Eastern Counties Railway into East Anglia.

Peter Bruff's railway — the Eastern Union, as it was to be called — would first extend to Ipswich at a cost which was but a fraction of the sum which Braithwaite had estimated would be required. Bruff's proposed route and gradients were, of course, completely different, and no doubt he had argued their merits with his chief, to the detriment of the relationship between the two men. Worst of all, he had found backers for his ideas among the small group of E.C.R. shareholders who had so long and so bitterly fought against the decision to stop at Colchester, and who had for so long been a sharp thorn in the side of the directors.

The Eastern Union Railway was almost entirely promoted and initially financed within the town of Ipswich, which at that time had only about 30,000 inhabitants. The company's headquarters were always in the town; and the chairman and many of the directors were always local men, members of a few influential families which dominated every aspect of local government, commerce and social life; they had their counterparts in every part of the land.

The Eastern Union launched Bruff upon his successful career and in return he served it with extraordinary loyalty. He built it, at first as resident engineer under the nominal supervision of Joseph Locke but soon as engineer in his own right. He equipped it and latterly he managed it. And when at last its working was taken over by its more powerful neighbour, the Eastern Counties Railway, he had the satisfaction of returning to that company as engineer.

At the time he first approached J.C. Cobbold, Bruff was living at 22 Charlotte Street, Bloomsbury, but when it became clear that his future lay in East Anglia he moved to Ipswich, where he lived for the rest of his life, although he had an office in London in his later years.

His first home in the town was a medium-sized detached house close to the River Orwell, in the district known as Halifax; the building is now part of a garage. In December, 1845, an abnormally high tide flooded the lower part of the house to a depth of five feet, and it is not surprising that the Bruffs moved soon afterwards. For a time they lived in Norwich Road; but about the end of 1846 they moved to Handford Lodge, "a genteel family

Joseph Locke (1805–1860) at the age of thirty-two; a mezzotint from a portrait bequeathed by his widow to the Institution of Civil Engineers.
National Railway Museum

residence" standing in seven acres beside the River Gipping. Here Bruff was to live for his remaining fifty-three years.

A delightful story survives of Bruff travelling down from London one night with a stranger in the same compartment. They found that they were both going to Ipswich, and the stranger asked Bruff if he knew Handford Lodge. The engineer said he did, without disclosing that he lived there.

The other remarked that he had often, in years gone by, attended parties there when he was stationed at the barracks in the town. Once, at a card party in the drawing room, a lady was accused of cheating by one of the officers present. Her escort denied it and a hot dispute arose.

There was a challenge to a duel, which was accepted; pistols were produced and they shot it out in the room, there and then. One stood to one side of the door and the other in front of the window. Each fired twice — and missed — and honour was then considered satisfied (What their host thought of all this, we are not told!)

The stranger concluded by saying that he believed that the marks of the two bullets could still be seen on the wall by the door. Bruff went home, and there they were. The room was never re-papered in his lifetime and he carefully preserved the marks, hidden behind two small pictures.

Handford Lodge, Ipswich, Bruff's home from 1846–1900. It was demolished shortly after Bruff's death.

20

IT SEEMS probable that Bruff, fully aware of the efforts of some E.C.R. shareholders to secure the extension of the railway beyond Colchester, was already giving attention to his own proposals for this, going over the ground with maps and note-books in hand while the contractor at Stanway, a man named Worswick, was making such a poor job of the embankment there. Unfortunately, we do not know exactly when or how Bruff first approached J.C. Cobbold, as neither of them seems to have left any correspondence or diaries of this time.

Braithwaite had estimated that the cost of extending the E.C.R. on to Ipswich would be £800,000. Bruff conceived his scheme about eight years later, and in those eight years the steam locomotive had undergone considerable improvement; in particular it was known that it could ascend steeper gradients than had been thought possible in the mid-thirties without loss of adhesion or the need for cable assistance, using fixed winding engines. Unlike the almost straight alignment favoured by Braithwaite, which swept across the countryside and strode over the valley of the Stour on a vast brick viaduct, Bruff's proposed line deviated to take advantage of the contours of the ground and descended to the floor of the valley to cross the river on a couple of short low-level timber bridges before climbing up the other side.

J.C. Cobbold and his friends were keenly interested in Bruff's scheme. The Bill for the Yarmouth and Norwich Railway had received the Royal Assent on 18th June, 1842, and the E.C.R. seemed to be interested in extending to Bury St Edmunds from Kelvedon. Ipswich, which had always been an important port, had just completed its Wet Dock, a scheme in which the town had been encouraged at the outset, in 1836, by the prospect of rail communications over the E.C.R. and to Bury. If there was no railway the new dock would be something of a white elephant, particularly as there was also talk of a railway from Colchester to Harwich, Ipswich's ancient rival at the mouth of the Orwell.

A public meeting, presided over by the Mayor, was called in Ipswich Town Hall on 8th August, 1843, "to consider the plans and estimates prepared by W. Tierney Clark and P. Bruff, for extending the Eastern Counties Railway from Colchester to Norwich by way of Ipswich, with branches to Harwich Harbour and Bury". It seems that Bruff had approached William Tierney Clark merely to get the name of an older and better-known engineer associated with his scheme. Clark was primarily a bridge engineer and seems to have had little to do with railways. His name does not recur in the story of the Eastern Union and he was not even present at this first meeting.

A newspaper announcement of the proposal to build a railway between Norwich and Yarmouth, from the Norwich Mercury of 8th January, 1842.

YARMOUTH AND NORWICH RAILWAY.

MR. ROBERT STEPHENSON'S OR VALLEY LINE

CAPITAL £150,000.

Engineer in Chief—Robert Stephenson, Esq.

SOLICITORS.

Messrs. White and Borrett, 35, Lincoln's Inn Fields.

Messrs. Rackham and Cooke, } Norwich.
John Oddin Taylor, Esq.

Charles John Palmer, Esq. Great Yarmouth.

ACCORDING to the Estimates of Mr. Robert Stephenson, the above line from Yarmouth to Norwich, may be constructed for the unusually small sum of £150,000.; and the traffic between the two towns having been taken by the Eastern Counties Railway Company at upwards of £60,000. per annum, and being certainly at a low estimate calculated to produce a revenue of upwards of £40,000.; the shareholders may rely with confidence upon receiving a high rate of interest upon their capital.

The Shares are £20. each, on which a deposit of £2. per share will be required, *which will however be returned in case the proposed Bill be not introduced into Parliament in the next Session.*

Shares and a printed Prospectus, with a copy of Mr. Stephenson's Report, may be had at the offices of any of the Solicitors, where Plans and Sections of the Line may be seen.   (255

Bruff explained the proposals. The line was to follow the route proposed by Braithwaite for a distance of two and a half miles from the Colchester station of the E.C.R., and for which that company had already acquired the land. Thence, swinging away to the east, it was to follow the course of a small stream down into the broad valley of the Stour. Crossing over the turnpike road at Cattawade, the line was to be continued along the north side of the Stour estuary to Shotley, from where there would be a ferry to Harwich. This length would be carried on a low embankment and it was estimated that some 2,000 acres, occasionally covered at high water, would thus be protected and could be reclaimed.

The main line would turn away northwards at Holbrook Bay, climbing up the valley of a small tributary to a summit at Freston and then descending to Ipswich, where the station was to be "opposite the Bourne-road meeting house" on the site where the first terminus was actually built. This would allow easy access to the dock and other quays, and the line could be extended "several hundred yards nearer the town, if found advisable". The maximum gradient was to be 1 in 132.

However, Bruff had no intention of continuing the main line very far round the projecting spur of Stoke Hill. Even at this early stage he envisaged a tunnel. It was to be 590 yards long, passing under the hill at a maximum depth below ground of 87 feet — deeper into the hill than it was in fact later driven.

The line was to continue up the valley of the River Gipping, climbing out beyond Stowmarket at a gradient of 1 in 245 for two and a quarter miles, with a short length of 1 in 132, up on to the plateau of mid-Suffolk. Near Scole it would join the route which the Eastern Counties Railway had proposed to follow and would be continued thus to Norwich.

The branch to Bury St Edmunds would leave the main line near Stowmarket and run through Woolpit on a route apparently to the south of that eventually chosen.

In contrast to the mighty embankments and viaducts which Braithwaite had proposed, the maximum height of embankment anywhere on this line would be a mere 23 feet in the Stour valley and not much more in the Gipping valley.

Bruff concluded by saying that Clark and he had carefully considered every aspect and the cost of the whole "Projected Eastern Union Railway", with a double main line and single branches, would be less than £16,000 per mile, including land, stations and rolling stock, "and he might say that few estimates were in that preliminary stage so complete".

The report was adopted and a committee, including, of course, John Cobbold with J.C. Cobbold as honorary secretary, was immediately appointed to carry the project further.

Another public meeting was held at Ipswich on 10th October. The committee reported that they had submitted the scheme and estimate to Joseph Locke for his comments. He had expressed his approval but as he was at that time concerned with a proposed line from Colchester to Harwich, the first four miles of which would coincide with the Eastern Union line, he had suggested that the proposed branch from Holbrook to Shotley should be abandoned and that the line should be double throughout, except for the tunnel at Ipswich.

Perhaps also at the suggestion of Locke, an alternative route between Cattawade and Ipswich, through Bentley, had been surveyed. This would be shorter than the Holbrook route and would avoid the opposition of some landowners, although the constructional costs would be somewhat heavier.

At that time Locke was away in France, but he wrote saying that he had received an offer from "an experienced contractor" to build the Eastern Union line for the estimated sum. He referred to Thomas Brassey, the leading contractor of the day, whom he had first met on the construction of the Grand Junction Railway about ten years before. Brassey had since carried out several large contracts under Locke, who recognised the advantages of dealing with a single, reliable main contractor with adequate resources, and a bond of mutual trust had grown up between the two men. Brassey, in partnership with William Mackenzie, another well-known contractor, had built the railway from Paris to Rouen under Locke's direction, and they were still busy in France, on the extension line from Rouen to Le Havre.

Thomas Brassey (1805–1870), the great railway contractor.

It seems to have been the policy of Locke, in which he was followed by his pupil, Bruff, to choose his main contractor and have only one tender to consider. No doubt there was haggling behind the scenes before the bid was submitted in writing for formal acceptance. In March, 1846, the directors authorised Bruff to obtain an estimate of the cost of the Harwich branch from George Wythes, "provided he will take the contract at Mr Bruff's prices".

In contrast to Locke, Braithwaite let the works on the Eastern Counties line in some thirty separate contracts, for which competitive tenders were invited — and Braithwaite's estimates of costs went sadly awry! Of these contracts, Bruff's No. 29 at Stanway (when he was sacked) extended for a distance of only about 90 chains (a mile and an eighth) from the Roman River towards Colchester.

At the first public meeting to promote the Eastern Union line, on 8th August, it had been decided to invite the mayors of Ipswich, Norwich, Bury St. Edmunds, Eye and Harwich to serve on the provisional committee, but all except the first had declined to do so. The committee had also invited the Eastern Counties Railway Company to nominate a representative to join them but this invitation also had been refused on the grounds that the company was promoting its own scheme for a line from Colchester to Bury,

Eastern Union Railway.

A T a numerous meeting of the Owners and Occupiers of Land, and inhabitant Householders of
Harleston and its neighbourhood, in Norfolk and
Suffolk, at the Magpie Inn, on Wednesday, the 25th
of October; and by adjournment, at the Swan Inn, on
Wednesday, the 1st day of November, 1843, for the
purpose of taking into consideration the expediency of
giving aid to the projected Eastern Union Railway,
Charles Etheridge, Esq. in the Chair, the following
resolutions were passed:—
Resolved—That it is highly important to the interests of the Eastern parts of Norfolk and Suffolk, that
a Railway should be extended from the present terminus of the Eastern Counties' Railway, at Colchester,
by Ipswich and Scole to Norwich.
Resolved—That in the opinion of this meeting, the
line proposed from Ipswich to Norwich by way of
Scole, with a branch to Bury St. Edmund's, is far
preferable to that by way of Brandon and Thetford;
inasmuch, as from the great population on the one
line as compared with the other, the passenger traffic
by way of Scole would be far the greatest, from which
traffic it is well ascertained that the principal source of
income on all railways proceeds; independently of
which, there can be no doubt but that the transit of
cattle on the line by way of Scole, would be greatly in
favour of that line; and further, that in the event of
the main trunk being completed, the level of the
country from Scole to Bungay and Beccles, is sin-
gularly favourable to a divergent line in that direction.
Resolved—That a Public Meeting be convened, by
advertisement in four of the provincial papers, to be
held at the Swan Inn, Harleston, on Wednesday, the
15th day of November instant, at Eleven in the Fore-
noon, at which the Landlords be requested to attend,
to determine upon the best mode of giving aid to and
co-operating with the Ipswich Committee.   (4734

*An expression of support
for the Eastern Union
Railway from the people of
Harleston, November,
1843.*

and on to Thetford, and they proposed to serve Ipswich by means of a branch from Hadleigh. The Ipswich meeting thereupon resolved to carry on alone, but initially with a line from Colchester as far as Ipswich only.

It was necessary, of course, for the project to be authorised by an Act of Parliament but, to comply with the standing orders of Parliament, the promoters of a railway had to attend to many things.

Firstly, plans and sections of the proposed line had to be deposited with the Clerks of the Peace for each county through which the line would pass. On these plans, every different piece of land the line would pass over in each parish was numbered and all were set out in a so-called "book of reference" giving the owner, lessee and occupier of each.

The promoters had to advertise for three successive weeks in the *London Gazette* and in local newspapers saying that they intended to apply to Parliament for powers to build a railway from A to B, listing all the parishes that it would pass through and declaring that plans and books of reference could be seen by applying to the various officials. Copies of this notice had to be displayed on the doors of county court buildings. The officials issued certificates that all these things had been done at the right time.

Zero hour was midnight on 30th November, by which time the Bill with all the supporting documents had to be in the offices of Parliament. By 31st December, in addition, copies of parts of the plans and books of reference relating to each and every parish had to be deposited with the parish clerks.

Early in November, 1843, therefore, the Eastern Union Company's intent to promote a Bill was duly advertised. The list of parishes indicated that the route was still undecided but in the course of the month the Bentley route was chosen.

The plans showed the line diverging from the Eastern Counties Railway about half a mile to the west of the terminus and passing about 300 yards to the north of the Eastern Counties station to cross the Nayland road at a point where there would presumably be a separate Eastern Union station, although proposed stations were not shown. After about two and a half miles the Eastern Union line ran tangentially into the old alignment of the Eastern Counties, just at the point to which that company had already purchased land.

The line then descended into the valley of the Stour, presumably as originally proposed by Bruff and Clark (although as far as I am aware their plan no longer survives), at 1 in 132 and climbed out of it at a similar gradient. For part of the way to Bentley the line followed the valley of a small stream flowing into the Stour from the Suffolk side, but to enter this valley there would have to be a cutting through a spur of high land at Brantham. This cutting would be over 50 feet deep, the heaviest work on the line. The final descent into the valley of the Orwell at Ipswich was also to be at 1 in 132, generally down the valley of the tributary Belstead Brook.

There was comment on the delay in issuing a prospectus, and it was not until the end of November — when the Bill had to be deposited in Parliament — that it appeared. The capital was to be £200,000 — Locke's estimate of the total cost — and subscriptions were invited in £50 shares. It was estimated that if the number of passengers travelling between Colchester and Ipswich by coach was only doubled, there would be a dividend of seven and a half per cent, after allowing forty per cent of receipts for working the line.

The prospectus stated that

> the Line has been selected under the superintendence of Mr Locke, and an offer has been made by an eminent and responsible Contractor to furnish all materials and execute the work for the amount put down for the same in Mr Locke's Estimate; the public, therefore, have the best assurance of its sufficiency.

The provisional committee of directors had done all that they could to ensure that the scheme would not fail because of ever-rising costs, like those that had frustrated the Eastern Counties Railway.

The *Ipswich Journal* commended the scheme to its readers:

> We congratulate our townsmen on the favourable auspices of the Union Railway, but we would suggest to them, that it is desirable to establish a local interest in the concern by the possession of shares. That it will be a profitable one we have no doubt, yet it must be apparent that those whom it will practically affect ought to have some voice in the management, which might be accomplished were interest enough taken in the matter to produce a goodly number of persons in the town each to purchase one or two shares in the undertaking.

J.C. Cobbold said later that he and his friends had originally subscribed a tenth of the capital between them, so that the Bill could be submitted to Parliament, and, finding the public reluctant to invest, they later increased their holding. There is nothing to suggest that shares were ever widely taken up in Suffolk. Although all the capital was subscribed within three weeks of the company's Act of Incorporation passing on to the Statute Book, much of it seems to have come either from the directors or from the North of England.

Cobbold himself was tireless in his efforts to raise capital. He was, as we shall see, also chairman of the Ipswich and Bury St Edmunds Railway. He was also one of the two treasurers of the Ipswich and East Suffolk Hospital; and, with his co-treasurer, Dykes Alexander (probably also a shareholder), he offered to advance the railway company £600 at five per cent interest, "on receipt of a temporary acknowledgement for such loan until the

Directors were authorised to issue debenture bonds". A modern auditor would not consider this to be a suitable trustee investment!

Before the end of 1843, the E.C.R. had decided to drop an earlier proposal for a line from Colchester to Thetford through Bury St Edmunds, but a group of Bury people were themselves wondering how their town could be provided with a rail link to London and they favoured the shorter route to Colchester rather than the Eastern Union line by way of Ipswich. In February, 1844, a deputation from Bury met the directors of the E.C.R. to discuss the subject and, finding the company unwilling to consider building a line from Colchester even as far as Hadleigh, the Bury group decided to promote their own line — the East and West Suffolk Railway — all the way to Colchester, with Sir John Rennie as engineer. This scheme received considerable support from mercantile and shipping interests in Colchester, where the line was seen as a means of making the town the port of West Suffolk, whereas the Eastern Union would inevitably confer this role upon Ipswich.

In April, Cobbold told the promoters of the East and West Suffolk that the Eastern Union would not oppose any scheme for a line from Bury to Ipswich by way of Hadleigh, which he thought would benefit all parties, provided that they did not oppose his direct line from Colchester to Ipswich. He added that he personally would not even object to a line from Ardleigh to Hadleigh if it belonged to a genuinely independent company. The lack of response to this offer merely confirmed his suspicions that the Eastern Counties was behind the Bury promoters.

Meanwhile the Eastern Union Bill had received its first two formal readings in the House of Commons on 14th and 22nd March, 1844. On 29th April it came before a Committee of the House, where the case in support was opened by Charles Austin, one of the leading advocates of the time.

Austin was a Suffolk man, the son of a miller at Creeting. For his work before Parliamentary Committees during the few years of the "Railway Mania" he was estimated to have earned £100,000, a vast sum in those days. He retired in 1848, at the age of forty-nine, and lived at Brandeston Hall, near Framlingham, until his death in 1874.

Petitions in favour of the E.U.R. Bill were presented from Ipswich, Manningtree and Stowmarket, and even from Eye, Halesworth and Lowestoft. The promoters of the East and West Suffolk Railway had no Bill in direct opposition, but they had organised petitions against the E.U.R. from Bury St Edmunds and Colchester. Locke gave evidence in support of the Bill, and the opposition called George Bidder, an engineer associated with the Stephensons, to speak against him.

The promoters of the Bill had one undeniable trump card in their hand: Parliament had already sanctioned a line running

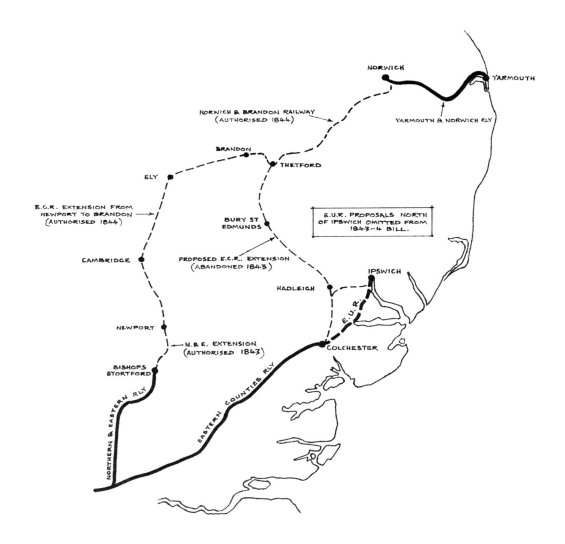

NORWICH

YARMOUTH

NORWICH & BRANDON RAILWAY
(AUTHORISED 1844)

YARMOUTH & NORWICH RLY

BRANDON

THETFORD

ELY

E.C.R. EXTENSION FROM
NEWPORT TO BRANDON
(AUTHORISED 1844)

BURY ST
EDMUNDS

E.U.R. PROPOSALS NORTH
OF IPSWICH OMITTED FROM
1843-4 BILL.

CAMBRIDGE

PROPOSED E.C.R. EXTENSION
(ABANDONED 1843)

IPSWICH

HADLEIGH

E.U.R.

NEWPORT

N. & E. EXTENSION
(AUTHORISED 1843)

COLCHESTER

BISHOPS
STORTFORD

NORTHERN & EASTERN RLY

EASTERN COUNTIES RLY

straight from Colchester to Ipswich, so no one could now condemn it as a madcap scheme. Moreover, the Eastern Union line would cost only a quarter of the sum which Braithwaite estimated would be necessary to extend the Eastern Counties Railway to Ipswich.

Much of the case against the Bill was that the estimates of traffic to be expected were too optimistic, because the line would only connect two ports which were already handling the traffic of their respective districts cheaply and effectively. There was already an established and thriving steamer service for passengers to and from London.

The Eastern Union Railway and its rivals, 1843–1844. Railways open in 1844 are shown by solid lines.

The cross-examination of witnesses went on for several days, during which the strength of the case in favour of the measure became increasingly obvious. On 9th May the Commons Committee decided that the preamble to the Bill was proved — in other words, it was in the public interest that the railway should be built. The next day a detailed examination of the proposals began.

Bruff's plans had been altered by Locke so that the first four miles from Colchester coincided with a proposed line to Harwich. But John Braithwaite had also designed a line to Harwich, and Bills for both these schemes (see Chapter thirteen) were among the many then being considered by Parliament as the "Railway Mania" gathered momentum. At one stage, the Eastern Union Bill was amended so that the Suffolk line would branch from Braithwaite's line, if the latter were to be authorised, at a point which was also four miles out of Colchester. In the event, both these Harwich schemes were thrown out on 10th May, and the Eastern Union Bill passed with the proviso that the line should meet the E.C.R. at a point two and a half miles from Colchester, as Bruff had originally proposed.

To this point the older company had already purchased land, and they were to be allowed six months to begin construction of a railway to it from their station at Colchester, After a further year, this section of line was to be completed to the same gauge [3] and to

The birthmark of the E.U.R. The intended sweeping curve of the line from Ipswich to Manningtree was straightened to take it further from Brantham Hall, hidden behind the trees on the left.

levels suitable for an end-on junction with the Eastern Union. The latter, if it wished, had the right to ask the Essex county magistrates to appoint an independent engineer to see that the work was properly carried out. If the E.C.R. defaulted, the Suffolk company was empowered to acquire the necessary land and build its own line, which would join the E.C.R. west of Colchester station, as provided for in Locke's plans.

Two diehard opponents of the Bill were a certain Robert Whalley and a Mrs Mary Spooner, lessee and owner respectively of Brantham Hall, who had at last agreed to a diversion of the line which would take it about 100 yards further away from the hall. The third reading of the Bill in the Commons had to be delayed while the diversion was advertised in the *London Gazette* and fresh plans were drawn up and deposited with the county authorities. Even after the Bill had become law these two delayed the start of the work until the last possible moment by refusing to agree to any price which was named and insisting that the full compulsory purchase procedure be gone through.

The company's agreement with Whalley obliged them to employ a policeman specifically to protect the Brantham Hall estate from the depredations of the navvies. Early in December, 1844, the directors themselves interviewed and appointed John Tunmer to be this policeman, at a weekly wage of seventeen shillings (85p); he seems to have been the first outdoor servant of the company. Some months later Whalley complained that Tunmer was neglecting his duties and the constable was summoned to Ipswich and "requested to be more attentive to his duties in future, as upon a second complaint being made he would be forthwith dismissed".

Land charges and compensation at Brantham Hall cost the Eastern Union Railway Company about £2,500, a modest sum compared to what the Eastern Counties Company paid to some of the landowners with which it had to deal.

Among the other railway Bills before Parliament in this same Session was that authorizing extension of the Eastern Counties Railway from Newport to Brandon, and another to sanction the line from Norwich to Brandon. If both Bills were successful Norwich would have a rail link with London. The Eastern Union promoters had therefore confined their Bill to a line from Colchester to Ipswich and, indeed, their prospectus had stated that nothing further was to be attempted until the result of the Norwich and Brandon application was known. It was hoped thereby to avoid the opposition of any Norfolk interests and to reduce to a manageable number the points upon which the Eastern Counties Company might be provoked.

The last real hurdle for the Eastern Union Bill was the Committee in the Lords, which stage it reached on 4th July. Here, at last, there was open opposition from the E.C.R. When asked

A newspaper announcement of the proposal to obtain an Act for a railway between Norwich and Brandon, November, 1843.

Norwich and Brandon RAILWAY.

Notice is Hereby Given,

THAT application is intended to be made to Parliament in the ensuing Session for an Act to make and maintain a Railway, with all proper works and conveniences connected therewith, commencing in a field in the parish of Weeting, otherwise Weeting All Saints, in the county of Norfolk, adjoining or near to the high road leading from Brandon to Swaffham; passing thence from, in, through, or into the several parishes, townships, town lands, extra parochial, or other places of Weeting, otherwise Weeting All Saints, and Weeting Saint Mary, Broomhill, Brandon, otherwise Brand, Santon, West Tofts, Saint Peter Thetford, Croxton, West Wretham, otherwise Little Wretham, East Wretham, otherwise Great Wretham, Kilverstone, Bridgeham, otherwise Bridgham, Roudham, Snetterton, East Harling, Illington, Quidenham, Larling, Eccles, Hargham, Attleborough, otherwise Attleburgh, Old Buckenham, Besthorpe, Morley Saint Peter, Morley Saint Botolph, Wymondham, otherwise Wyndham Suton, Hethel, Hethersett, Ketteringham, East Carlton, Intwood, otherwise Intwood cum Keswick, Cringleford, Keswick, Marketshall, otherwise Markshall, Caister cum Marketshall, Arminghall, otherwise Armeringhall, Swardeston, Trowse Newton, Thorpe Saint Andrew, or some of them in the County of Norfolk; Eaton, Lakenham, Trowse otherwise Trowse Millgate, Carrow, Bracondale, Thorpe, or some of them, in the City and Borough of Norwich and County of the same City, and terminating by a Junction with the line of the Yarmouth and Norwich Railway, as at present authorised to be made in or near a Field in the Hamlet of Thorpe, in the City and Borough of Norwich and County of the said City numbered 15 in the Plan of the said last-mentioned Railway, deposited with the Clerk of the Peace for the County of the said City. And also to make and maintain a Branch Railway, diverging from and out of the Main Line of the said intended Railway in a certain Heath or Common, known by the name of Two Mile Bottom, in the Parish of Saint Peter's, Thetford, in the said County of Norfolk, and passing in, or through, and terminating within the said last-mentioned Parish, and the Parish of Saint Cuthbert, Thetford, or one of them, in the said County, near the Town of Thetford. And it is intended by the said Act, to incorporate a Company for the purpose of executing the said proposed Railway, with powers for the compulsory purchase of Lands required for the construction thereof, and levying Tolls for and in respect of the use of the same, and with powers also of entering into and carrying into effect, arrangements with the Yarmouth and Norwich Railway Company, or any other Company in reference to the construction of the said intended Railway, or any part thereof, and the use and working thereof on such terms and conditions as may be mutually agreed on, and to enable the said Yarmouth and Norwich Railway Company, or any such other Company, also to enter into and carry into effect such arrangements, and to raise and provide such funds as may be necessary for the purpose. And it is also intended by the said Act to vary and extend all rights and privileges which may in any manner interfere with the objects aforesaid, and to confer other rights and privileges.—And notice is hereby lastly given, that Plans and Sections, describing the line and levels of the said proposed Railway and Branch, and the works connected therewith, and the lands to be taken for the purposes thereof, together with Books of Reference to such Plans, containing the names of the reputed Owners, Lessees, and Occupiers of such Lands, will be deposited on or before the thirtieth day of November inst. with the Clerk of the Peace for the County of Norfolk, at his Office in Aylsham, and with the Clerk of the Peace for the City and County of the City of Norwich, at his Office in the City of Norwich, and a Copy of so much of the said Plans, Sections, and Books of Reference as relate to each of the Parishes through which the proposed Railway and Branch will pass, will be deposited on or before the thirty-first day of December next, with the Parish Clerks of such Parishes respectively, at their respective residences.

Dated this 1st day of November, 1843.

PARKER and HAYES,
1, Lincoln's Inn Fields, London,
Solicitors for the Bill.

upon what grounds they were opposing the Bill, their counsel replied that they were promoters of a competing line from Colchester to Bury St Edmunds.

Austin, who was said to have "entered with feeling into the merits of the case" because it concerned his native Suffolk, argued that the Committee should take no account of that scheme, because no Bill had been brought forward for it and, so far as their Lordships were concerned, it did not exist. Their Lordships agreed with him. The Eastern Counties Company then objected as landowners; but again Austin, "in a most able speech", argued that on this basis they were virtually a competing company. After some discussion, the Committee decided that the E.C.R had no basis for its case and declared that the preamble to the Bill was proved. It received the Royal Assent on 19th July, 1844.

The Act was a lengthy one of 358 sections, some of which now seem very strange. In the early days a railway was considered to be like a canal or a turnpike road, and anybody had the right to use their own locomotives and carriages upon it, on paying the tolls. At least on the E.U.R. all traffic was required to conform to the company's regulations (it had not always been so on some railways!). Locomotives were to be approved, and faulty ones taken away. Particulars of all vehicles using the line were to be lodged with the company, and privately owned ones were to have their numbers, weights *and gauges* painted on them. The names of the toll collectors were to be displayed, in letters two inches high, on any building where they were on duty. Any collector who failed to display such a notice, or who declined to divulge his name, or gave a false one, or who used "scurrilous or abusive language" to any person lawfully using the railway, could be fined £10.

In 1845 many routine provisions were collected together into the Railway Clauses Consolidation Act and the Companies Clauses

The original E.U.R. office building in Lower Brook Street, Ipswich. Coincidentally, it now houses the legal practice established by George Josselyn, the Mayor who presided over the inaugural meeting in 1843, and one of the directors of the company.

Consolidation Act; later railway Acts, by merely referring to these two general statutes, were made much shorter.

The Eastern Union share capital was to be £200,000 in £50 shares, but in addition the company could borrow £66,666 on mortgages or bonds when all the share capital had been subscribed for and half of it actually paid up. This power to borrow up to a third above the share capital was usual.

There were to be at least nine directors, and not more than twelve. The first board members, eleven in number, were named in the Act:

J.C Cobbold	(Ipswich)	J.G. Hart	(Stowmarket)
John Cobbold	(Ipswich)	Geo. Josselyn	(Ipswich)
R.D. Alexander	(Ipswich)	Joseph Shaw	(Huddersfield)
John Footman	(Ipswich)	C.H. Jones	(Huddersfield)
T.D. Burroughes	(Ipswich)	William May	(Ipswich)
Jeremiah Head	(Ipswich)		

John Chevallier Cobbold (1797–1882), chairman of the Eastern Union Railway.

The redoubtable John Chevallier Cobbold was elected chairman; he held the position throughout the life of the company. John Footman was elected vice-chairman and managing director; he was a member of a family of well-known drapers in Ipswich, and the business, now a large department store, carried his name until 1972. However, unlike another draper, the notorious George Hudson, he retained the trust of his associates until other commitments obliged him to give up active participation in Eastern Union affairs in March, 1849. He died in October, 1854, at the early age of fifty-two. He seems to have had a latent talent for railway administration and in particular he handled the acquisition of the land required for the line between Colchester and Ipswich almost single handed.

Early in 1846, Shaw and Jones resigned from the board of directors, and James Grayston of York and William Hawkins of Alresford Hall, near Colchester, were co-opted in their places. Both were to serve for many years; Hawkins was to be associated with Bruff in other enterprises.

James Ferguson Saunders was appointed secretary of the company, a position which his younger brother Charles already held with the Great Western Railway. Joseph Locke was retained as engineer, although all the day-to-day work was handled entirely by his former pupil, whom he appointed resident engineer. The Eastern Union directors confirmed the appointment, at an annual salary of £400, with the condition that Bruff was to serve "not only on the present line but in the future extensions of it".

The company leased a house in Lower Brook Street, Ipswich, as offices; a few years later, if not at once, Bruff had an office a few doors away.

Construction of the Line 5

B RASSEY and William Mackenzie wasted little time in commencing work on the line.

The contractors had intended to start where the heaviest earthworks occurred, at the deep cutting at Brantham, and they began landing plant and materials from barges at Cattawade towards the end of August, 1844. In those days land transport was difficult and expensive, and it was fortunate that navigable water came within easy reach of the proposed railway at intervals of only about nine miles from the existing railhead at Colchester.

Because of delays in obtaining entry to all the necessary land, construction actually began on 1st October at Bentley, some three miles nearer to Ipswich, under a sub-contractor named Larke. Within the next two months work was in full swing at Brantham and elsewhere in Suffolk. It seems that no work was started on the Essex side of the Stour until the end of the year.

Victorian England looked askance at the armies of workmen assembled for building railways; never before in living memory had so many men been gathered together, except in time of war. Vice and violence were often rampant among them. As had been done elsewhere, it was suggested that a chaplain should be appointed to minister to the spiritual needs of the men working on the Eastern Union, and a meeting was convened in Ipswich in December. Well-meaning clergymen and others spoke of what had been done on other railways; of how Peto, the Baptist contractor on the Norwich and Brandon line, had paid for Bibles to be distributed to his navvies and had employed two persons to attend to the spiritual condition of the men. It was decided on the Eastern Union works to set up places of worship at Brantham and Wherstead, and possibly schools as well. A fund was started.

In the following October, a correspondent wrote to the *Suffolk Chronicle* saying he had subscribed a guinea and asking what progress had been made. Answer came there none.

It was Brassey's custom, as with most other contractors engaged on railway building at that time, to sub-let the work extensively, and some of the larger sub-contractors sub-let their portions again. The larger sub-contracts would comprise the construction of several miles of the line for a lump sum, laid down by Brassey on a "take it or leave it" basis — a sum which he estimated would allow a reasonable profit to those carrying it out if the work was undertaken in a proper manner — although he would invariably agree to extra payment if difficulties which he had not foreseen arose. He did not ask for such extras himself from the companies employing him.

His success as a contractor came about partly from his skill in estimating the cost of work, partly from his genius for organising the execution of it and getting the best out of those whom he employed, and partly from his unshakable integrity. Just as these factors recommended Brassey to the engineers for whom he worked, so they did to those who worked under him; it is not surprising that many of his sub-contractors and employees continued with him for years.

Some of the larger sub-contracts might be worth anything up to £25,000 but the value was carefully fixed to be within the capability of each sub-contractor. Much of the bulk excavation of earth would be let, or sub-let, to gangs of about a dozen men known as "butty gangs" who undertook the work at so much a waggonload, the price being agreed by their elected ganger.

Brassey provided the materials, except the actual rails and fittings for the permanent way, which on the Eastern Union — as often in more modern times — were provided by the railway company. He also provided items of plant such as the earth waggons, some of which were shipped to Ipswich direct from Rouen as work on the French contract was completed; he later ordered 2,400 of these waggons from the Ipswich firm of Ransomes & May (now Ransomes, Sims & Jefferies Ltd.) for use on the Great Northern Railway contract. On his earlier contracts, Brassey provided the horses for hauling these waggons, but by the time the line was constructed between Colchester and Ipswich the sub-contractors were responsible for their own animals.

Alexander Cummings, a sub-contractor on the Norwich Extension, advertised his plant and tools for sale at Mellis when he had completed his work in October, 1848. There were ten horses, with their harness, and also

> a timber drug with 6 inch wheels, nearly new; with the Working Tools, etc — comprising 30 picks, 8 keying and adze hammers, 12 augers, 12 iron crowbars and 12 piles, 6 beetles, 24 shovels, 5 levers, 5 spring bars, 15 lamps with irons (complete), an 8-coomb corn chest, several mangers, racks, etc, 7½ cwt Cart Grease, about 2 tons of nails, spikes, etc; quantity of boards, planks, etc . . .

The augers were for boring holes in the sleepers for the treenails, or oaken pegs, securing the chairs. The adze hammers were used for driving in the pegs, and also the keys which held the rail in the chair; the adze part was probably used to cut a "flat" for the chair upon the rounded sleeper (see Chapter ten). The piles referred to were stout wooden stakes which were driven in to dislodge overhanging masses of earth when cuttings were being excavated; they were driven in with beetles, or heavy mallets. The spring bars were devices used in hitching the horses to the earth waggons for speedy release when "running the tip".

Bridges were sub-let to specialist contractors; the fine five-arch bridge across the Brantham cutting was built by a man named

Barnard, who was also responsible for the massive underline bridge adjacent to the station at Bury St Edmunds.

Brassey and Mackenzie were not partners in any permanent firm, for again it was Brassey's custom to enter into temporary partnerships with others for only one or two contracts, and even to be working simultaneously on different contracts with different partners. The partners appointed Alexander Ogilvie as their site agent to manage the Eastern Union contract, but before it was finished Brassey had taken the contract for the line from Ipswich to Bury St Edmunds in partnership with Ogilvie, who remained as agent.

Alexander Ogilvie, a Scot, was born in 1812. He was trained under the Bridgemaster of Cheshire, where he became acquainted with Brassey, although it seems he first worked with the great contractor on the Eastern Union. Later, in partnership with Brassey and others, he constructed the Portsmouth Direct Line, the Runcorn Viaduct over the Mersey and the Great Eastern lines from Sudbury to Shelford and Bury St Edmunds. Under Bruff's directions, he built the Waveney Valley Railway and the first section of the Tendring Hundred Railway from Colchester Hythe to Wivenhoe. Much of his subsequent work was abroad, chiefly in Argentina.

He must have liked East Anglia, for about 1860 he purchased Sizewell House from Richard Garrett, the Leiston engineer, and it remained his home until he died there in 1886. His family later

Making a cutting. A rather stylised picture, probably based on one of a cutting blasted through rock, from Our Iron Roads, *by F. S. Williams, 1852. A cutting through earth would have been progressively stepped at the working face, which this artist has hidden.*

became much involved with the development of the modern seaside hamlet of Thorpeness.

Towards the end of May, 1845, the *Ipswich Journal* reported:

> The works are now proceeding with great rapidity; the lights on different parts of the line indicating that the night is not suffered to interpose any hindrance to the labours of the excavators.

But either by day or by night, conditions on the sites would have appalled modern engineers. In 1846 a Parliamentary Select Committee was appointed to investigate the welfare of railway labourers, but none of its recommendations was immediately adopted. The working and living conditions of the navvies were generally accepted by contemporary opinion as unworthy of comment.

One thing however which contemporary opinion would not accept was the continuation of work on Sundays.

"A strong feeling was excited last week by some of the men being employed in laying the rails on the Sunday, but a representation on the subject being made to J.C. Cobbold, Esq., he, in the most prompt and decided manner, took steps to prevent a repetition of this unseemly violation of the Sabbath", said the *Bury Post*, concerning work near that town.

The Mayor of Colchester went even further. As chief magistrate, he went out personally ordering the contractors to stop work, and issued instructions that summonses were to be taken out against any ganger whose men were found to be doing Sunday work within the borough boundary. The men were glad enough not to work seven days a week, but feared they would be dismissed if they refused.

In those less safety-conscious days it was inevitable that there should be accidents. The railway from Colchester to Ipswich was constructed at the cost of seven lives; three others were killed while working on the south side of Ipswich tunnel, which included levelling the site for the Eastern Union terminus. Others were seriously injured.

Most of these unfortunate people came from the villages of the district and it seems likely that the majority of the labour force consisted of local men, apart from the gangers and skilled tradesmen. Except at Ipswich tunnel there was none of the fighting which characterised railway construction in the North and in the Midlands. East Anglia had plenty of impoverished agricultural labourers who were glad of the better-paid work on the railway and there was less industrial work in the towns to attract men away from the countryside. Witnesses before the 1846 Select Committee spoke of agricultural workers in Devon and elsewhere finding railway work too hard for them for long, and no doubt there was a high turnover of labour on the Eastern Union line also; certainly the numbers working on the railway rose after harvest time.

The railway under construction at the foot of Belstead Bank, with the Orwell in the distance; an etching by Henry Davy dated 11th July, 1845. Note the rails and half-round sleepers in the foreground and the navvies' huts in the trees.

Author's collection

The excavations for the cuttings were all done by hand; by a hazardous technique known as "holing out", a mass of as much as fifty tons of earth would be dislodged at a time. An engineer described it to the Select Committee thus:

That kind of material that will permit of the operation is worked at a vertical face of from 8 to 12 feet, the men working at the front of it . . . take a space of two yards in width, and with their picks they work underneath it for . . . a yard back, leaving a solid space of from one foot to two feet; they take another interval of two yards, and so on, as the width of the face. At the same time that the men are holing it at the bottom, there are other men at the end, clearing down the end, cutting a channel two feet wide, to loosen the sides of it, and when this has been done, the men then set another, if they are careful, to watch upon the top, to see if the ground gives any notice of cracking or falling; they then knock away these piers, or as they term it, knock its legs from under it; and if the earth does not fall, after it has been so weakened, piles are driven in upon the top, to drive it down. Where it is well managed, it will fall over; that is the object, and as it breaks itself into pieces, it requires little trouble, and they can fill it with shovels into the waggons . . .

Experienced men knew the exact height of face to be tackled; if the height was too great the earth would merely subside downwards and forwards in one piece. "The great aim is to make the dirt fall over", it was said. Risky by day, the process was positively perilous by night, when only the more "careful" men thought to station one of their mates on top, to feel the width of any crack with his hand and try to give warning of the impending collapse.

In April, 1845, there was an inquest at Colchester on a young man from Aldham, near Hadleigh, who had been killed by an earth fall.

> . . . one of the men called as a witness stated that they did not apprehend any danger, as they had only undermined the earth about nine inches, while they had sometimes gone as far as 3½ feet. The Coroner cautioned him about taking such great risks but the man replied that the soil was very stiff, and as they had taken the work at a low price, they were obliged to do it the "gainest" way they could to get a livelihood.

The victim was obviously a member of a butty-gang.

On the Stour Valley line to Sudbury, a Bures man was similarly killed on his first day at work. "The Jury on viewing the body expressed their astonishment at its horribly mutilated state; and the Coroner observed that he had never before witnessed anyone so shockingly crushed", said the *Ipswich Journal*.

The earth waggons ran on temporary tramroads; as they were filled they were moved along the formation to where the soil was required to be tipped out to form the embankments. If the gradient allowed, the waggons were pushed so that they ran by gravity. In January, 1845, William Worlledge was pushing a loaded waggon on what is now called Belstead Bank when he was overtaken by another waggon pushed by four men. He did not hear their shouts of warning and was crushed between the two waggons. He was the first fatal accident victim on the line and had only started on the railway that day, having come from Framlingham to seek work, together with his son-in-law and two others.

To stop the trundling waggons, it was usual to thrust an iron bar or "brake pole" through the spokes of one of the wheels. Running beside the waggons to do this, it was easy to trip, as fourteen-year-old David Garwood did on the Ipswich dock tramway in 1847; he died under the leading waggon of a set of five. Near Colchester, on the Eastern Union in 1846, a labourer had inserted his bar when it was torn from his hands and thrown up into his face, seriously injuring him.

If the waggons could not be moved by gravity, or to hasten the work, horses were used, often tended by young boys. At night, at any rate, some contractors forbade their workers to drive the horses faster than at a walking pace. One night in April, 1845, a West Bergholt man named Spooner was ignoring this rule when he tripped and was killed under the waggons near Ardleigh.

By day, horses were used for the dangerous practice of "running the tip". Each waggon in turn was uncoupled from the others and hitched to a horse which was urged forward into a gallop by the driver running alongside. When nearly at the end of the embankment, the driver loosed the horse and the animal was trained to turn off to one side and stop. The waggon ran past under its own impetus and on to the brink, where it struck a sleeper placed across the rails. The body of the waggon tipped forward and the earth was shot down the face of the embankment. A youth from Hockham, in Norfolk, was engaged in this "ingenious but perilous employment" near Bury St Edmunds in November, 1845, when his horse turned to the wrong side. The lad tried to run across the track to retain control of the animal, but he tripped and fell to his death under the lumbering waggon. The *Suffolk Chronicle* commented primly:

> a circumstance which we should have hoped would have created serious reflection in the minds of the men employed . . . but the oaths and blasphemous expressions used by these men while employed in the most dangerous positions are horrid in the extreme.

The *Bury Post* was more practical:

> We would strongly urge upon the Railway Contractors the necessity of so arranging the gear that the driver may not have occasion to cross the rails before the truck, thereby risking his life upon the sureness of his foot or his hold of the horse.

Giving evidence before the Select Committee, John Sharp, a contractor on the South Devon Railway, claimed that the earth waggons he used were safer in this respect. The shorthand writer faithfully recorded his halting sentences:

> . . . we have no spring attached to them; you have only a horse to pull it on the one side, the hook comes out, there is no spring to miss; you have only to pull the horse away from the waggon and it clears itself; it is simply a straight bar that comes out on one side of the waggon and when you hitch the horse on . . . you put it to the side you want to send the waggon, and as soon as the horse is turned about the hook drops out.

The process was dangerous enough, but the foolhardiness of some of the navvies was incredible. An Ipswich man employed tipping on the Woodbridge extension of the Eastern Union some ten years later was actually running between the rails, in spite of repeated warnings from his ganger not to do so. The coroner could only shake his head in amazement. It is difficult, too, to decide by what gymnastic feat a man named Wilden encompassed his fate at Tostock, near Bury St Edmunds. According to the *Suffolk Chronicle,* he "in unhooking the tip chain, caught his neck in the chain, so that his head went between the bumpers of the waggons".

At 10.30 p.m. on 12th August, 1845, when it was dark, a sixteen-year-old lad named Chaplin was leading a horse when he tripped and received fatal injuries under a waggon near the bridges at Cattawade. The coroner's jury heard how the sub-contractor's agent sent for Mr Smith, a surgeon at Manningtree, who did not come but sent his assistant instead. This assistant ordered Chaplin to be removed to the hospital at Ipswich, nine

Running the tip, from
Our Iron Roads, *1852.*
All too often the horse ran
between the rails.

miles away. A cart was obtained and the wretched lad, fortified with brandy for the ordeal, began his journey at 4.30 a.m. He was dead on arrival at 7 a.m.

The agent explained that the surgeon was under contract to attend the men in cases of accident "at the rate of three half pence per week, per man, whether sick or well. The average number Mr Smith had to attend was about 100 and the average rate of payment 12s. 6d. per week". The jury deplored the attempt to move the patient.

The evidence given to the 1846 Select Committee included many instances of similar medical insurance schemes, both on construction sites and in mines. The schemes were usually organised by the men themselves, although some of the more enlightened employers, such as Morton Peto, made the contributions compulsory. In some cases the subscriptions were higher so that a weekly payment could be made to the sick or injured.

A couple of months after Chaplin's death Mr Smith's anonymous assistant attended to another lad, fatally injured under a waggon on a Mr Brown's sub-contract at Ardleigh. Although the victim had received first aid (including the inevitable shot of brandy) and was on his way to Colchester Hospital in a butcher's cart all within about twenty minutes, the Colchester coroner was strongly critical. He

> thought it a great pity that no provision was made by the railway contractors for the reception of persons meeting with accidents. It would be easy for them to have a small travelling hospital of their own; a caravan might be obtained at a trifling expense, in which might be placed a bed . . . it could be removed with facility from place to place . . .

Although railway companies were often accused of being indifferent to the working conditions and sufferings of the men who built their lines, the Eastern Union Railway Company, at least, donated £50 each to the hospitals in Colchester and Ipswich. The Ipswich and Bury Railway Company, too, made donations to the hospitals at each end of its line "in consequence of the accidents that had occurred". After a mishap in which a navvy from Buckinghamshire lost an arm in August, 1846, "Mr Hart, one of the Directors, kindly visited him on Friday, and his case will no doubt be liberally considered by the Company". In 1849, a nineteen-year-old lad, Joseph Lambert, from Bramford, was appointed as a gate-keeper at a wage of ten shillings a week, "he having lost an Arm during the Construction of the Company's Works". This had happened when he had been "running the tip" at Gislingham on the Norwich Extension. At the time they lost their limbs, neither of these men was directly employed by the company.

As a cutting was excavated wider and deeper into a hillside, earth from the higher parts was sometimes barrowed out along stagings and tipped into waggons below. In the southern approach cutting to the tunnel at Ipswich, one man's barrow slipped off the staging. He tried to prevent it from falling but overbalanced and fell himself, sustaining spinal injuries from which he died. His funeral in the town was attended by a hundred of his workmates "cleanly and neatly attired".

In the deepest cuttings extra tramroads would be laid at

Making an embankment, from Our Iron Roads. *The size of the figures on top indicates the height then tipped in a single operation; nowadays the earth is always carefully compacted in horizontal layers only a foot or two deep. The underline bridge shown would have had the bank tipped up to and over it; the original bridge adjacent to the present Ipswich station collapsed under such treatment.*

higher levels, positioned so that they formed ledges on the sides of the completed excavation. These "turn-off" lines, as they were called, were particularly useful where there was more earth to be dug out than was required for adjacent embankments; they reached the original ground surface in a shorter distance than the formation, or floor of the cutting, and the surplus earth could be tipped out on the adjoining sloping ground.

In August, 1845, William Leighton, a sixteen-year-old lad from near Norwich, was driving a horse with an empty earth waggon on the turn-off line in Brantham cutting when the animal left the line of the track. As Leighton was trying to regain control, the horse kicked him and he fell down the bank on to the tramroad on the cutting floor, right in front of two loaded waggons which were trundling out towards the tip. He was killed.

It was not only the men and boys who stumbled in front of the waggons; a number of horses were lost in this way and others bolted away over the edge of the tips. Webb, the sub-contractor at Wherstead, lost three of his animals in the space of a few weeks in 1845. I do not know whether Webb's contract extended right to the Ipswich terminus, but there, in the following April,

Navvies' shanties among the trees near the foot of Belstead Bank; a detail from Davy's etching, shown in full on page 36.

> as a man was driving a waggon load of earth along the line . . . the horse stumbled, and before it could recover itself the waggon passed over its hind legs, one of which was completely crushed. As soon as the accident occurred, the driver informed some men in the workshop of it, and is then supposed to have absconded, as he was not seen during the rest of the day. The animal, which is the third that has been lost through the carelessness of this man, was immediately killed.

The men employed on the works — and by the summer of 1845 they numbered about a thousand — lived in rough shanties beside the line, if they could not obtain lodgings in nearby villages. Two of these shacks can be seen in the illustration of the works at Wherstead.

One night in January, 1846, a temporary stable, similarly built of faggots roofed with thatch, was burned down on the works of the Ipswich and Bury Railway near Norton. It belonged to a sub-contractor named Robert Sallis, who had worked for Brassey for several years. Sallis got his wife and family out safely from an adjoining hut, but both structures were completely destroyed and the family lost everything they possessed, including five horses and a week's supply of food for the workmen. With his loss estimated at £125, Sallis was destitute, but an appeal organised throughout the district on his behalf brought in £117 (see Appendix one).

The company's originally authorised capital of £200,000 was based upon an estimate for a single line only. However, it was always intended that the Eastern Union line should eventually extend to Norwich and it was obvious that the line should be double. Construction for a double line was undertaken right from the start, but it was not until the company's first general meeting on

11th December, 1844, that it was formally resolved that it should be so. It was estimated that the extra cost would be about £50,000 and the company obtained an Act of Parliament dated 21st July, 1845, permitting the creation of new shares to this amount.

By May, 1845, good progress had been made on the line. Between Ipswich and Ardleigh most of the earthworks were complete, apart from the deep Brantham cutting, but even this was so far through the hill that the Manningtree road had already been diverted and carried across on a temporary timber bridge. A length of the permanent way had been laid at Bentley.

The situation was less satisfactory where the E.C.R. had resumed work on the two-and-a-half-mile length near Colchester. Here Bruff discovered that the line was not being constructed in accordance with the original E.C.R. Act of 1836, as it should have been, but was on much steeper gradients. It was being built to form part of Braithwaite's proposed line to Harwich, but this had been rejected by Parliament long before, in May, 1844!

The E.U.R. directors had anticipated trouble on this length and, as provided for in their Act, they had already approached the Essex magistrates to appoint an independent engineer as arbitrator. James Walker, "the government engineer", had been chosen and the company now appealed to him.

Bruff hoped that Walker would allow the E.U.R. to discard the length and construct their own line, but eventually the two companies reached agreement on 22nd September, 1845. It was decided that the E.U.R. should complete the work and then purchase the length, for a sum to be agreed between Locke and Robert Stephenson, representing the two parties, with I.K. Brunel as umpire. A compromise was reached on the question of a line to Harwich.

The arrangement was authorised by an Act dated 26th June,

Spoil heaps still line the top of the cutting between Colchester and Ardleigh, dumped there by Wythes' navvies lowering the trackbed in 1846. This particular heap was removed to give working space when the adjacent bridge was reconstructed for the electrification of the line.

1846, by which the E.U.R. could raise additional capital of £20,000 for the purchase. The company's powers to build its own line to the north of Colchester station were annulled. Alas, when the time came the arbitrators fixed the price at £49,000, which made the section the most expensive part of the line.

The contractor building this short length for the E.C.R. was George Wythes, who later built many lines both at home and

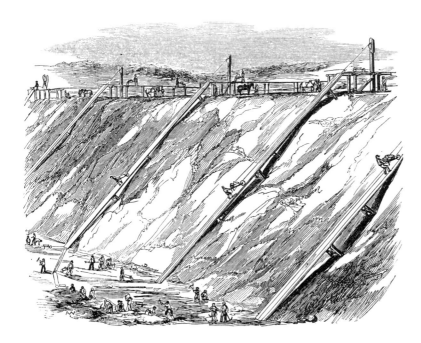

Making the running, from Our Iron Roads. *Although the cutting near Ardleigh is not nearly so deep as the one depicted here, this illustration shows the highly dangerous technique used to haul spoil up the slope. The rope was attached to both the barrow and the man's belt.*

abroad. Bruff may have disapproved of the gradients, but he seems to have been impressed by Wythes, for he kept him on, and he was among the official guests at the opening of the line to Ipswich. Bruff later employed Wythes to construct the branches to Hadleigh, Sudbury and Harwich, negotiating prices with him alone, in the manner of Locke.

Both the timber viaducts over the arms of the Stour estuary at Cattawade were complete by December, 1845, although the embankment between them was not quite finished. On the Essex side of the river, the embankment was being extended steadily out from the high ground at Lawford, where a steam locomotive was used to haul the empty earth waggons back up to the cutting.

The lofty bridge over the Brantham cutting was not begun until 1846. The gradients between Ardleigh and Colchester were restored by lowering the floors of the cuttings and taking the spoil up over the top with "barrow runs". These involved another

Brantham Bridge under construction in 1846, from the Illustrated London News. *The cutting seems to have been left with perilously steep sides where the temporary bridge was carried across on a single span.*

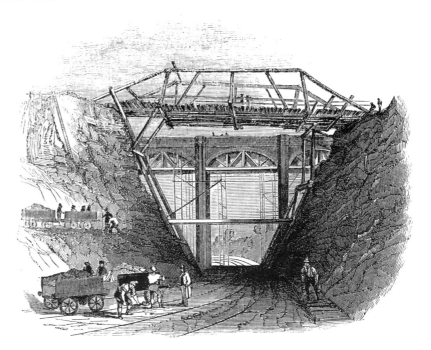

dangerous practice, in which both a wheel barrow and the man using it were pulled up a sloping plankway by a horse at the top.

The embankment at Cattawade was finished at the beginning of May, 1846, the last length of permanent way was laid, and the line was complete throughout. In the words of the *Ipswich Journal:*

> The junction of the embankments at Cattawade causeway having been effected on Saturday last [2nd May, 1846], Mr Ogilvie, the agent of Messrs Brassey and Mackenzie the contractors, decided on traversing the entire line with a locomotive engine, and on Tuesday morning an engine and tender arrived from Lawford at the Ipswich station, about seven o'clock in the morning. The engine has for some time been upon the line, having been employed in drawing the earth waggons between Ardleigh and Manningtree. At nine o'clock a large party left Ipswich by the train which consisted of a number of open luggage wains. Peter Bruff Esq, the Company's engineer, took the direction of the locomotive, and the journey to Colchester was accomplished in about an hour and a half. At twelve, a larger party left Colchester in the train, which now consisted of some new and very elegant first, second and third class carriages, built for the Company, and reached Ipswich in 1 hour 25 minutes.

The *Suffolk Chronicle's* account was less detailed, but it concluded:

> The party then proceeded to the Coach and Horses, Brook Street, and spent the rest of the day in social conviviality.

All the navvies were given a day's holiday and appropriate liquid refreshment.

On 7th May one of the company's own locomotives arrived from the builders, bringing with it a further batch of carriages from Colchester.

Shortly afterwards the company applied to the Board of Trade for the official inspection so that the line might be opened for passenger traffic but General Pasley,[4] who was to carry it out, was away inspecting railways in the North.

In the meantime, according to the *Ipswich Journal* (23rd May):

The Company's new engine has several times traversed the line with material for the roads at Bentley and Cattawade, and on Monday last [18th May] took a party in a first and second class carriage to the latter place, and were only prevented from extending their trip to Colchester, because it was deemed inexpedient to disturb the workmen engaged at Cattawade. At this point an iron girder bridge is erecting, which will be completed this day. This bridge is an addition to the original plan of the railway, by which a level crossing only was intended, but the height of the embankment admitting of a space of 10 or 11 feet, the bridge was thought desirable, as the ordinary traffic of the road will not be interrupted by the gates of the railway.

This bridge, now of steel, and the adjoining level crossing are still to be seen close to Manningtree station.

In 1985 Brantham Bridge was again surrounded with scaffolding as the road was widened. The ledge for the "turn-off" tramway when the cutting was made can still be discerned on the left.

The formal opening of the E.U.R. at Ipswich on 11th June, 1846; an etching by Henry Davy published only eight days later.

Author's collection

The scene at Colchester on 11th June, 1846, from the Illustrated London News. *The building in the centre opened as the Victoria Hotel in 1844, a venture which had already failed by this time.*

Goods traffic began on Monday, 1st June, 1846,[5] and it was noted that "the powerful engines of the Company surmount the gradients without difficulty; the ascent between Ipswich and Bentley being accomplished at the rate of 30 miles the hour."

On the Tuesday, General Pasley "was expected at Colchester and the Directors, as in duty bound, were in waiting to meet him, but after cooling their heels there for some time, they returned without having seen the gallant Government official. However he made his appearance on Thursday" when the directors and officials of the company, having again turned out with a special train, greeted the General and Joseph Locke as they alighted from the London train at Colchester shortly after eleven o'clock.

Pasley and Locke, with Bruff, took their places on the footplate of the Eastern Union locomotive for the journey to

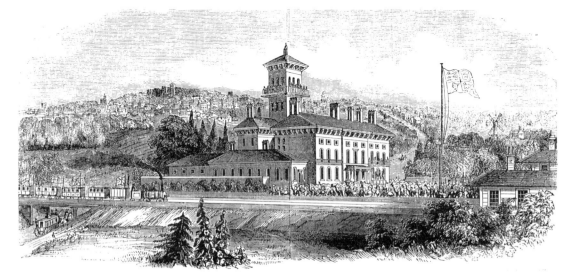

Ipswich. At intervals the train was stopped and the party got down to examine various works, such as the "substantial and scientifically constructed viaducts" over the Stour.

The line having been passed for public passenger traffic, the official opening took place on 11th June, 1846. In Ipswich, shops and workplaces were closed and the day was a general holiday, by special request of the Mayor. At 10.30 a.m. a train left the station, hauled by "two of the Company's noble engines"[6] and consisting of twelve carriages and a truck carrying a band.

At Halifax Junction, where the line to Bury St Edmunds diverged towards the tunnel mouth, a triumphal arch had been erected. Nearby, a grandstand accommodated six hundred ladies who waved "snowy kerchiefs" as the train passed by with the band playing the National Anthem. On the leading locomotive, driven by Robert Taylor, the locomotive foreman, rode Bruff and John Squire Martin, the traffic superintendent. It was a proud moment.

J.C. Cobbold joined the train at Bentley, where another arch spanned the line. There were other stops at Manningtree, at Lawford Mills — to take in water — and at Ardleigh. Everywhere the train was greeted by cheering crowds; many other people watched from the bridges and any suitable vantage point. At 11.45 the train arrived at Colchester. There, of course, it was no novelty, and "the good people of Colchester did not appear to be so much moved by the opening of the line, as were their more vivacious brethren of Ipswich", as one Suffolk journalist quaintly put it.

Waiting to meet the party were George Hudson, chairman of the E.C.R., Joseph Locke and others who had travelled down from London in a special train of six carriages. The two trains were joined together and, worked by the two engines, arrived in Ipswich

One wall of the original engine shed at Ipswich survived until the loco depot closed in 1968. On the other side was the lean-to stable (see the plan on page 132); this, converted to an enginemen's rest-room about 1863, was latterly just a mess-room.

The viaducts at Cattawade, 1846, from the Illustrated London News.

after a journey lasting slightly less than an hour. Again, there were stops at every station. At Halifax Junction the ladies waved again from their stand — one wonders whether they were the same ladies and, if so, what they had been doing in the intervening two and half hours. Guns were fired and church bells pealed.

After lunch, some of the visitors went for a steamer trip down the Orwell to Harwich. On their return, a gathering of about two hundred sat down to a banquet in the Assembly Rooms, which began at about 5 p.m. and went on for five hours, with many toasts and speeches.

While the banquet was going on, the contractors entertained about 270 of their workers at Manningtree, and at Ipswich there were dinners for the company's staff and for the sub-contractors. The navvies from the tunnel were given a meal at the *Railroad Tavern*, Stoke Hill; this seems to have been a temporarily converted house above the tunnel,[7] catering for the needs of the thirsty miners as they came up out of the shafts.

In the course of the evening the celebrated aeronaut Charles Green made a balloon ascent over the town, and the festivities concluded with a firework display by the Wet Dock. It was all typical of how our forefathers celebrated with what they termed "éclat".

The line opened for public passenger traffic on 15th June, 1846.[8]

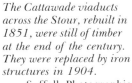

The Cattawade viaducts across the Stour, rebuilt in 1851, were still of timber at the end of the century. They were replaced by iron structures in 1904.
Suffolk Photographic Survey, Suffolk Record Office

Stopped in the Tunnel and Lost in the Bog 6

AS SOON as the E.U.R. Company was incorporated in July, 1844, surveys were undertaken for extending the line to Norwich and Bury St Edmunds, and beyond. Committees to encourage subscriptions were formed in those towns, and also in Newmarket and Cambridge.

Norwich was likely to have one rail link to London, for earlier that summer the E.C.R. had obtained powers to extend the Northern and Eastern Railway from Newport to Brandon, and the Norwich and Brandon Railway had been incorporated.

In September, J.C. Cobbold and other members of the Eastern Union Extension Committee met the local committee in Norwich Guildhall to discuss the proposed line from Ipswich. One gentleman was certainly not present. According to the *Ipswich Journal*:

> We are requested to correct an error into which we have fallen, by inserting the name of R.H. Gurney, Esq, among the committee formed at Norwich. Mr Gurney, we learn, is resolutely opposed to railways in general, and determined not to afford any his approval or support.

At the meeting, it was decided that a prospectus should be issued as soon as possible; and if there was support from the locality, a branch from the line to Dereham should be promoted, and a survey for it undertaken by Locke. The capital required for the double line extension was estimated to be £650,000, and subscriptions were invited in £25 shares at the beginning of October.

At the same time, several schemes were being put forward for railways to Bury St Edmunds, and a public meeting was called in the Shirehall there to try to decide which of them the townspeople should support. The E.C.R. was proposing a branch from Cambridge, where there would soon be a railway. An extension from the E.U.R. at Ipswich was another option. Francis Eagle, a prominent local resident, was advocating a London and Norwich Direct Railway from near Stansted to Thetford, where it would join the Norwich and Brandon; and there was Sir Hyde Parker of Long Melford, with his pet scheme for a line from Chelmsford, via Long Melford, of course. (See map.)

Local support for the East and West Suffolk Railway of the previous year had dwindled away when it was revealed that it would receive support from the E.C.R. only if there was no link with the port facilities at Colchester, and no extension northwards to Thetford. After much discussion, the meeting decided by a small majority that the Norwich Direct would be the best railway for Bury.

These advertisements from the Norwich Mercury *of 31st August, 1844, indicate both that the Eastern Union was going ahead with its plans and that there were people looking in other directions.*

Eastern Union Railway.

Immediate Extension from Ipswich to Norwich & to Bury St. Edmund's.

NOTICE is hereby given, that the Surveys being in progress under the direction of Mr. Locke, the Provisional Committee are prepared to give every attention to the communications of parties interested in these undertakings.

By order,
JAMES F. SAUNDERS,
Secretary.
Railway Office, Brook Street, Ipswich,
August 17th, 1844.   (3514

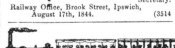

AT a *Meeting of the General Committee for promoting the West Suffolk Railway, held the 28th day of August,* 1844—

It was resolved—

That public attention having been drawn to a proposed Line of Railway from Thetford to Bury and onwards, by or near Haverhill, to join the Northern and Eastern Line at Newport, and no definite answer having been received from the Directors of the Eastern Counties Company, in reply to the resolution of this Committee, dated July 26th, this Committee expresses its readiness to receive any proposal that may be made to it, relative to the above line from Thetford by Bury to London.

That this Meeting be adjourned to this day week, at Two o'clock in the afternoon, for the purpose of receiving such information, and that the same be advertised in the Norwich Papers and Railway Times
J. HANBY HOLMES,
3680)   HONORARY SECRETARY.

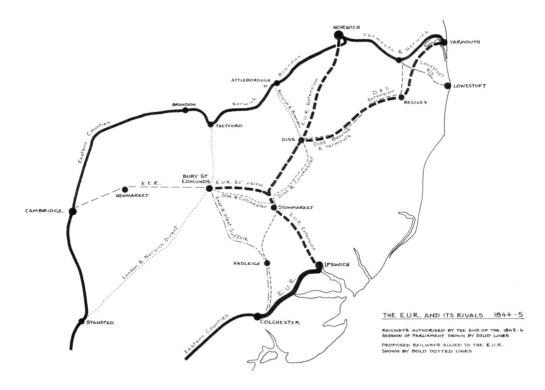

THE E.U.R. AND ITS RIVALS   1844-5

RAILWAYS AUTHORISED BY THE END OF THE 1843-4
SESSION OF PARLIAMENT SHOWN BY SOLID LINES

PROPOSED RAILWAYS ALLIED TO THE E.U.R.
SHOWN BY BOLD DOTTED LINES

J.C. Cobbold, with his Extension Committee, was preparing Bills for two completely independent schemes — Ipswich to Norwich and Ipswich to Bury. These were identical for the first fourteen miles, and there was thus a double chance of Parliament sanctioning a line as far as Haughley. If one scheme should fail, a later application need be only for a comparatively short line, which would then be more likely to be favoured than longer rivals.

It was the E.U.R.'s intention of reaching Norwich which the E.C.R. was determined to thwart. Hudson wanted all the traffic between London and the Norfolk city to pass over the already-sanctioned Cambridge line, of which he would control eighty-seven miles — as far as Brandon — as opposed to only fifty-one miles down to Colchester, on the overall shorter route by way of Ipswich.

In a further bid to strangle Cobbold's schemes, the E.C.R. backed a Colchester and Diss Junction Railway, laid out by Robert Stephenson under the chairmanship of his father, George. This would serve both Norwich and Bury. The E.C.R. also revived its Colchester to Bury line, part of which could easily be combined with the C.&D.J.R.

With these irons in the fire, Hudson wrote to Cobbold offering to take over the Colchester to Ipswich line at cost and to co-operate with the Extension Committee to obtain powers for a line from Stowmarket to Bury, if the committee would abandon their plans north of Stowmarket. If they agreed, the proposed Colchester to Diss line would be dropped. A reply was demanded within three days, but Cobbold and his colleagues had had enough of the E.C.R. and rejected the offer.

Some Colchester people had never forgiven the Eastern Counties Railway for building its terminus so far away from their town. To remedy this, and also to provide a rail link to Hythe quay, a Colchester Port and Junction Railway was proposed in the autumn of 1844. This line was to leave the Eastern Counties main line about two and three-quarter miles on the London side of the terminus and pass in a loop nearer the centre of the town to rejoin the Eastern Union line at Ardleigh. The total length would be about six miles, by-passing Lexden viaduct, and there was to be a short tunnel.

At the first general meeting of the Eastern Union Company, at the Ipswich office on 11th December, 1844, Locke spoke of "the offensive action of the Eastern Counties Company to keep the Eastern Union from anywhere except in a field" at Ardleigh, and he recommended that the promotion of the Colchester loop line should be supported. This point was taken up again at the next meeting on 12th February, and it was resolved to subscribe towards the Colchester Port and Junction the cost of building the line from Ardleigh to the Eastern Counties terminus — the famous two and a half miles. The meeting also resolved to purchase, rent, or at least try to obtain running powers over the Colchester loop line if it were ever constructed.

In the 1844/45 Parliamentary struggle in which the Eastern Union and its protégés were involved, Norwich and Bury St Edmunds were not the only goals. Since May, 1844, Yarmouth had been linked by rail to Norwich, and would have a through route to London when the line through Cambridge was complete.

To provide a shorter route between the Norfolk port and the capital, the Eastern Union supported an independent Diss, Beccles and Yarmouth Railway as an adjunct to its Norwich Extension. The Colchester and Diss promoters put forward an extension of their line to Reedham, a station on the existing Yarmouth and Norwich Railway. Access would be gained either from Colchester, if their main line was sanctioned, or from Attleborough, if the Norwich and Brandon Company's branch to Diss was successful.

By the end of November, 1844, Bills for all these schemes — except Locke's projected line to Dereham — had been deposited in Parliament. In due course they were referred to a special department of the Board of Trade which had been set up to examine projected railways and the claims of potential traffic made for them, and to advise Parliament accordingly. Towards the end of January, 1845, the Board of Trade reported in favour of the

An advertisement for the Diss, Beccles and Yarmouth Railway, October, 1844.

Diss, Beccles, & Yarmouth
RAILWAY.

CAPITAL, £260,000, in 10,400 Shares of £25 each.
Deposit . . . . £1. 10s. per Share.

PROVISIONAL COMMITTEE.

The Viscount Acheson, M. P. Worlingham Hall
The Rev. A. A. Arnold, Ellough Parsonage
J. J. Bedingfield, Esq. Ditchingham, Norfolk
The Right Hon. and Rev. Henry Lord Berners, Kirby Hall, Norfolk
Calverley Bewicke, Esq. Barsham House
T. C. Brettingham, Esq. Brockdish Place, Norfolk
Samuel Brooke, Esq. Diss
John Cooper, Esq. North Cove Hall
W. H. Crowfoot, Esq. Mayor of Beccles
W. J. Crowfoot, Esq. Beccles
Francis Cupiss, Esq. Diss
Sir Wm. Windham Dalling, Bart. Earsham House, Bungay, and Manchester Square, London
Capt. Dalling, R. N. Earsham House, Bungay
H. W. Davey, Esq. Deputy Mayor of Beccles
H. S. Davey, Esq. Beccles
John Day, Esq. Beccles
John Kerrick, Esq. Geldeston Hall
Richard Mann, Esq. Towne Reeve, Bungay
James T. Margitson, Esq. Ditchingham House, Norfolk
Edward P. Montagu, Esq. J. P. Beccles
H. Read, Esq. Worlingham
Lieut.-Colonel John Smith, Ellingham House, Norfolk
Thos. O. Taylor, Esq. Starston Hall, Harleston and Diss
Charles T. Thompson, Esq. Diss
Capt. Sir Eaton Travers, R. N.
The Hon. Henry W. Wilson
Wm. Freeman, Esq. Mayor, Norwich
Wm. May, Esq. Deputy Mayor, Ipswich
Wm. Back, Esq. Stratford, Suffolk
T. O. Springfield, Esq.
John Wright, Esq.
With power to add to their number.

Engineer—Capt. W. S. Moorsom.
Secretary—Richard Mosse, Esq.

SOLICITORS.

Messrs. Stevens, Wilkinson, and Satchell 6, Queen Street, Cheapside, London
Messrs. Margitson and Hartcup, Bungay
Messrs. Bohun and Rix, Beccles
Messrs. Fisher, Lucas, and Steward, Yarmouth
Messrs. Steward and Tillett, Norwich.

BANKERS.

Messrs. Oakes, Fincham, and Co. Diss
Messrs. Taylor and Dyson, Diss
Messrs. Gurney and Co. Harleston, Bungay, Beccles, and Yarmouth.

Eastern Union extensions to Norwich and Bury, and against their rivals. Some schemes were recommended for postponement, among them the Colchester Port and Junction and the Diss, Beccles and Yarmouth Railways.

All Bills, whether or not they were favoured by the Board of Trade, were then scrutinised by a Standing Orders Committee to see that they complied with all the requirements of Parliament and contained no material errors. This Committee Room was the graveyard of many schemes as opposing interests showed that there were mistakes in the drawings, or that legal technicalities in the Bills had been overlooked by those who drew them up.

The sections showing the gradients proposed for Locke and Bruff's line to Norwich came under attack when it was alleged that some of the levels shown were 10 feet in error. One of Bruff's

A levelling party, from Our Iron Roads, *1852.*

assistants, giving evidence, stated that he and his assistants had been turned off the land and their surveying instruments taken from them, but counsel for the landowner said that his client had not objected to the surveyors "until they had brought poachers and other disreputable people with them". These were probably navvies or other burly characters hired to protect the survey parties from gamekeepers and estate workers.

It was also pointed out that in the subscription list Thomas Brassey was shown as having taken up shares totalling £10,000 and £33,000 at different addresses, but the point was allowed when it was explained that the contractor had homes in both Kingston-upon-Thames and Rouen.

The drawings must have stood their test, but the Norwich Extension Bill did not comply with Standing Orders, because one of the subscribers, Walter Cobbold (a brother of the E.U.R. chairman), was also one of the trustees to enforce the payment of calls. It was held that in the event of a dispute he could not sue himself! And so the Bill was thrown out.

Among the Bills which survived all the vicissitudes of passing through Parliament in that session was that of the Lowestoft Railway and Harbour Company. This received the Royal Assent on 30th June, 1845, and was an important step in the development of the Suffolk port by Samuel Morton Peto. The railway which it sanctioned would connect Lowestoft to the Yarmouth and Norwich line at Reedham.

Lowestoft harbour in the nineteenth century, from an album of views by Rock.

Although several schemes were brought forward in the "Railway Mania" to connect Yarmouth to the Eastern Union system, there was probably too much Yarmouth capital involved to envisage a branch to serve its rival, Lowestoft. After an unsuccessful Lowestoft to Beccles promotion in 1845, it was to be many years before the Suffolk port would be connected directly to J.C. Cobbold's lines by Peto's East Suffolk Railway.

The Bill for the Bury Extension went forward and in its later stages was unopposed; it received the Royal Assent on 21st July, 1845. A separate Ipswich and Bury St Edmunds Railway Company was thereby incorporated, with a share capital of £400,000 and the usual power to borrow an extra third of this amount when all the shares had been taken up and half the capital actually paid up.

The Act laid down that there were to be at least nine directors and not more than fifteen; the first of them, thirteen in number, were named in the Act:

John Chevallier Cobbold	(Ipswich)
John Cobbold	(Ipswich)
John Footman	(Ipswich)
George Pratt Barlow	(London)
Frederick Pratt Barlow	(London)
William Crake	(London)
Edward Willett	(Norwich)
Alexander Shafto Adair	(Flixton, near Bungay)
Thomas O. Springfield	(Norwich)
George Josselyn	(Ipswich)
William May	(Ipswich)
William Stitt Wilson	(Norwich)
William Bulkeley Hughes[9]	(Anglesey)

J.C. Cobbold was elected chairman, with G.P. Barlow as his deputy. Two other directors were immediately co-opted to the board to bring the number up to the maximum allowed; these were Samuel Bignold and John Wright, both of Norwich. Five directors of the Ipswich and Bury company were also members of the Eastern Union directorate, namely, the two Cobbolds, Footman, Josselyn and May. The two companies shared the same secretary and engineer, and also the same offices in Ipswich.

As soon as it became obvious that the Bill would be passed, the promoters began negotiating for the acquisition of land and the work of construction commenced within a few days of the Bill becoming law, long before the completion of the Eastern Union line from Colchester to Ipswich. The contract was awarded to Brassey and a ceremony of breaking the first ground took place on 1st August, 1845.

The line to Bury St Edmunds was to leave the original Eastern Union line about half a mile from the Ipswich terminus, at Halifax Junction, a name commemorated on a signal box long after the junction itself had ceased to exist. Swinging away on a curve of half a mile radius, the new line was to pass through a short tunnel under Stoke Hill.

This tunnel was the only one which Bruff ever constructed and, although its length of 361 yards is insignificant, Ipswich Tunnel was probably the first ever driven on so sharp a curve throughout its length.[10] There is a tradition in the locality that Bruff decided to have a tunnel here merely from motives of personal vanity; Locke was invariably opposed to tunnels. Certainly, too, at the initial public meeting in the town, back in 1843, Bruff spoke of the hill as being of "compact dry loamy gravel" when, in fact, springs could be found issuing out of it. Be that as it may, he took no chances in setting out the curve and sank no fewer than three intermediate shafts from the surface of the hill. It was the southernmost of these, not far from the proposed position of the mouth, which was the scene of the inaugural ceremony.

A line of twelve wheelbarrows was drawn up and the Mayor of Ipswich, William Rodwell, took off his coat and tied a handkerchief round his head "in the true style of a railway operative". He then shovelled earth into the first barrow, wheeled it along a plankway to the appointed tipping place and dumped his load, to the cheers and applause of the assembled gathering. As a reward for his efforts, he received a pot of beer from Mr Hawley, the sub-contractor for the tunnel.

He was followed by J.C. Cobbold, and the next eight barrows were similarly dealt with by prominent local people, directors of the Bury and Eastern Union companies among them. The eleventh barrow was wheeled by Edmund Ayres, the assistant secretary to the two companies, and the last by Peter Bruff. All received a pot of beer and the gathering then moved off to a marquee on the top of the hill, where a "déjeuner à la fourchette" was provided. There were the usual speeches with mutual congratulations, in the course of which it was announced that Brassey expected to finish the whole line by the beginning of October, 1846.

A week later the shaft had been excavated to a considerable depth and the work was being hampered by large stones. "No water has yet been found", said the *Suffolk Chronicle*, "though the exterior foot of the hill is very shaky and boggy".

Much of the ground overlying the southern half of the tunnel was glebe land of the parish of St Mary Stoke, and an agreement was made with the rector, the Reverend Stephen Croft, for the earth hoisted up the shafts to be spread about upon it. In return for this concession, the rector required the company to appoint a policeman at the tunnel works, as had been done at Brantham Hall. It was a wise move because, as it turned out, it was only here that there was any serious fighting among the men engaged in the work.

On 3rd October, Bruff reported to the directors:

> The tunnel works are now almost exclusively devoted to drainage .... by day and by night .... although great difficulties have been encountered from the loose and fine nature of the sand which runs off with the water . . . we have very nearly accomplished the object which we have been contending for, having stopped back the water in No 1 shaft and in another week the top heading for the drainage of No 3 shaft will be completed. No 2 shaft it is probable will be affected by the drainage of No 3 shaft, in which case we shall be able to proceed with the construction of the Tunnel almost immediately. Centering for the work is now preparing and will be ready in time for the Brickwork.
>
> I have seriously considered the subject of constructing the Tunnel to a width adapted for the Broad Gauge and the attention of the Contractor and his agents have been directed to the subject in accordance with your expressed wish to Mr Brassey and they appear indisposed to name any sum for the extra width.

With the Battle of the Gauges then raging in Parliament it seems incredible that the Ipswich and Bury Company can have seriously considered the Broad Gauge, particularly as the nearby Eastern Counties Railway had by then abandoned even Braithwaite's modest increase to 5 feet. Was this something that Bruff had originally talked them into? If his tunnel could not be long, did he wish it at least to have portals of an impressive size? We do not

The northern entrance to Ipswich tunnel before 1859, from a stereoscopic photograph by Richard Dykes Alexander. Note the gravel-ballasted track and the absence of the loop line for the present station.
Suffolk Record Office

55

know. Bruff's report went on to say that eventually he had received a letter from Ogilvie, in which the contractor advised that the width should not be increased on account of "the treacherous and weak nature of the strata". The engineer therefore recommended that Ogilvie's advice should be accepted, and the directors agreed.

On 11th October, 1845, the *Suffolk Chronicle* reported:

> Near the horizontal shaft driven beneath the first mill on the hill at Stoke, a caving recently took place of an extensive nature . . .

It appears that a quantity of crag and sand had been washed out by the water, and possibly at this juncture Bruff decided to open out the hill where the slip had been, and shorten the tunnel. Certainly it was originally intended to be 380 yards long and, assuming that the line of Belstead Road which passes over it has remained unchanged, the northern mouth was to be about 30 yards further out than it is now. The tunnel also extends about 10 yards further south from the position shown on the Parliamentary plans.

The three shafts were lined with brickwork, probably by the method, long used for sinking wells, of building a few courses of brickwork upon a kerb and then excavating the ground from beneath the kerb, so that it sank by the weight upon it, and more brickwork was then added. It seems strange that the shafts should have been so lined, but the *Chronicle* reporter, who seems to have watched progress carefully, was specific on the point; Bruff may have entertained some idea of making the shafts permanent, if only to provide some ventilation.

The first few months were a trying time for Bruff. He admitted later that he nearly abandoned the tunnel at that time and it became known as "Bruff's folly". By the end of January, 1846, however, he was able to report to the directors:

> The Tunnel through Stoke Hill has anxiously occupied my attention, but I am happy to state that the difficulties which at one time appeared seriously to interpose against our progress have now been surmounted. By great exertion the Contractor succeeded in driving a bottom-heading through the Hill, in the position of the intended Tunnel, and also other headings in different directions and levels, to collect and lead off the water, and to prevent its flowing in upon our works. In these operations he has been successful and the permanent brickwork for the Tunnel has been commenced from each of the Shafts and is proceeded with day and night; all the side lengths are now completed.

These last few words are interesting, for they indicate that the tunnel was taken through *at its full size* before any of the brick lining was commenced.

The usual method of tunnelling at that time, in England, was to drive a short length of pilot heading at the level of the top of the intended bore — a "top heading", as it was called — which was then widened out so that the roof could be completely supported on a timber lining, or "lagging", before the lower part was excavated.

This pilot heading was taken only about 20 feet in advance of the complete brick or masonry lining, so that the timber roof lagging could be supported at one end upon the lining already completed. The length of working where slips might occur was thus reduced to a minimum.

This technique was all very well in a straight tunnel, but with the novel complication of a continuous curve at Ipswich it appears that the tunnel was enlarged to its full size right through, so that the curved side walls could be set out from end to end before any bricks were laid. This would have necessitated much more timbering than usual, and a delay before the roof was safely supported.

The initial bottom heading, for drainage, was probably driven in straight lengths between the shafts, which were close together (it would not have come outside the limits of the full size tunnel), and out sideways by the shortest route, from No 3 shaft at the northern end. According to one contemporary account, the influx of water at this stage was at times so great that the men were unable to work in the heading for more than three or four hours before being relieved by another shift.

One effect of the water being drained away was that the wells belonging to nearby houses dried up. The company was liable to a penalty of five pounds a day for this, but they seem to have managed to avoid paying it. They did, however, by the summer of 1847, get around to providing a well and pump for the use of the poor in the parish and "to celebrate the munificence of the Company, between thirty and forty old women were treated to a cup of tea, at the yard near the church". The old women would not have known that the five pounds a day was specifically to be laid out in restoring their water supply.

The brickwork in the tunnel was carried out by another sub-contractor, named John Fisher.

The brick lining for the roof was commenced at No 1 shaft, the southernmost, towards the end of December, 1845, when it was reported that "on each side the excavation is approaching the intended entrance". This brickwork seems to have been built entirely from the three shafts and not from either end of the tunnel. At the end of July, 1846, Bruff reported that of the total length of 360 yards, 320 had been bricked and completed, as follows:

	Work done	Work to be done
From No 1 shaft	103 linear yards	4 linear yards
From No 2 shaft	105 linear yards	19 linear yards
From No 3 shaft	112 linear yards	17 linear yards
Totals	320 linear yards	40 linear yards

He added that up to that time there had been no serious accident, either to the work or to any of the men employed, although it "threatened at the outset to be a tedious, expensive and dangerous work, arising from the position and nature of the strata, viz: London clay interspersed with beds of septaria, and overlaid with crag and sand surcharged with water". He spoke too soon, for only about a week later, on 5th August, there was a serious slip to the south of No 3 shaft. It happened at about 9 a.m. while the men were at breakfast, and so no one was hurt, but a crater about ten yards across and eight feet deep appeared in the Belstead road, some 50 feet above the crown of the tunnel. Some of the brickwork to the south of No 3 shaft had to be rebuilt, but work was able to continue as usual to the north of No 2, although that week a total of only 10½ feet was completed instead of the usual 21 feet.

One person at least who was concerned with the driving of the tunnel did not live to see it completed. In April, Bruff's assistant engineer on the job, Samuel Bowman, aged twenty-two, of Carrickfergus, died of pulmonary tuberculosis at Bruff's home in Norwich Road, Ipswich; his chief paid for the headstone on his grave in St Matthew's churchyard. Bowman was succeeded by Edward Sheppard, who had had experience of the Thames Tunnel under Brunel.

As there were no serious accidents to the miners, little information about them has survived. The name of one, George Cooper, has at least been recorded as the defendant in a case of assault upon the landlord of the *Boar's Head* public house, at the bottom of the hill. Something about the beer displeased Cooper and he started throwing mugs about, one of which struck the landlord and gashed his head. The landlord and others then locked the door and tried to seize the miner, who leapt from the

A horse gin such as is likely to have been used to remove spoil from the shafts when excavating Ipswich tunnel, from Our Iron Roads, *1852.*

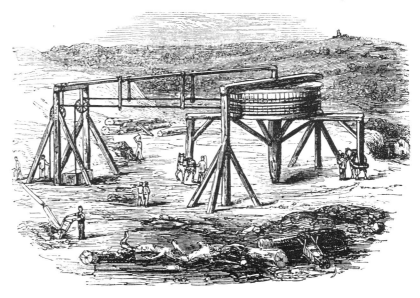

table at the closed window in a manner since adopted by stunt men in Western films. Unfortunately for him, the window frame was rather too stoutly constructed for this method of egress and Cooper remained caught up in the wreckage long enough for his pursuers to secure him and hand him over to the police. He was fined ten shillings and ordered to pay the cost of the damage, eleven and sixpence.

There was always hostility between the miners and the local labourers who worked in the approach cuttings to the tunnel, over rates of pay. In April, "both parties, highly exasperated, sought each other at several public houses, and at one time the streets presented a mob of about 200 persons, one party being headed by a labourer who exhibited a £5 note on a pole, as a challenge to single combat". Eventually the police, helped by the men's gangers, managed to disperse the mob but for a time the shops in one street had to put up their shutters.

When the first trial run was made on the Eastern Union line on 5th May, the beer given to the men for them to celebrate revived the old grudges and again the streets near Stoke Bridge were the scene of drunken brawls.

> As soon as possible, nearly the whole of the police were sent to quell the disturbance. Upon their arrival several of the labourers had large clubs in their hands, which they were wielding on all sides with the most ferocious threats. The police acted with becoming forbearance, as they were quite unable to subdue the combatants.

The free beer would "better have been dispensed with", according to one journalist.

Fighting continued in the ensuing weeks until people complained to the Mayor. "Every day in the week, not excepting the Sabbath, presented disgraceful scenes of riot and intoxication, associated with the most obscene language, and disgusting pugilistic exhibitions".

In the meantime, the tunnel lining had been creeping forward at about a yard a day and on 15th August the length between shafts Nos 1 and 2 was completed. According to one account, the brickwork was five or six feet thick in places, "entirely set in cement, and strengthened by iron banding of great substance".

At last, on 19th September, about fifty guests attended at Ogilvie's invitation to witness the ceremonial insertion of the last four bricks in the lining. The party assembled at the northern end of the tunnel and, headed by George Humfress' brass band[11] playing *See the Conquering Hero Comes*, they marched in for about 125 yards to where a large platform had been erected on scaffolding at a height of about 12 feet. Two tables were spread for the inevitable banquet — another opportunity for a local caterer to demonstrate his skill in serving dinner in the most improbable and inaccessible surroundings.

Brick with graffito dated 1850, in the wing wall at the southern end of Ipswich tunnel. The wall was refaced about 1970.

The first brick to go in was inscribed with the name of John Footman, the deputy chairman. "Mr Footman's brick having been dipped and received its due share of cement, that gentleman placed it in its resting place, with his gloves on, which gave rise to sundry jocose remarks on the part of his friends. Mr Bruff followed and manfully seizing the trowel, laid on the cement, and quickly disposed of his brick". This had his name on it, as engineer. The third had the date on it and was laid by Sheppard, the assistant resident engineer. The fourth brick was inscribed with the name of the chairman of the company. "Mr Cobbold placed in the last, the band playing *God Save the Queen* and the company cheering most lustily."

With tingling ears the gathering then sat down at the two long tables, Ogilvie presiding at one and Bruff at the other. Afterwards, healths were drunk, including those of Bruff, Sheppard and the sub-contractors, Hawley and Fisher. In his reply, Bruff said that great credit was due to Brassey and his agents for completing the work "without one shilling extra expense to the Company, or a single casualty to the workmen employed".

Sheppard said that the difficulties encountered had been as great as those in the Thames Tunnel. He went on, "So admirably had Mr Bruff and the contractors performed their work, that though the tunnel was on a curve, the junctions of the brickwork were effected within a small fraction of an inch".

Outside, "the railway police force were in attendance, and discharged their duties with exemplary temper and moderation, although they had some difficulties, the railway labourers having been treated upon the occasion".

By the middle of October the drainage culvert extending the full length of the tunnel was complete and work began on filling in the shafts. Ballasting and the laying of the permanent way followed, and by 26th November, 1846, the works, not only at the tunnel but all the way to Bury, were sufficiently complete for a trial run over the line.

At that time, work was still in progress on the tunnel portals; there had been some speculation as to what form these would take, and whether or not they should be built of stone, but eventually it was decided to use brick. The splendid watercolour painting of the tunnel mouth in the Borough Museum's collection at Ipswich (bequeathed to the town by Bruff himself) can only show a projected design which was never carried out; there is not room for it in the cutting.[12]

In the G.E.R. General Powers Act of 1899 the company was empowered to purchase about 11 acres of land, and a score of houses, on top of the hill and open out the tunnel; but the powers lapsed and the work was never carried out.

The proposed portal for the southern end of Ipswich tunnel; a watercolour by Fred Russel. Note the policeman's signal hut.
Ipswich Borough Museums and Art Galleries

The tunnel has always defied the efforts of the engineers to make it watertight. A Scottish stationmaster is still remembered, who was wont to send a lad inside it to fill a jug with the water falling from the soffit, or roof, so that he could add it to his whisky. It was, he maintained, real natural spring water, not like the stuff out of the tap. (If only the engines had burned peat!)

At the time of writing, the line through the tunnel has been electrified. When the extension of electric traction from Colchester to Norwich was first proposed it was quickly realised that the tight, dripping bore under Stoke Hill might well prove an insurmountable obstacle. Surprisingly, it was found that there was sufficient headroom to accommodate the overhead equipment, even for double track; Bruff had designed the tunnel to admit locomotives with tall chimneys, but not long rolling stock, fitted with bogies. For many years, the curvature of the tunnel had been a problem, with the need to maintain accurate alignment of the permanent way — difficult enough on a curve, even in dry surroundings.

British Rail have taken the opportunity to replace the conventional track with slab track, in which the rails are attached directly to a reinforced concrete slab, laid by special plant to very accurate levels. Track maintenance work in the tunnel will be very much reduced.

It is ironic that the problem would not have arisen, apart from the dripping water, had the tunnel been constructed "to a width adapted for the Broad Gauge".

For the trial run on 26th November, 1846, a special train consisting of five carriages and the 2-2-2 locomotive *Bury St Edmunds* was backed out of the Ipswich station to Halifax Junction. The locomotive was driven by Taylor, the superintendent, and also riding on the footplate were J.C. Cobbold, John Footman, James Saunders, Peter Bruff and J.S. Martin — presumably there was a fireman as well. As the train moved forwards towards the tunnel mouth, the cheers of the passengers were echoed back by those gathered along each side of the cutting. According to the *Ipswich Journal*:

> Little time was allowed for reflection — shriek went the whistle of the engine, and amidst shouts of "Down with your heads, gentlemen", to those who travelled as "outsiders", the train shot into Stoke Tunnel, and was soon threading its dark recesses. The scene was extremely novel to those who had never before travelled through the bowels of the earth — the shrieks of the engine, the clatter of the carriages, the whizzing of the steam, the shouts of the passengers, mingling together in uproarious and strange confusion.

A minute and a half later, the train emerged from the tunnel to the cheers of those who had gathered at the other end. The first stop was at Claydon and the next at Needham, where "a number of people were assembled who appeared to be highly amused with the novel spectacle". Amid the usual scenes of enthusiasm, the train

The southern entrance to Ipswich tunnel about 1968.

continued along the valley of the River Gipping to Stowmarket.

Here, the line was — and still is — carried on a low embankment only a few feet high, which it was proposed to form by "side cuttings", i.e. excavating a ditch on each side and banking up the spoil in the middle. Bruff had reported on 28th July that this embankment had absorbed much more material than had been expected. In fact, Brassey's sub-contractor for this section of the line, a man named John Douglas, had been battling for a couple of months to form about 100 yards of bank immediately on the Ipswich side of the site of Stowmarket station.

In the last week or so of May, 1846, the work had shown a slight tendency to subside, but this was expected in view of the nature of the ground, which at that time was an open marsh intersected with various ditches draining into the nearby river. However, on 1st June — Whit Monday — "the labourers were astonished to find several yards of the embankment had almost disappeared". More men and waggons were laid on to make it good, but the hard top crust of the ground had been broken through and the earth was absorbed as fast as it was tipped. Efforts to advance the embankment continued for no less than nine weeks, until on 1st August about 40 yards of the bank previously formed just disappeared in the night, complete with rails and sleepers.

The next week's work was all in vain, but by the following Saturday (15th August) the embankment had advanced a few feet, although men stood by over the weekend to salvage the tramway if further settlement seemed imminent. By that time a total of about 25,000 cubic yards of material had been swallowed up; and the effect of it was to force up the ground for about 50 feet on each

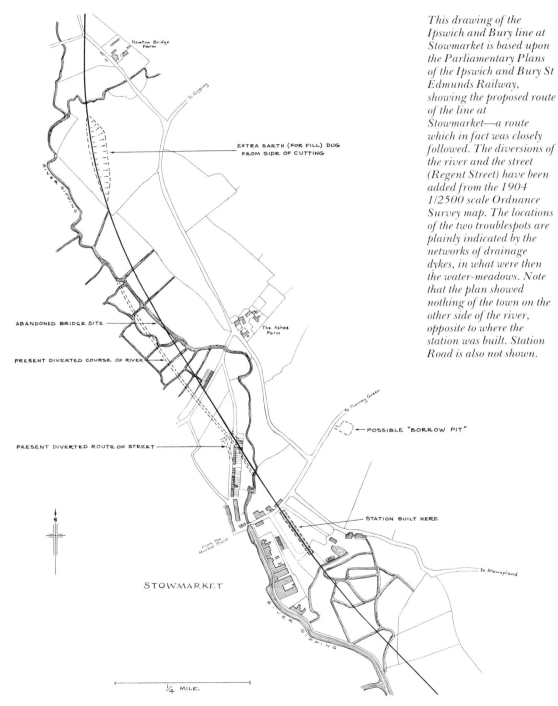

Newton Bridge Farm

RIVER GIPPING

To Gipping

EXTRA EARTH (FOR FILL) DUG
FROM SIDE OF CUTTING

ABANDONED BRIDGE SITE

The Ashes Farm

PRESENT DIVERTED COURSE OF RIVER

To Thorney Green

PRESENT DIVERTED ROUTE OF STREET

POSSIBLE "BORROW PIT"

STATION BUILT HERE

From the Market Place

STOWMARKET

To Stowupland

RIVER GIPPING

N

¼ MILE

This drawing of the Ipswich and Bury line at Stowmarket is based upon the Parliamentary Plans of the Ipswich and Bury St Edmunds Railway, showing the proposed route of the line at Stowmarket—a route which in fact was closely followed. The diversions of the river and the street (Regent Street) have been added from the 1904 1/2500 scale Ordnance Survey map. The locations of the two troublespots are plainly indicated by the networks of drainage dykes, in what were then the water-meadows. Note that the plan showed nothing of the town on the other side of the river, opposite to where the station was built. Station Road is also not shown.

side. It broke and heaved up, "as if a miniature earthquake had happened". In some places the surrounding ground rose by as much as seven feet above its original level.

As the bridge to carry the line over the Gipping at Badley, midway between Needham and Stowmarket, was still incomplete at that time, the fill had to come from nearby. No doubt it was dug from where a large and overgrown pit could until recently still be seen a short distance along the Stowupland road. The site has now been developed as an industrial estate.

No mechanical plant was used here in 1846, every particle being dug by hand. That summer was extraordinarily hot, too; at some places along the line work was carried on only at night. No wonder there was even a special waggon for carrying beer along the line to the sweating labourers at Stowmarket! There was some small comfort in all this for the contractor. At some places, work had been hindered by crowds of sightseers, but the swamp at least kept the spectators at bay. Towards the end of August a journalist recorded:

> Mr Bedingfield, surgeon, of Stowmarket, very narrowly escaped losing his life last week, in going to see the extraordinary phenomena at the Ipswich and Bury Railway near Stowmarket. About a hundred yards from the spot, but in the line which the embankment is to traverse, he slipped into a ditch which it appears contained no less than seventeen feet of mud. He was alone, and was only saved by catching hold of the grass on the bank, by which he held until two persons who had previously observed him, and were surprised at his sudden disappearance, came up, and found him buried up to his neck in the mud, from which perilous position he was extricated without material injury.

Half a mile north of the station site, another 80 yard length of embankment began to sink on 9th August. Although desperate efforts were made to lift the tramway much of it was lost. In the succeeding week 2000 cubic yards of fill were tipped to advance the bank by less than a yard, with the surrounding ground heaving up as before.

Some trouble had been expected here, but Bruff estimated that the cutting through a hill of good gravel, immediately to the north, would yield an ample supply of fill. Today, this short cutting — the first north of Stowmarket — is of extraordinary width and considerably deeper than the formation level for the permanent way, which runs along a ledge on one side. Its great size is a silent testimony to the amount of earth swallowed up in the low embankment.

Along here, 45 foot timber piles for the foundations of a bridge over the river sank from view in the morass by their own weight! Probes showed that there was no hard bottom until a depth of 80 feet was reached — the bog was twice as deep as the notorious Chat Moss on the Liverpool and Manchester Railway! George Stephenson's solution to the problem there was well known, and it

The great borrow pit at Stowmarket, looking towards Norwich. Earth was dug from here to make the embankments near the station.

seems strange that it was not until September that the decision was taken to float the Stowmarket embankment on a raft of faggots and brushwood.

The idea of a bridge where the piles had disappeared was abandoned, and instead the course of the river was diverted. The original course, now little more than a ditch, can still be traced — marking the boundary of the parish of Stowmarket.

By 26th November, 1846, when the special train steamed triumphantly along the valley, it was evident, in the words of the *Bury Post*, "that engineering skill had surmounted all difficulties".

> Nothing is to be seen except a low embankment, not more than four to five feet high, across a swampy marsh; but that something unusual has been overcome is apparent from the great width of the embankment, which, in some places, is more than 100 yards, all laid upon immense layers of faggots, brushwood and hurdles, crossed and re-crossed, strengthened by rows of timber, so that in fact, the whole forms a huge mat-work of earth, bushes and timber; upon this, longitudinal timbers, extending the whole length of the bogs, are laid, firmly scarfed and plated together with iron, and upon these again the cross sleepers are laid for the rails, which appear stronger and closer together than usual.

This broad embankment (which was, and is, only about 50 yards wide) later carried sidings which concealed its significance; but a train passing at speed "makes the whole place shake like a jelly", I have been told.

It is small wonder that almost every inhabitant of Stowmarket turned out, not only to see the first train but what would happen to it at this spot. As it passed safely over, a great cheer went up. There

The diverted River Gipping—the "New Cut" at Stowmarket. The house on the right indicates the original line of Regent Street (see plan on page 64).

The view from the new footbridge at Stowmarket, looking towards Ipswich. Now that most of the sidings have been lifted the width of Bruff's embankment to carry the two running lines across the bog once more becomes apparent; it extended from the row of trees on the left to some still-surviving tracks on the extreme right.

The formal opening of the railway at Bury St Edmunds on 7th December, 1846, as depicted in the Illustrated London News. *Note the temporary platform on the Ipswich side of the bridge.*
Paul Fincham

was a short stop at the intended site of the station, but the building work had hardly been started.

Stops were also made at Haughley, Elmswell and Thurston, where none of the station buildings were very far advanced. In the great cutting 38 feet deep through Norton Great Wood, where the contractor had had to resort to blasting the heavy clay with gunpowder, there was only a single line at that time; and at other places only temporary track had been laid for the occasion.

Eventually, nearly two hours after leaving Ipswich, the train reached Bury and stopped at a temporary platform just on the Ipswich side of the bridge over the Northgate road. This was as far as the company's Act of Parliament authorised the construction of the line, but the land on the western side of the road had been purchased by agreement with the owner and the work of levelling the site for the permanent station had already begun. The city fathers of Bury, mindful of the need for a future rail link to the westward, had gladly given their consent to the "noble arch" over the road.

There were the usual scenes of jubilation. The *Bury Post* noted:

As the turn tables were not fixed, it was necessary to send a second engine, reversed, to take the train back again, the *Bury St Edmunds* following at a suitable distance.

Upon returning to Ipswich, Ogilvie gave a dinner at the *Golden Lion Hotel* to those who had been concerned in the building of the railway. In his speech, he referred to the problems which had been encountered and to Bruff's part in dealing with them: "without his

skill, and the aid of his able assistants, he thought they would have stopped in the tunnel and been lost in the bog".

The formal opening of the line took place on 7th December, when a special train ran from Shoreditch, making several stops on the way to Ipswich. Here it was made up to seventeen first-class and two second-class carriages, with an open truck containing Humfress' band, and two locomotives. The stalwarts in the band played *See the Conquering Hero Comes* as the train left Ipswich station; it was a piece which they could probably play with their eyes shut — maybe they had to as the train entered the tunnel.

With the celebrations all along the line, it was an hour and three-quarters before the train arrived at Bury St Edmunds, where the people cheered again, as they had done not a fortnight previously. Flags flew and cannon were fired.

According to the *Bury Post*, the only mishap in the festivities occurred when a gunner in the Royal Artillery, "recruiting here", was firing off the guns; "and not having the means of properly spunging after the discharge, an explosion took place as he was reloading". He broke his arm.

The visitors were met by the Mayor and Corporation of Bury and everyone formed a procession and marched off for the customary banquet. The Bury paper concluded by saying:

Mr Fuller, the Master of the Poor Boys' School, takes this opportunity of thanking the Mayor, on behalf of the boys, for his liberal distribution of buns on the day of the opening of the Ipswich and Bury Railway.

The line had been opened for goods traffic to Bury St

Charles Russell's massive bridge across the Fornham road at Bury St Edmunds. Writing in 1961, Professor Jack Simmons referred in his The Railways of Britain *to "the monumental railway bridge at Bury, which can certainly claim to be the finest bridge of any kind in Suffolk".*

Edmunds on 30th November.[13] The *Suffolk Chronicle* meticulously recorded that the first train carried 24 tons of general goods and 90 tons of coal. Due to heavy snow, however, it was found necessary to divide the train at Needham and take it forward to Stowmarket in two sections. There it waited until a second train arrived, when the two were joined and proceeded, double-headed, to Bury.

The Board of Trade inspection was carried out by Captain Coddington on 15th December; the tunnel and the embankment at Stowmarket were closely examined and the inspector congratulated Bruff and Ogilvie upon them.

It was announced that the line would open for passenger traffic on the 21st, but to the consternation of all concerned the certificate did not arrive from the Board of Trade. When notices were posted up, saying that the opening would unavoidably be delayed for a few days, it was rumoured that the line had once again sunk at Stowmarket; another theory circulated was that approval had been withheld because there were no gates at the level crossings. In fact, Captain Coddington had been ordered at short notice to go to Ireland, and had not had time to submit his report in London until he returned on the 21st. It was not until the afternoon of the 23rd that permission to open the line was telegraphed to Ipswich and a special train with notices to all stations left at four o'clock the next morning. The first public train left Ipswich at 9.10 a.m.[14]

Detail of the arch of Charles Russell's bridge at Bury St Edmunds.

Expansion

7

THE 1845/46 session of Parliament marked the climax of the "Railway Mania". In East Anglia the aim of many of the schemes was to provide more direct routes from London to Norwich than the one which had opened, via Cambridge, on 30th July, 1845.[15]

The Ipswich and Bury St Edmunds company put forward Locke and Bruff's proposed Norwich Extension again. With lines from Colchester extending north of Stowmarket, Cobbold's companies were in a strong position; they sought powers to build only just over thirty-one miles of railway to reach Norwich. To branch from it at Diss, hopefully, would be the Waveney Valley and Great Yarmouth Railway, successor of the previous year's ill-fated Diss, Beccles and Yarmouth promotion. If the I.&B.R. failed to reach Diss, the new Yarmouth company was prepared to build its own line down to Haughley. Better still, they did not propose to cross Bruff's line at Diss on the same level and have their own terminus on the other side like the D.B.&Y!

Opposition to these lines came from the Norfolk Railway, which had been formed on 30th June, 1845, by the amalgamation of the Yarmouth and Norwich and the Norwich and Brandon railways.

The Norfolk Railway proposed its own scheme for a shortened line to Norwich from the capital, the Spooner Row and Stowmarket Railway, which would involve even less construction than the Bury company's extension. To safeguard its monopoly of all traffic to Yarmouth, a line was proposed from Thetford to Reedham, via Diss and Beccles.

The Norfolk Railway also undertook to lease two other lines, if they were authorised by Parliament. One was the Thetford, Bury and Newmarket, a truncated alternative to the London and Norwich Direct line of the previous session. The other was the Ipswich, Norwich and Yarmouth, intended to traverse East Suffolk to Bungay, where it was to diverge one way via Beccles to Reedham and so to Yarmouth, and in the other direction to join the Norfolk Railway at Trowse.

Part of the I.N.&Y. Railway's application to Parliament was being duplicated as the Halesworth and Norwich Railway, just as the Ipswich and Bury company had had two identical schemes for lines from Ipswich to Haughley in separate Bills in the previous session of Parliament.

The I.N.&Y. Railway would generally have followed the route taken by the present East Suffolk line from Ipswich to Wickham Market. It is interesting to note that it was not intended to pass through Saxmundham on its way to Halesworth, but was to follow

The coming of the railways had a drastic effect on coach services.

a route about five miles to the west through the village of Peasenhall.

Here was a small but flourishing ironworks producing patent seed drills (and which only ceased to do so in recent years). James Smyth, the then owner, was a keen supporter of the proposed railway, and he appeared before a Parliamentary Committee to give evidence in favour of it. He said that he found it economical to dispatch his drills for London by road as far as Witham, from where the rail freight charge was eight shillings per ton. If he put them on a train at Colchester, the Eastern Counties Railway charged twenty-five shillings per ton.

J.C. Cobbold and his associates were also looking westwards, where the land was bright with the prospect of connecting the railways of East Anglia to those of the Midlands and the North. In the autumn of 1845 the Eastern Counties line from Ely to Peterborough was under construction, and from Peterborough there was already a line to Blisworth, on the London and Birmingham Railway.

In the previous session of Parliament, a proposed E.C.R. line from Cambridge to Bury St Edmunds had been rejected because of opposition from racing interests over the route to be taken at

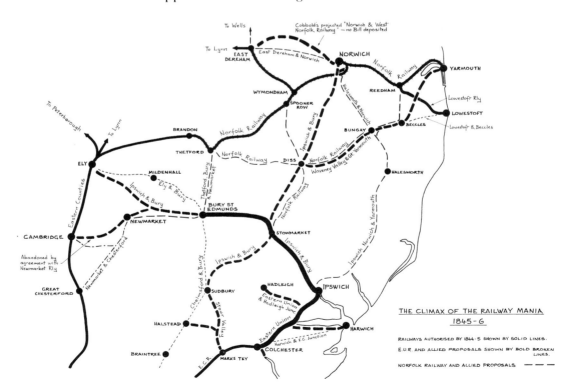

THE CLIMAX OF THE RAILWAY MANIA 1845-6

RAILWAYS AUTHORISED BY 1844-5 SHOWN BY SOLID LINES.

E.U.R. AND ALLIED PROPOSALS SHOWN BY BOLD BROKEN LINES.

NORFOLK RAILWAY AND ALLIED PROPOSALS — — —

Newmarket. Taking care not to offend the Jockey Club, the Ipswich and Bury St Edmunds company deposited a Bill for an extension from Bury to Cambridge, with a branch to Ely from Kentford. Shortly afterwards they came to an agreement with the promoters of the Newmarket and Chesterford Railway, whose Bill was also before Parliament, to meet that line and abandon their scheme beyond the racing town.

Bruff's line to Ely was countered by a parallel one laid out by J.U. Rastrick and promoted by parties in Ely and King's Lynn.

J.C. Cobbold again tried to promote a direct line from Norwich to Dereham, a town to which Parliament had now approved lines from Wymondham, on the Norfolk Railway, and — more important to him — from King's Lynn. Such a line could be expected to carry much of the coal trade to Norwich. Many Norfolk interests supported a Direct Norwich and Dereham Railway, with its own terminus in the city near the site of the later City Station; so he and T.D. Burroughes, another E.U.R. director, joined a rival faction, the Norwich and West Norfolk. This would join their own hoped-for line from Haughley; but alas, once more they failed to get a Bill introduced.

In the southern part of Suffolk, Bruff had laid out the Stour Valley line from Marks Tey to Sudbury (see Chapter thirteen). There was a threat from two almost identical schemes, Hyde Parker's Chelmsford and Bury and the Essex and Suffolk, which were intended to by-pass Cobbold's territory altogether. The directors of the Ipswich and Bury, without even waiting for sanction from their shareholders, immediately took steps to deposit a Bill for a double line branch from Stowmarket to Sudbury, to draw traffic on to their own Norwich line if either of the rival lines should be successful.

In addition to all these, many other railways were promoted in East Anglia. Some, scarcely plausible, never even reached Parliament; for example, a modified London and Norwich Direct, to be worked by atmospheric traction, and the Cheltenham and Ipswich Direct. There was even a proposed Harwich Docks, Birmingham and Central England Railway, whose promoters seem to have been providing for Britain's entry into the European Economic Community.

In November, 1845, the notices relating to all the Bills necessitated daily supplements to the *London Gazette*, and one issue was not published until ten minutes before midnight on the 30th, "just in time to secure a literal compliance with the Standing Orders of Parliament". In the following April, Sir Robert Peel told the Commons that no fewer than 519 railway Bills were being considered, involving a total capital expenditure of some £304 million.

The battle for shorter rail routes to Norwich was fought through Parliament, with Locke and Bruff as expert witnesses for

In 1845 the columns of local newspapers were full of advertisements concerning railways existing and projected.

the Ipswich and Bury company's bill against Robert Stephenson and G.P. Bidder, who were giving evidence for the Norfolk Railway and other opposing companies. In the event, it was the I.&B.R.'s Bill which passed through to receive the Royal Assent, on 27th July, 1846.

On the following day, at the half yearly general meeting of the shareholders, it was agreed that the name of the company should be changed to "The Ipswich, Bury and Norwich Railway". Votes of thanks were passed to Saunders (the secretary) and to Bruff, of whom the proposer said, "A more able, or more indefatigable, or painstaking, or more unimpeachably honest and faithful man, was not to be found in England; for even the great Mr Stephenson and the subtle Mr Bidder[16] had not been able to put a finger upon his plans, so ably had they been got up".

Apart from branches from Bentley to Hadleigh and from Marks Tey to Sudbury, all the other Bills with which Bruff or Cobbold were involved were either thrown out by Parliament or withdrawn to save money when their rivals were defeated. There had to be a limit.

The strain on those principally involved can be imagined. Engineers had not only prepared many schemes in great haste, but they spent long hours before Parliamentary Committees as expert witnesses, not to mention the supervision of schemes under construction at the same time. Locke, for example, was busy not only in England but in Scotland and France, too. There were no rapid means of travel or easy communication available. It is no coincidence that he, Brunel and Robert Stephenson all died in middle age.

With railway schemes being proposed literally by the hundred, surveyors were in such demand that they could command salaries of five and even seven guineas a day (how does one put this in modern figures? It was about three times the rate then usually paid to senior executives).

The Act for the Norwich Extension provided for a two-way junction with the Ipswich to Bury St Edmunds line at Haughley, although the leg which would have allowed direct running from Norwich to Bury was never constructed. The terminus at Norwich was to be near St Stephen's Road on the site of the Victoria Gardens, from which the station was later to take its name. At Lakenham the line was to cross both the River Yare and the Norwich to Brandon line on a viaduct, and there would be a branch leading down to join the Norfolk Railway at Trowse.

The I.&B.R. was authorised to increase its share capital by £550,000 and to borrow a further £183,333 upon mortgage or bond. An important provision of the Act empowered the company to lease or sell its entire system to the Eastern Union, if three-fifths of the shareholders of each company agreed.

It had long been the intention of J.C. Cobbold and the

directors of both the Eastern Union and the Ipswich and Bury that the two should be united as soon as possible. On 8th December, 1846, special meetings of both groups of shareholders were called, one after the other, at the Brook Street offices in Ipswich to approve the amalgamation, which was proposed to be on 1st January, 1847.

The capital of the E.U.R. Company at that time was £400,000, and that of the I.&B.R. £1,266,666. It was proposed that the capital of the combined company, to be known as the Eastern Union, should be £1,866,666 — an increase of £200,000. Different amounts had been called on the old shares, and there were to be arrangements to take account of this and of how many new shares everyone should have.

Each group of proprietors seemed to think that the other would get the best of the bargain, but eventually agreement was reached.

The two railways were worked as one from 1st January, and the amalgamation was formally sanctioned by an Act dated 9th July, 1847, which was subject to the approval of details by the Railway Commissioners.[17]

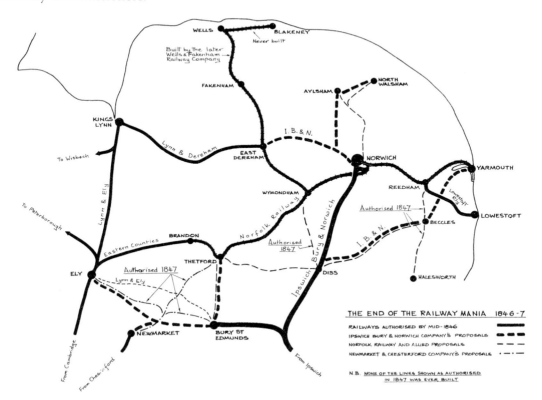

But — and it was a big but — the Commissioners required certain alterations to be made in the amalgamation arrangements; in particular, they disapproved of the way in which the company's capital was to be increased, apparently without any reason. It took many months for all the points to be resolved, and the Commission did not issue its formal certificate of approval until February, 1848.

In the meantime, neither of the two companies could take any major step without obtaining the consent of the other, and the delay was to prove fatal. They lost the chance to take over the working of the Norfolk Railway.

The directors of the two companies had been having joint meetings to consider matters of common interest since before the Ipswich to Bury line was opened. Both boards were anxious that the construction of the Norwich Extension should be pressed forward without delay, but the letting of the contract was held up by the absence of Locke in Scotland. Early in October, 1846, Bruff was authorised to make the necessary arrangements himself, but Locke returned to London in time to lay before a joint meeting of the two directorates on 21st October an offer which he had received from Brassey to construct the extension for £289,230. No other tender seems to have been invited. Locke reported that this figure could be reduced to £283,232, but the tender was not a fixed price one. He recommended that it should be made so, and that Brassey should be allowed to increase his tender by not more than five per cent if he agreed to make no subsequent claim for extra payment.

Locke was able to present Brassey's amended tender, dated 21st October, to the directors of the Ipswich and Bury company on the 30th. It was remarkably simple:

Sir,

After examining the Parliamentary Plans and Sections I hereby offer to execute the same from Hawley to Norwich a distance of 32 miles 65 chains . . . to your perfect satisfaction for the sum of two hundred and ninety seven thousand three hundred and ninety three pounds (£297,393) — the Company providing Rails and Chairs, Land for the Line, Spoil Banks and side cutting.

This tender includes all excavation, masonry, brickwork, drains, culverts, Gates, Crossings, ballasting, sleepers and fastenings for the permanent way, also all extra bridges and crossings which may be agreed to be built for land owners . . . in short, everything that is necessary to the completion of a double line of railway its entire length, but exclusive of all points, crossings or sidings, or other work necessary for Stations. It is understood that I have the use of the permanent materials for the execution of the work subject to your approval, being accountable for any loss or damage they sustain.

I remain, Sir, your obedient servant,

Thomas Brassey
21st October 1846

The Board accepted the price, but instructed company secretary Saunders to point out to Locke that there was no mention of a completion date. They suggested that the line should be opened to Diss within twelve months, and completed to Norwich in another twelve after that. What was agreed with Brassey is not recorded.

The work did not begin until the line from Ipswich to Bury had been completed; the ceremony of breaking the ground took place on 25th February, 1847, on Markshall Hill, just south of the River Yare, where the deepest cutting on the line was to be.

A plankway had been laid down, and the dignitaries were to dig earth from one end of it and barrow it to the other. A polished oak wheelbarrow, made by a firm of Norwich coachbuilders, and an elaborately carved spade were provided for their use.[18]

J.C. Cobbold, the chairman of the company, took off his coat and offered the spade to Jeremiah Colman, the Mayor of Norwich. "The Mayor willingly responded and after turning a few sods, of course done in a workmanlike manner, he placed them into the barrow, which Mr Cobbold wheeled away ... The barrow was successively filled by different gentlemen, and wheeled away by others, till it was thought sufficient had taken part in the ceremony". In fact, the digging went on for about an hour, causing Edward Willett, one of the directors from Norwich, to remark that "if they went on at that rate they would leave little work for the navvies to do". At last the gathering moved off to the marquee for lunch, at which the table was presided over by Brassey's partner, Alexander Ogilvie.

As work on the line from Ipswich to Bury St Edmunds was completed, Brassey transferred men and plant to the Norwich line.

The spade used in the ceremony of cutting the first sod, as depicted in the Illustrated London News. *It is now in the National Railway Museum at York.*

A somewhat fanciful view of the cutting of the first sod for the Norwich Extension, 25th February, 1847, from the Illustrated London News.

He divided the earthworks between Norwich and a point near Mellis into five sub-contracts:

(a) From the Norwich terminus to the southern end of the Markshall cutting, which was over half a mile long and had a maximum depth of 60 feet, was let to a man named Evans, who had dug some at least of the great cutting at Brantham.

(b) From this point to Swainsthorpe, a mere couple of miles or so, was entrusted to one George Sillitoe.

(c) The next eight miles, to a point near Tivetshall, was carried out by a man named Edward Parry.

(d) The next four miles or so to Burston was let to a certain John Frohawk.

(e) The remainder was entrusted to John Douglas.

Douglas had emptied substantial parts of the surrounding landscape into the bog at Stowmarket. No doubt he was assigned to this part because the going was likely to be soft near the River Waveney and a couple of miles further on there would be about a quarter of a mile of embankment across a marsh at Thrandeston.

By July, 1847, a total of 1,200 men and 150 horses were employed along the route. Where the line was to cross the Waveney by means of a three-span brick bridge a firm foundation was found at a depth of about 20 feet, and the workings were kept dry by means of "one of Shalders' pumps[19] in constant operation". Thrandeston Marsh kept Douglas busy for many months — according to one account it proved almost as difficult as the notorious bog at Stowmarket — but the remedy of floating the bank upon a raft of faggots and brushwood was quickly adopted. Even so, the bank continued to sink until a vast amount of material had been absorbed and the surrounding ground heaved up as it had done at Stowmarket.

This was a time of recession after the "Railway Mania" and the money market was tight. The directors were reluctant to embarrass the shareholders by making calls and construction work gradually tailed off for lack of funds. Although Cobbold announced in August that the line would be opened as far as Bacton — about three miles from the junction at Haughley — in the autumn, this was not achieved and early in October most of the work was suspended.

Meanwhile, with the Ipswich and Bury Railway virtually, if not completely, amalgamated with the Eastern Union, Cobbold had been seeking to strengthen his hold on the railway routes to Norwich. As far back as March, 1844, the E.U.R. directors had decided that they should amalgamate not only with the "Eastern Union Extension Railway Company", which was eventually incorporated as the Ipswich and Bury, but even with the Norwich and Brandon Railway Company if suitable terms could be arranged and the shareholders' consent obtained. Some preliminary correspondence had produced a favourable reaction.

In February, 1847, the directors of the E.U.R. agreed with those of the Norfolk Railway Company that the amalgamation should take place, with the Norfolk shareholders receiving a guaranteed seven and a half per cent on their holdings. A few days later the proposals were briefly outlined to the proprietors of the Norfolk and the Eastern Union Railways at their respective half yearly meetings, but it was decided not to vote on the question until the Eastern Union and the I.&B.R. were fully amalgamated and a special meeting of the combined company could be called. Norfolk Railway shareholders were told, "In the present state of the railway market, the directors had thought it best to accept the 7½%". The *Railway Record* hailed the merger as a step towards the abolition of the ruinous competition in which railway companies engaged over their Bills in Parliament, and commented:

> A more promising Company than the Eastern Union does not exist; nor one that has from the outset been conducted with more honourable regard to the permanent interests of the proprietors. Again and again have we had the pleasure of commending the management of Mr Cobbold and his colleagues . . .

However, Cobbold's two companies could not amalgamate without a certificate from the Railway Commissioners and this was not to be forthcoming for over a year. In the meantime, the shareholders of the Eastern Union and the I.&B.R. had time to consider the state of the Norfolk Railway and what the take-over would mean. The Ipswich and Bury, in particular, faced a daunting prospect of attracting investors to finance the building of the Norwich Extension; even so, its capital debt was lighter than that of the Norfolk Railway, which had leased the as yet incomplete Lowestoft Railway and even lumbered itself with the moribund navigation from Lowestoft to Norwich.

In July, 1847, an influential group of Ipswich and Bury proprietors met in York and resolved to oppose the purchase or lease of the Norfolk Railway (whereas the Eastern Counties Railway had a large number of shareholders in Lancashire, Cobbold's companies seem to have attracted a considerable investment from Yorkshire; their calls were payable at several banks in the White Rose county, apart from London and the Eastern Counties).

On 29th October a special meeting of the I.&B.R. was called to consider not only the proposed takeover of the Norfolk Railway but the general financial state of their own. Money was coming in too slowly for the work on the Norwich Extension, yet at the same time the company was erecting elaborate stations at Bury, Needham and Stowmarket. Today, these stations are among the most splendid monuments of the Railway Age to be found in eastern England, but the angry men who rose to their feet at that meeting were not thinking of posterity. Some were anxious to see

An 1848 view of "the palace-like station at Needham Market"; a watercolour by Fred Russel.

Ipswich Borough Museums and Art Galleries

their railway carried to Norwich and earning more revenue. Others thought that all new work should be suspended.

The directors were further criticised for maintaining an office in London. Cobbold explained that it had been invaluable while the company was involved in considerable Parliamentary work, but it was shortly to be closed.

Of the stations, only that at Needham had then been completed. One speaker complained that £5,000 had been spent on what he called "a palace-like station at Needham Market, which, despite its name, was not even a market town". Bruff replied that the building had cost only about half that sum (the accepted tender had been £3,150), but the *Ipswich Journal* commented sarcastically:

> Still the size is a matter of wonder, though, of course, the engineer and directors no doubt understand better than other people the requirements of the *extensive* traffic of that *stirring* town.

The chairman explained the position of the works on the Norwich Extension and managed to satisfy the meeting on that account. The proposed takeover of the Norfolk Railway, however, came under heavy attack. Among the loudest critics was a certain Mr Swann, the chairman of a committee which had been appointed by the Yorkshire shareholders to organise opposition to the move. His argument that the dividend of seven and a half per cent proposed for the Norfolk Company's shareholders was about three times as much as their railway had been earning was irrefutable. Even Cobbold was forced to admit that conditions had altered since the provisional agreement had been concluded by the respective boards of directors.

John Muskett, a prominent shareholder from Bury St

Edmunds (and the father-in-law of company secretary Saunders), begged the meeting to approve the lease, saying that if they did not take over the Norfolk Railway others would. But it was all in vain, and the proposal was rejected by forty-three votes to five.

A few months later John Muskett's warning proved all too true. The Eastern Counties took over the working of the Norfolk Railway in May, 1848, bringing the entire system from London to Norwich and Yarmouth by way of Cambridge and Ely under their sole control. Within a few days fares were increased and large numbers of Norfolk Railway employees were declared redundant as the organisation was transferred into that of the larger system. The *Norfolk Chronicle* commented:

> The travelling, for the greater part, and the conveyance of light goods, must, in this age of competition and excitement — when all the steady, quiet and regular modes in which our forefathers did business, are discarded — be by rail; and for both, the public is completely at the mercy of the Eastern Counties Railway. The amalgamation . . . renders it still more necessary than ever that the Ipswich and Norwich line should be completed without delay.

However, the expected lease of the Norfolk Railway by the Cobbold companies had resulted in a truce between the two factions in the struggle during the 1846/47 session of Parliament. They agreed not to oppose each other's Bills, and some measures which had been promoted merely to safeguard territory and not with the serious intention of building railways were withdrawn.

Stephenson's and Bidder's proposed line from Thetford to Bury St Edmunds was abandoned in favour of an almost identical one laid out by Locke and Bruff, but the Bill was thrown out.

Cobbold shelved once more his ambition of a line up the Wensum Valley from Norwich to Dereham. The scheme included a branch from Drayton to Aylsham, and a link to the proposed Wells and Dereham Railway.

For its part, the Norfolk Railway withdrew its Bill for a proposed extension from Norwich to Aylsham and North Walsham. The plans show that this would have branched from just outside Thorpe Station and passed through a short tunnel under what is now Rosary Road.

This time, the I.&B.R. introduced a Bill for its own branch to Yarmouth from near Diss, and it is interesting to note that it would have passed, like its two predecessors, between the ruins of Burgh Castle and the river and would have terminated near the site of the later Southtown Station at Yarmouth. The scheme was thrown out in favour of a Norfolk Railway proposal for a line from Diss to Reedham, with a branch to Halesworth from Beccles.

The Norfolk Railway's application for a line from Thetford to Diss was unsuccessful, but an Act was obtained for a link between Wymondham and Diss.

81

Westwards from Bury St Edmunds the honours went to the Newmarket and Chesterford Railway, which was authorised to extend its line to Thetford, Bury and Ely. But neither this nor the Norfolk company was ever able to proceed, and the powers conferred upon them lapsed. Elsewhere in the region, however, lines laid out by Bruff were approved by Parliament, as we shall see in Chapter thirteen.

So ended the "Railway Mania" in East Anglia.

* * *

Following the approval of the Railway Commissioners to the amalgamation, the first general meeting of the enlarged Eastern Union Railway Company was held on 2nd June, 1848, at Radley's Hotel, Blackfriars, London. The following directors of the constituent companies were elected to the new board:-

J.C. Cobbold, of Ipswich	(E.U.R. and I.&B.R.)
John Cobbold, of Ipswich	(E.U.R. and I.&B.R.)
John Footman, of Ipswich	(E.U.R. and I.&B.R.)
George Josselyn, of Ipswich	(E.U.R. and I.&B.R.)
J.G. Hart, of Stowmarket	(E.U.R. and I.&B.R.)
George Alexander, of Ipswich	(E.U.R.)
James Grayston, of York	(E.U.R.)
William Beresford, of Essex	(E.U.R.)
W.W. Hawkins, of Colchester	(E.U.R.)
George Pratt Barlow, of London	(I.&B.R.)
Frederick Pratt Barlow, of London	(I.&B.R.)
Samuel Bignold, of Norwich	(I.&B.R.)
William Crake, of London	(I.&B.R.)
Edward Willett, of Norwich	(I.&B.R.)
Wm Stitt Wilson, of Norwich	(I.&B.R.)
John Wright, of Norwich	(I.&B.R.)

They were joined by two new members who had not previously sat on the board of either company, Robert Williamson of Scarborough and Edward S. Cayley, a Yorkshire M.P.[20]

The meeting decided that interest payments on the existing loans should be suspended until the line to Norwich was opened and that £100,000 should be raised by means of a special issue of six per cent debentures. Not to be outdone in the general round of belt-tightening, the directors agreed to forego their fees until the Norwich line was complete, and before the meeting was over they announced that they would all take up their maximum allotment of the new debentures, leaving only about £30,000 outstanding.

Not long afterwards, in February, 1849, Footman resigned his position as managing director and Bruff voluntarily shouldered the duties of general manager for no extra pay, again until the line reached Norwich. Well might the directors acknowledge that his "general capability and intimate knowledge of the locality and its resources are highly appreciated by the Board". Rigorous economies followed, but a few months later one shareholder was still complaining of "reckless extravagance in the management", alleging that "for three years, to enable him to pay up his calls, he had been compelled to subsist on bread and water".

Work was resumed on the Norwich Extension early in 1848, and by the end of May the labour force numbered about 450 men. At that time, permanent way had been laid as far as Finningham, so that a locomotive could haul a load of materials there for building a wooden station. Public goods services to Finningham began on 7th June, 1848.[21]

Immediately to the north of the station there had been a long delay in the acquisition of land, and the work of construction had hardly begun, but it was proceeding apace at many other points all the way to Norwich. Most of the embankment across the treacherous Thrandeston Marsh had been completed. In July, the brick arches of the bridge across the Waveney at Diss were finished.

The autumn of 1848 was very wet and, as much of the earthwork was in heavy clay, the rate of progress fell. The earth clung to the navvies' shovels and picks, making the work more laborious. Then, under the action of feet, hooves and wheels — and more rain — it became a sticky, treacherous substance which impeded traffic and could not be consolidated in embankments. It was liable to slide and sink in frustrating, unpredictable and dangerous ways of its own.

Under any conditions, clay was useless for ballasting the permanent way, and for the length between Haughley Junction and Finningham, gravel ballast[22] had to be taken all the way from

The Ipswich and Bury St Edmunds Railway gravel pit at Gallows Hill, near Needham Market, from where the ballast was dug for the line from Haughley to Mellis. It is now a refuse tip.

Gallows Hill, near Needham. On the Norwich Extension itself, no suitable material was found in the cuttings down to Flordon, although some ballast was obtained from a field near Diss, but it was somewhat off the alignment and a tramway had to be laid to it. The heavy earthworks near Norwich were mostly in gravel. There the work was delayed not so much by the weather as by shortage of capital.

It was obvious that the line should be opened in sections, progressively from the Haughley end, and in adopting this policy Cobbold was not obstructed by the Norwich shareholders, as he himself had sought to obstruct the Eastern Counties directors ten years earlier.

In spite of all the setbacks the earthworks between Finningham and Diss, including the embankment across Thrandeston Marsh, were completed early in the new year. Track of some sort was laid down and on 19th January the contractor's ballast engine reached Diss. This locomotive was probably ex-Eastern Counties Railway No 141, an 0-4-0 with 5 foot diameter wheels, built by Braithwaite, Milner and Company in 1839 and sold to Brassey in that same January ten years later. It was apparently named *Woodlark*, but was usually referred to as the *Mudlark*; as the first engine ever to arrive in Norfolk over the Eastern Union line it was given a tumultuous welcome.

Banners and greenery were festooned over it, the Diss brass band blared away from a truck behind and crowds turned out to cheer and fire off cannon. The driver was Mrs Alexander Ogilvie, the contractor's wife, assisted by John Mitchell, Bruff's chief assistant on the line, and another engineer named Read.

Several trips were made up and down the line as far as Burston — "the fair driver performing her task in gallant style", according to the *Norfolk Chronicle* — until some enthusiast turned the points so that the locomotive went up a siding, into what was to be the engine shed and out through the back! Fortunately no great damage was done.

In March the collapse of a large culvert near Finningham isolated the Diss section, but soon a single line of permanent way stretched from Flordon to Mellis and was being continued steadily southwards, ballasted with gravel brought up from Norfolk. By 16th May the culvert and embankment had been made good and the road completed so that the ballast engine could run through to Finningham and return with materials for the station buildings at Mellis and Diss.

Single line working for goods traffic began to Mellis and Diss on 28th May.[23] A train left Finningham every afternoon and immediately upon arrival at Diss the locomotive returned with another, "on account of a deficient supply of water at Diss, whereby the engine cannot be retained in that neighbourhood. The water of the river Waveney is so impregnated with extraneous matter as to

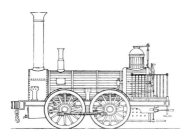

An E.C.R. goods locomotive with 5 ft wheels, of which a pair was built by Braithwaite, Milner and Company in 1839. In January, 1849, one was sold to Thomas Brassey, and this was probably his "new engine" used on the construction of the Norwich Extension of the E.U.R.

be detrimental to the machinery, and the supply drawn from springs is not more than sufficient for the engine now stationed at Diss". On 11th June the service was extended to Burston.[24] Within a short time the second line of permanent way was completed and passenger traffic between Haughley Junction and Burston began on 2nd July.[25]

Presumably for the first week both the old and the new Haughley stations (see Chapter ten) were open, for it was not until 6th July that the company issued an announcement:

> On and after Monday next, July 9th, the Haughley Station will be closed, and the business transferred to the Haughley Junction.

Although the foundation stone for the Lakenham viaduct near Norwich had been laid as long before as 30th August, 1847, with suitable ceremony and broaching of beer barrels, the work had been proceeding at only a slow pace. The scaffolding stood for so long that the rope lashings rotted and the staging round one of the piers collapsed, injuring four men. In February, 1849, it was still only up to springing height. Not until June was the Markshall cutting completed, and at that time the permanent way hardly extended north of Burston, although an isolated length had been laid from the Norwich side of the viaduct to Peafield, an area of Lakenham which was one of the early Norwich suburbs. In July, the Royal Agricultural Society was to hold its meetings and show in the city, and many people hoped that the Eastern Union would be able to extend its line at least as far as Dunston, some three miles short of the intended terminus.

On 8th June, Colonel G. Pratt Barlow resigned from the vice-chairmanship of the company and his place was taken by Samuel Bignold, secretary of the great Norwich Union Fire Insurance Society and at that time Mayor of Norwich. He knew that the company's difficulties stemmed from shortage of capital and, again in sharp contrast to Cobbold's tactics with the Eastern Counties Railway, he took immediate steps to provide money. Before the month was over he wrote to the chairman expressing the concern felt by many in Norwich:

> There is to be sure a little going forward . . . but nothing at the Viaduct, causing people to ask whether our line is abandoned. I am assured about £9,000 will finish everything to the Viaduct. To this extent, I and two or three ardent spirits here are willing to be answerable . . .

His colleagues accepted his offer with gratitude. Within a few weeks the centering was in position at Lakenham and early in September bricklayers commenced turning the arches.

By the beginning of October, a double line of permanent way stretched from Haughley to Flordon and a single one onwards as far as Swainsthorpe. The great skew bridge at Dunston, carrying the highway from Norwich to Scole over the railway at an angle of

The buildings of the original "Haughley Road" station, closed in 1849, as they were about 1970. The shadow is cast by the road bridge, and the tracks are out of sight below the picture.

Lakenham viaduct, near Norwich, built to carry the E.U.R. across the River Yare and the tracks of the Norfolk Railway.

only about 32 degrees, was complete; the Lakenham viaduct, with its six arches each of 30 feet span, was nearly finished, with the embankments almost closed up on each side.

A large quantity of bricks and drainage tiles were supplied from a brickground at Tharston, "across the fields" to the east of the railway, between Forncett and Flordon, which was owned by Sir Robert Harvey, the first vice-chairman of the Eastern Counties Railway Company. Perhaps on the proceeds — or more likely to use some of the bricks when progress on the railway works fell behind expectations — he built a new house nearby having, according to the *Norfolk Chronicle*, "a large stone in front inscribed 'This house was built by Major-General Sir Robert Harvey, in 1847, in which year two millions of bricks were burnt for this railway'."[26]

The bridge carrying what was then called Brazen Doors Road (now Grove Road) over the line just by Victoria Station had caused some red faces among the city fathers when one of them claimed that it was higher than the Corporation had agreed. Alas, no one could say positively what the Corporation had agreed, for the Town Clerk was unable to produce any document or correspondence on the subject, and even the minutes of a meeting between the council's Railway Committee and representatives of the company had been lost.

Another committee was appointed to search the Town Clerk's office, but the missing agreement could not be found. Some councillors denied that any such document had ever existed and the Mayor, Samuel Bignold, said he had never seen it or signed it. After some debate, a councillor reminded his colleagues that the railway was coming so far into the city only at the request of the citizens; the railway company was doing its best for Norwich and only one person objected to the bridge. Embarrassed by the course

The plaque on Sir Robert Harvey's cottage "Vittoria" at Tharston recording the burning of bricks for the railway.

that events had taken, the council resolved the matter by dropping it.

Bignold had given much inspiration and practical help to the company as the railway extended nearer to Norwich and great efforts were made to complete the line during his term of office as Mayor of the city.

Evans, the sub-contractor for the Norwich end of the line, had

The Tharston cottage, with the plaque still to be seen above the door.

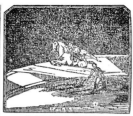

An advertisement of 1839 for entertainment at the Ranelagh Gardens. Ten years later the Gardens had become Victoria Station.

men working in shifts all round the clock. Sixty men were busy on the Lakenham viaduct. On 15th October, the Mayor, with a party of local worthies, went to the viaduct to lay the last bricks of the structure. The Sheriff, Robert Chamberlin, laid two and the final two were laid by Bignold himself. The workmen listened to a short speech or two, cheered and turned their attention to the contents of two barrels of beer which had been brought along.

By 3rd November a single line of permanent way had been laid over the viaduct and Brassey's *Mudlark*, hauling a single carriage containing representatives of the contractors and the company, with a party of their guests, traversed the entire line from Diss down to the Norwich terminus. The Victoria Gardens, the site of the station, had earlier been known as the Ranelagh Gardens. The station building itself had been adapted from the "Pantheon" which had been a feature of the gardens — a building used for circuses and other entertainments. It now housed the booking and luggage offices, and "the exterior orchestra being removed, three plain but lofty arches are turned, under a pointed pediment, and surmounted with the city arms".

The opening of the line was advertised to take place on 7th November, when there would be a public dinner in St Andrew's Hall. The *Norwich Mercury* noted with satisfaction:

> The dinner, as will be seen, is by ticket — the Company's resources being very prudently in no way made use of for such a purpose.

The day turned out to be wet, with flurries of sleet driven by a biting wind, but Norwich was determined to celebrate the occasion in a fitting manner. Even the arrival of the empty carriages for the inaugural train was marked by the firing of cannon. At about 11.15 a.m. the train pulled out, hauled by a locomotive named *Goliath*, driven by Mitchell. Just behind the tender was an open truck containing a band and the rest of the train comprised about fourteen carriages (contemporary press accounts varied as to the precise number) in which rode some 550 people. Somebody had gallantly ordained that the ladies should occupy the first class carriages and the gentlemen travelled second class. A journalist commented that this broke up parties, but the real reason may well have been to avoid giving offence. At least there was no wild rush for a more privileged ride.

It was the usual story, told at great length in the contemporary press: the cheering crowds, etc. The *Norwich Mercury* said:

> We trust that now the Line has thus nearly approached completion, care will be taken in future to avoid in the construction of stations, that lavish and ridiculous expenditure which must have struck everyone who has passed along the Line from Diss to Stowmarket and Ipswich.

In the same column, however, it dismissed Mellis station as "a very unpretending structure of brick" and Finningham "partakes of the utilitarian if not of the picturesque character".

About noon, another train left Ipswich, drawn by the locomotive *City of Norwich*, with Bruff as driver. It carried a large party, invited from the surrounding district, but "a few persons who paid fares to Burston, though they had often derided the railway, and made sport of the losses of the projectors, were generously allowed to take their seats in the carriages".

The intention was that the two trains should reach Stowmarket, where a lunch had been arranged, at about the same time; but in fact the Ipswich contingent arrived there about an hour before the train from Norwich, and some had had their meal before the second train pulled in. Cobbold greeted Bignold, and then there was "a perfect scramble of no very creditable kind" as everyone "tried to secure something edible and potable".

Afterwards, the two trains were joined together and "impelled by the *City of Norwich* and the *Ipswich* engines" started off towards Norwich. Another engine, the *Diss*, was waiting at that station to assist the train of twenty-four carriages, if required. At the terminus, which was reached after a journey of about two hours, the train "extended from the station nearly to the second bridge".

The dinner in St Andrew's Hall was no more decorous than

Victoria Station, Norwich, as it was about 1910. The top of the original Rotunda can be seen above the roof.   Peter Larter

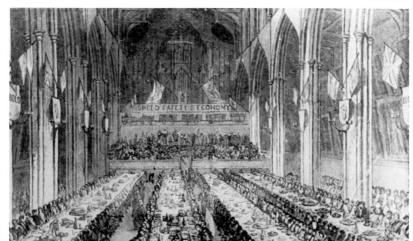

The dinner in St Andrew's Hall, Norwich, on 7th December, 1849, to celebrate the opening of the E.U.R. Extension.
Suffolk Record Office

the lunch had been. The food, "considering the difficulty of the task, was placed on the table with reasonable promptitude, notwithstanding the occupants of a side table had clamorously to demand the attention of the waiters". According to another account, this was "by keeping up a continual clatter on the plates. The Mayor very justly treated their conduct with contempt".

Goods traffic through to Norwich began on 3rd December[27] and the line opened for passengers on 12th December, 1849.[28] The Eastern Union looked forward to a considerable increase in its traffic. The directors knew there would be opposition from the Eastern Counties Railway, which controlled the entire route to London by way of Ely and Cambridge, but they also knew that some of the E.C.R. shareholders regarded the lease of the Norfolk Railway as a costly blunder and were thinking that each route should have an agreed share of the traffic.

Construction of the short branch to the Norfolk Railway at Trowse did not begin until the autumn of 1850. It was just over a mile in length and, most of it being at an incline of 1 in 84, it was the most steeply graded stretch of the Eastern Union system. The official inspection was carried out by Captain Wynne, R.E., on 25th August, 1851,[29] and the company probably just managed to comply with the stipulation in the Act that all work on the Norwich Extension should be completed within five years of the Act becoming law. By a notice dated 29th August,[30] the company announced that the Trowse branch would be brought into use for special excursion trains to Yarmouth Races on Tuesday, 9th September, and the following day, but it was not used regularly until:

> On and after the 1st October, a daily communication will be opened for Passengers and Goods, between the Eastern Union line and all places on the Norfolk and Eastern Counties Companies' lines via the Trowse Junction at Norwich.
> Eastern Union Railway Company Offices 27th September 1851.[31]

The Trowse link was the last section of the Eastern Union Railway to be built and operated by the company before the working of its whole system was taken over by the Eastern Counties Company. The E.C.R. refused to allow any E.U.R. locomotive to run upon their metals and the engines of the latter company had to run round their trains and follow them down the gradient to Trowse Lower Junction.

Victoria Station later became somewhat superfluous, but Norwich Corporation managed to get a clause prohibiting its closure inserted in the E.C.R. company's 1854 Act which authorised the lease of the E.U.R. Thorpe Station naturally became the principal station in the city, but nevertheless Victoria continued to handle a small amount of local traffic until the former terminus of the E.U.R. closed to passenger traffic on 22nd May, 1916.

Men of the Eastern Union

8

FOLLOWING the appointment of John Tunmer in December, 1844, as the Eastern Union's first policeman, a second constable was engaged in March, 1845, and two more in July. Their job was to see that the contractors' workmen behaved in an orderly and law abiding fashion, and upon taking up his duties each constable was issued with a suit of uniform clothing.

But their beats lay along muddy cuttings and over raw embankments and it was not long before they requested the issue of a second suit of clothing. The directors instructed the secretary, Saunders, to find out what clothing was issued to policemen serving with other railways, and a few days later he reported that the police on the Eastern Counties Railway received an annual issue of "1 Body Coat, 2 Prs Trowsers, 1 Hat, 1 Stock and 2 Pairs Boots". Every second year they were given a greatcoat and a cape. Upon hearing this the Eastern Union directors decided that a cape and a second pair of "trowsers" should at once be issued to their men, together with a brush and button-stick for cleaning the buttons of their coats.

As the time for the opening of the line between Colchester and Ipswich drew nearer, senior officials were appointed. On 30th March, 1846, J. Dent took up his duties as superintendent of the goods department, at a weekly "salary" of forty-two shillings, and a Mr Williams followed a few days later as police superintendent, with special responsibility for the management of the station at Ipswich. Both probably had previous railway experience. Early in May the directors appointed a "Superintendent and Chief Station

An E.U.R. cuff button dug up in a Stowmarket garden in 1986.

John Day

Barnes' station at Mellis, described at the time of its building as "a very unpretending structure"; now demolished.

Clerk" to manage the passenger traffic at a salary of £250 a year. He was John Squire Martin, lately "Deputy Superintendent of Bristol Station", and his application had been backed with an excellent testimonial from Charles Saunders, secretary of the G.W.R. At the same time J. Dutton came from Shoreditch station to be chief clerk in the goods department of the Eastern Union.

At Ipswich station there were to be fourteen policemen, headed by a sub-inspector, and twelve porters, the duties of the constables being as follows:

1 Policeman	Lodge Gate	Day
1 Ditto	Departure Platform and Bell	Day
1 Ditto	Arrival Platform and Bell	Day
1 Ditto	Front of Station	Day
1 Ditto	Ditto	Night
1 Ditto	Goods Shed	Day
1 Ditto	Ditto	Night
1 Ditto	Arrival Switches	Day
1 Ditto	Ditto	Night
1 Ditto	Engine House	Day
1 Ditto	Ditto	Night
1 Ditto	Signal Post	Day
1 Ditto	Ditto	Night

At Ardleigh there were two posts for policemen — "Front of Station and Bell" and "Level Crossing Gates and Signal" — with day and night constables assigned to each. Three porters dealt with other duties.

These police duties remind us that constables then served as signalmen and pointsmen and that bells were rung to announce the arrival and departure of the trains. As only the mail trains ran at night to begin with, it is understandable that there were no policemen on platform duty at Ipswich by night and that bell-ringing was dispensed with; probably the constable on night duty at the front of the station supervised the receipt and dispatch of the mails.

John Brundley from the Eastern Counties Railway was appointed as the sub-inspector of police, at a weekly wage of thirty shillings, while James Otway, who had joined the Eastern Union as the second constable on the construction sites, was promoted to be one of the two sergeants in the company's service at a wage of twenty-two shillings and sixpence.

Even in these early days, when many people lived out their lives in the districts of their birth, there was obviously considerable mobility among railwaymen. It was a new industry and there were ready opportunities for promotion for those with experience. Of the first six constables appointed by the Eastern Union to be switchmen, at an enhanced weekly wage of twenty-three shillings, three came from the London and Birmingham, one from the Great Western, one from the London and South Western and one from the Eastern Counties Railway. At the same time, eight ordinary "policemen" were appointed, at a weekly wage of nineteen shillings; six of these came from the Great Western and the other two came from the Eastern Counties Railway. Twelve more constables were recruited locally, selected by the directors from twenty-five applicants whom they interviewed.

Police duties included permanent way inspection; day and night constables were assigned to the cuttings at Wherstead and Brantham, whereas Lawford cutting was to be patrolled only by day.

Two foreman porters were appointed at a weekly wage of twenty-five shillings; one of these came from the Great Western

DANGER   CAUTION   ALL RIGHT

Signals to be given by railway policemen, 1841. Russel shows a policeman giving an "all right" signal in his picture of Ipswich tunnel on page 61, and such hand signals continued to be used on the railways into the present century.

and the other from the London and South Western Railway. Of the first six ordinary porters to be engaged, three came from the Great Western and one from the London and Birmingham Railway; the remaining two were selected from four local applicants. The wage offered was nineteen shillings per week. A few days later twenty-one other porters were chosen from a list of thirty-three local applicants and three guards were appointed on the recommendation of Mr Roney, the secretary of the Eastern Counties company.

Williams' recommendation that the stations between Colchester and Ipswich should be manned by a staff totalling twenty-four porters and thirty policemen was closely scrutinised by the directors, who made all the appointments and caused details of all the applicants to be recorded in the minutes of their meetings. On the other hand, they were ignorant of technical matters, so that

Bruff, as engineer, was given a free hand in the locomotive and engineering departments, and few details of these have survived.

In March, 1846, the directors approved Bruff's appointment of Robert Taylor as locomotive foreman, at a weekly wage of three guineas, and "such other persons as he (Bruff) might think proper for the effectual working of the line".

Taylor was a thirty-four-year-old Cumbrian. In February, 1847, his remuneration was increased to an annual salary of £210, an almost unique example of a rise in the service of the company, which all too soon was imposing pay cuts at all levels. Taylor stayed at the Ipswich depot well into Great Eastern days, being still at his post in 1874.

Many of the tradesmen in the locomotive and rolling stock departments came from other parts of the country, and not surprisingly the unskilled workers were generally local men. An exception was John Hammond, carriage superintendent by 1851; he came from Leiston.

Most of the enginemen were under thirty when recruited and came mainly from Lancashire, where there were earlier railways and a tradition of steam power in the mills — and from where the company obtained its first locomotives.

The E.U.R. directors also decided to maintain their permanent way by direct labour and for this, too, Bruff was merely directed to appoint the necessary staff.[32]

As was usual on railways, those in positions of trust were required to find sureties for their honesty. The chief station clerks* on the Eastern Union had to have two guarantors of £150 each and the junior clerks two of £100 each. The juniors received an initial salary of £60 a year and the principal clerks were to be paid "as Mr Footman thinks proper". At Ipswich this post was held by one Gideon Hatchwell, another former Great Western man.

Having selected even its humblest employees with great care, the company did not tolerate any hint that there might be rogues among them. The following letter was published in the Ipswich local papers:

To the Editor . . .
Sir,
A paragraph appeared in the *Ipswich Express* of Tuesday last, the 2nd inst., stating that a man of the name of James Clarke, committed by the Magistrates for the robbery of some harness belonging to C.F. Gower Esq., Nova Scotia, was employed by this Company at this department. I beg to inform you that such statement is utterly without foundation, and you will much oblige me by contradicting it in your paper of this week.
I am, sir, your obedient servant,
J. Dent
E.U.R. Goods Superintendent's Office, Ipswich.   5th November 1847

*The term seems to have been synonymous with station master in the early days.

This image of the integrity of the company's employees was sadly tarnished a few months later, when the *Suffolk Chronicle* reported:

In the course of one day, about a fortnight ago, nearly a hundred individuals from the parish of Claydon, including a dry nurse and a washerwoman, called at the Audit Office of the Railway Company, Stoke, and sought interviews with Mr Footman, the managing director. They each and all stated that they had been referred to him for the settlement of some "little accounts" which had been contracted by a station master on the line. Upon making enquiry, it turned out that the eccentric station master had taken French leave of his situation the day before, and had gone to London by the steamer, not forgetting, however, to inform his numerous creditors that Mr Footman would be answerable for his liabilities. The annoyance to which the managing director was subjected may be conceived.

The final blow came in April, 1853, when the company's senior station master yielded to temptation. According to the *Illustrated London News*:

Mr H. Cole, the station master at Ipswich, has absconded. All moneys received at the station passed through his hands; and some discrepancy being discovered in his accounts, a rigid inquiry was determined upon. Apprehensive of the result, Cole took his departure by the late train on Monday night.

There was a sequel to this a few months later. A man named Cochrane had entered into a bond with the company for £200 for the honesty of Cole, and he refused to pay up, on the grounds that the bond had been with the original Eastern Union Railway, before it was amalgamated with the Ipswich and Bury Railway. He was successfully sued.

The highest standards of conduct were expected from the company's servants and even the most minor lapses were apt to be pilloried in the press. In June, 1847, an employee of the I.&B.R., alighting from a moving train at Needham, fell between the train and the platform. He was rolled over on the edge of the platform by the footboards of several carriages, but miraculously escaped without serious injury although his coat was torn to shreds. "As the passengers are strictly prohibited from getting in or out while trains are in motion, the Company's servants ought to set the example", commented the *Suffolk Chronicle*.

For its part, the company was understandably nettled by publicity of this kind. Not long afterwards there was alleged to have been a minor collision at Burston, but the only statement which the press could extract from a spokesman was:

An accident may have happened somewhere in the British dominions on that self-same evening, but I am happy to inform you that no accident has happened at or near Burston Station.

With a little less luck, several events could have caused a terrible disaster. It is well known that the safety which we take for granted in railway working today came about to a great extent from the application of lessons learned the hard way. Looking back to those early days we can often see instances of carelessness.

The following cases were all reported to the directors on one day in September, 1846:

> James Scrivener, policeman at Lawford, reported for not signalling special engine returning from Colchester . . . on the 14th . . . J.S. fined one week's wages.

> Constables Andrews and Tunmer reported for not giving the proper signal to a driver approaching Belstead Cutting on the 14th, when the rails were being lifted. They were called in and the Board having heard extenuating circumstances, it was ordered that Andrews and Tunmer be reprimanded by the Chairman, which was accordingly done.

> Switchman Cole having been reported asleep in his box on Sunday evening last upon the arrival of the Down Mail and not being in attendance as he had been ordered . . .

the directors gave instructions that he should appear before them the following week. When the time came, however, Footman reported that he had dealt with the man himself and fined him 2s. 6d. The constable Tunmer referred to here was no doubt the same man who had been appointed to patrol the construction works at Brantham, and who had already once been reprimanded for inattention to his duties.

"Switchman Cole" was probably the George Cole who was among the twelve ordinary constables recruited locally on 2nd May. A labourer of the same name joined the Ipswich Borough Police as a constable in December, 1842; there is evidence to suggest that a year later he was a sergeant. In September, 1845, he was dismissed from the force, having twice in the space of a few weeks neglected to visit men on their beats, falsely reporting that he had done so. Here was a man — if one and the same — gaining rapid promotion in two organisations; probably a very good man, but prone to nod off at the wrong moment, and saved from the wrath of the directors by a half-crown fine imposed by the general manager.

This was not an isolated instance; there were a number of cases of considerable leniency shown towards wayward employees. On one occasion after the amalgamation of the Eastern Union and the Ipswich and Bury Railways a complaint was received that a Bury train had been delayed for a long time at Haughley Junction. The stationmaster there, a man named Butcher, was sent a letter from the office in Ipswich asking for an explanation. At the next meeting of the directors' traffic committee, Bruff, who by this time was general manager as well as engineer, reported that "a letter had been received from Mr Butcher in which he intimated that in consequence of the small salary paid him, he was not very anxious to remain in the Company's service". He was immediately relieved of his responsibilities, but a couple of months later he wrote to apologise and asked if he might be re-employed. The committee resolved that Butcher be reinstated "as soon as arrangements could be made".

In 1851, a guard named Chapman was dismissed for detaining a train at Manningtree for thirty-five minutes; it was not his first offence of the kind. In his report to the directors, Bruff said that the man had not been very attentive to his duties for some time; on a previous occasion he had inexplicably detached a carriage from his train at Diss, so that five passengers going on towards Norwich were left behind!

By the beginning of 1848, although the Eastern Union company was still not actually amalgamated with the Ipswich and Bury, joint meetings of the two boards of directors were considering what economies could be made so that every available penny could be put towards the completion of the Norwich line.

A scheme of pay reductions was drawn up. Saunders agreed to accept a salary of £500 as secretary of the amalgamated companies, a sum which he had previously received from the I.&B.R. alone, besides £400 from the original Eastern Union and £200 from the Hadleigh Railway. Bruff's salary was similarly reduced, and in addition he lost £40 a year which he had been receiving as an office rent allowance (a few months later, however, the directors agreed to pay him an allowance of £100 per month for his expenses — assistants' salaries, etc. — until the Norwich Extension was completed). Other reductions were applied to all the head office staff.

A committee of directors visited every station to advise on ways of reducing expenditure, and widespread pay cuts and some redundancies were decided upon. The lower paid men had their wages cut by ten per cent or so, but the ticket collector at Stowmarket was singled out to have his weekly earnings reduced from twenty-five shillings to sixteen. By these and other measures it was estimated that an annual saving of £3,085 could be achieved.

The committee reported:

Although the Committee have no reason to consider the number of persons employed at the several stations or the amount of salaries and wages received by them to be at all excessive . . . they feel it to be their duty, in the present position of the Company, to recommend certain reductions . . . until the opening of the line to Norwich shall have produced such an increase of traffic as will render the capital of the shareholders productive; and until which period they are satisfied that all the parties to whom these reductions apply will cheerfully bear their share of additional labour and diminished receipt in order to aid in the early and successful completion of the undertaking.

The sole immediate result was the resignation of the station master at Bentley. Although enginemen on the Eastern Counties Railway had gone on strike for two days in December, 1839, when their overtime pay — a rarity in itself — had been reduced, such action was unusual. By the standards of the time, railway employment was considered well paid and, above all, fairly secure and this tended to induce acceptance of hardships.

Among those made redundant was Williams, the police superintendent, whose duties were transferred to Mr Worswick, inspector of permanent way in the engineer's department. The traffic committee of the board directed that Williams should be appointed to another post in the company's service but, as it turned out, he could not be offered anything which he considered a suitable alternative and he resigned. The traffic committee at once recommended that he should be paid six months' salary as a gratuity.

The directors, although not of course dependent on their fees for their bread and butter, did not overlook themselves in their quest for economy. They proposed that their new fees should be £600 a year, instead of £500 for those of the original Eastern Union and £800 in the case of the Ipswich and Bury; several had seats on both boards. In the event, they waived their fees altogether.

When Bruff succeeded Footman as general manager in the following February he received at first no extra salary, but as from 1st January, 1850 — the line being then open to Norwich — he was paid an annual salary of £800 for the combined duties of engineer and manager. But money remained desperately short, and on 30th January, 1850, he wrote to Saunders:

My Dear Sir,

From the many personal applications that I have made to you for the payment of the allowance of £100 per month, ordered to be paid me by the Board, by their minute of the 22nd Septr 1848, towards the expenses incurred by me on account of Engineering until the completion of the Norwich Line, you will be quite prepared to receive this application from me in writing for the payment of the £100 per month during the past twelve months, and unless you can make an arrangement by which I can receive this payment within the next few weeks, say during Feby, the consequences will be very serious indeed to myself and may render it necessary for me to make such sacrifices that the Co. would be unwilling to compensate me for, although in fact I should be raising money to pay debts incurred on their behalf and on faith of the payment ordered by the Board being strictly carried out. I have to request therefore, unless you can arrange to make payment of the £100 per month due to me for the year 1849 in cash during the course of next month, that you will let me have a Company's acceptance for the Amount at a date not exceeding two Months from this date, with which I believe I can continue to relieve myself of present embarrassments but I can only take it on the faith and promise that it will be honoured on its arriving to maturity.

I remain, dear Sir, . . .

Peter Bruff

As the time approached for the opening of the Norwich Extension, the E.U.R. directors realised that their Victoria Station was going to be a vital outpost deep in hostile territory. When the Trowse link was completed their line would provide a shorter route to London from a large part of Norfolk and the district round Lowestoft. For the key position of superintendent at Norwich they chose J.S. Martin. Gideon Hatchwell, from Ipswich station, went with him as "collector".

However, Martin resigned after a short time to become superintendent of the Norfolk Railway section of the E.C.R. (by 1857 he held a senior post on the Grand Junction Railway in Canada). He was replaced at Victoria by Joseph Dutton, previously stationmaster at Bury St Edmunds.

When Dutton arrived to take up his duties, "he found matters in a most unsatisfactory state, the officers and porters were almost beyond his control". He at once reported the situation to Bruff in Ipswich, and returned armed with powers to suspend anyone who would not obey his orders. Hatchwell was particularly obstructive. He later appeared before the directors to apologise for his remarks to Dutton, made "under excited feelings", and in June, 1850, he was posted to Bury. Shortly afterwards he met his death in circumstances which must be unique in British railway history.

On 4th October, the locomotive on the 8 a.m. train from Bury to Ipswich burst a tube as it was about to start. At that time, there

Thurston station shortly before the sidings were lifted.

Jannings' Bridge, Thurston, now more prosaically termed Bridge No 1158, which was the scene of the deaths of the two station masters in 1850.

was no telegraph north of Ipswich, but Hatchwell knew that the engine from the connecting down train to Norwich would be sent from Haughley Junction, on "the wrong road" towards Bury, to see what had happened to the train when it failed to arrive. To save time, he ordered four of the company's horses[33] to be hitched to the two-coach train to take it along until the engine met it. He wrote a letter to Bruff, explaining what he had done, and sent it by the train, upon which he rode himself. So that he might see the approaching locomotive at the earliest possible moment, he mounted the roof of the leading carriage, while a porter named William Baldry travelled on the roof of the other.

When the train reached Thurston, Hatchwell was joined by James Wolton, the stationmaster there, and the journey continued with the two men apparently enjoying an unaccustomed ride, perched on some luggage on the roof. They soon sighted the engine coming towards them, and met it at the second overbridge from Thurston station. The horses were then unhitched and the locomotive coupled up.

Incredibly, both stationmasters remained on the roof, seated on top of the luggage and, to crown their folly, with their backs to the engine! Their heads were well above the top of the chimney, and as the train passed under the fourth bridge from Thurston station[34] (known as "Jannings' bridge", after the farmer at the adjacent Grove Farm) they struck the arch. Wolton was killed instantly; Hatchwell rolled to the edge of the roof and, despite Baldry's efforts to hold him, fell to the ground; some platelayers working nearby had time to reach him before he died.

The horrified driver stopped the train as quickly as possible, and then reversed slowly back towards Thurston. Hatchwell was picked up and placed in the guard's compartment; Wolton's body remained on the roof until it could be lifted down at the station, where both were placed in an empty horse-box.

An inquest was held that same afternoon in the *Fox and Hounds* public house, which still stands close to the station at Thurston. Baldry admitted that the company's rules forbade anyone to ride on the roofs of trains, except guards, who were provided with proper seats. The guard related how he had immediately realised that there had been an accident and had applied his brake; the train had been travelling "at the usual speed of about 15 m.p.h.", and it came to a stand within about 200 yards. Verdicts of "Accidental Death" were recorded. The wretched Baldry was later dismissed from the company's service.

James Wolton, a Colchester man who had previously been stationmaster at Needham, was buried in Thurston churchyard, and Hatchwell at St Mark's, New Lakenham.[35] There was an extraordinary incident at the funeral when, with everyone standing round, the service had to be suspended for several minutes while the grave was widened, "in consequence of the great width of the coffin" — a bizarre final reminder that Hatchwell had been a Great Western man!

Although both men would have been dismissed from the company's service had they survived, the directors were not ungenerous to their widows. Both received payments of 50 guineas, and the *Ipswich Journal* invited the public to subscribe to a fund for the benefit of Mrs Hatchwell, who had been left with a number of young children. The directors were concerned, too, to learn that she did not wish to return to her relatives in Taunton, where her father was understood to be an innkeeper in comfortable circumstances who had offered a home to her and the children; she wanted to move back to Norwich. They ordered "that the Secretary do write Mrs Hatchwell, expressing the Directors' regret that such is her wish; and that he do urge upon her the desirability of her residing in future with her relatives at Taunton".

Saunders was doubtless able to pull a few strings at Paddington; the last we hear of the matter is a resolution of the E.U.R. board about a month later "that the Great Western Railway be thanked for agreeing to carry Mrs Hatchwell, her children and their furniture free from London to Bristol".

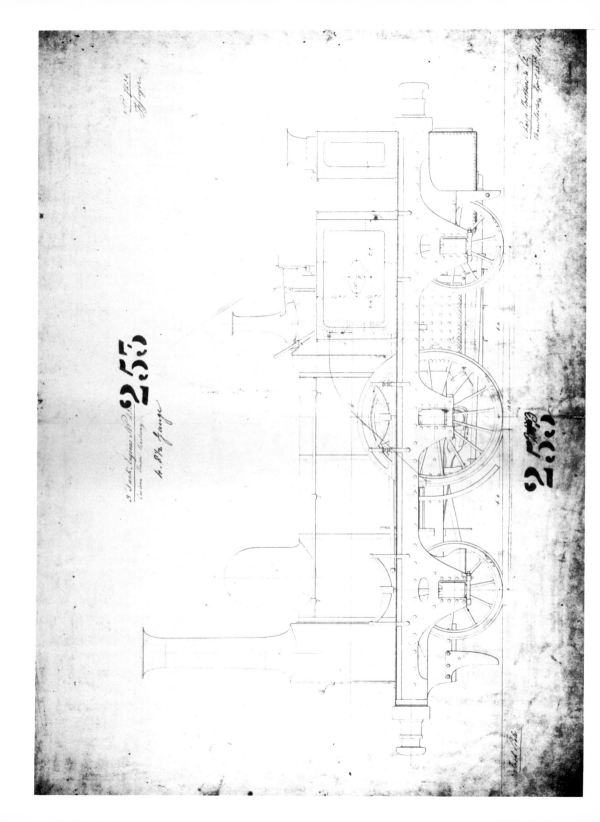

Locomotives and Rolling Stock 9

T HE DIRECTORS of the Eastern Union were expecting their line from Colchester to Ipswich to be completed in May, 1846. Early in September, 1845, Bruff was instructed to write to "the principal Engine Manufacturers" to see what they could supply.

Alas, this was the time of the "Railway Mania"; lines were under construction all over Britain — and overseas, too — and British locomotive builders were fully occupied. None could promise anything before the spring of 1847.

The reaction of J.C. Cobbold and his colleagues to this news provides us with a glimpse of the spirit which made Victorian England great. They immediately deputed the managing director, John Footman, with Bruff and their friend James Allen Ransome, the Ipswich agricultural engineer, to "proceed forthwith to the North of England for the purpose of communicating personally with those manufacturers to whom the Engineer would recommend that an order should be given". There was to be no reporting back for approval of prices or for further instructions; they sent men on whose judgment they knew they could rely and left them to get on with it, merely saying that the board would confirm any reasonable arrangements which they might make.

The deputation wasted no time. They "proceeded that afternoon towards Manchester" — the very wording of their subsequent report suggests the arduousness of the journey, which could hardly have begun with less than two hours' fast driving to the nearest railhead, at Colchester. The next day, 10th October, "they had a long conference with Mr C. Sharp of the firm of Sharp Brothers & Co". Little more than twenty-four hours after being told that they could not have any engines for about eighteen months, the delegation had arranged a provisional contract with Sharps for eight tender engines, of which three were to be delivered by 25th April, 1846 (in good time for the opening of the line), three more by 25th July and the remaining pair in May, 1847. The specification was as follows:

Cylinders 15 inches × 20 inches
Fire Box — Copper — 3 feet × 3 feet 6½ inches
Boiler — Best Plate Iron — 10 feet × 3 feet 6 inches
Tubes — Brass — 147 No. × 1¾ inches external diameter
Wheels — Six in number — Wrought Iron except the Naves
    5 feet 6 inches diameter driving wheels
    3 feet 6 inches diameter fore and hind wheels
Tenders to carry 1,000 gallons of water
    3 feet 6 inches wheels — six in number.

The prices were £1,580 per engine and £420 per tender, delivered

Opposite page: *The sole surviving contemporary general arrangement drawing of an E.U.R. locomotive, showing 2-2-2 well tanks Nos 29–31. Note the toggles actuating the brake blocks, a system favoured by Charles Beyer, chief designer for Sharp Brothers until he set up his own business with Richard Peacock in 1854.*
Science Museum

A rare photograph of a pre-G.E.R. locomotive: E.C.R. long-boiler 2-4-0 No 73 at Southtown. This was one of a class built by Robert Stephenson and Company in 1847; some were later rebuilt, but No 73 was scrapped in her original state in 1869. She would certainly have worked over E.U.R. metals in the years after 1854.   K. G. Leighton

in Manchester, or £35 on each engine and £10 on each tender if delivered at Shoreditch — nett cash on delivery.

On 14th October the directors confirmed their agreement and recorded that "the thanks of the Board are especially due to the Deputy Chairman and the Resident Engineer for the prompt and satisfactory arrangements". The full measure of the persuasiveness of these two gentlemen was revealed in a letter from Sharps to Bruff, dated 16th October:

Sir,
On ordering the plates for your Engines we find that we made an error in our Specification in respect of size of driving wheels. Those ordered by the Sheffield & Manchester and Blackburn & Preston Rway Companies having 5.0 driving wheels and not 5.6 as quoted to you; as it is our intention to give you some of the Engines ordered by the latter Rway so as to enable us to meet your views as to time of delivery, we shall be glad to receive your assent to the change by return of post so as to enable us to order the plates immediately — The diameter is sufficiently large to attain any velocity you may require.

Yours very respectfully,
p.pro Sharp Brothers & Co
(signed) John Robinson.

Sharp Brothers' original order book containing this, their order No 167, still survives in the Science Museum at South

Kensington. The prices were entered in code, presumably as a precaution against spies employed by the firm's competitors:

Eight Passenger Engines
Inside Cylinders } £dant

Eight 6 Wheel Tenders £pet

and the page is endorsed, "4ft 8¾ between the Rails".[36]

Other notes were added:

Oct 19. Agreed to our making the first 3 Engines with 5 ft Wheels, Same as Sheffield the remaining 5 to be 5f 6.

1845 (sic) March 19 Chimneys 13ft 3

Three Engines on or 25th April 1846 named 'Colchester' 'Ipswich' 'City of Norwich'

Three 'Bury St Edmunds' 'Orwell' 'Stour' 25th July '46
       No.4   No.5   No.6

Two   May 1847

On 27th March, 1846, a quantity of spare parts were added to the order:

One Set of Engine Wheels & Axles complete
Two pair of 3 f 6 Wheels & Axles for Tenders
Axle Bearings complete for the above
One Connecting Rod — Two Pistons & Rods
Two pairs of Connecting Rod Brasses, Large End
One set of Valve Balls & Seatings
Five Doz. Tubes
Two hundred Ferrules for Fire Box End
One hundred Ditto for Smoke Box
One Set of Tubing Tools
One Set of Taps & Dies with Screws & Stocks
One Set of Extra Taps for Engines
Six Plugs — Four Mud Cocks
Six Springs with adjusting Screws
A few Files of various kinds.

If this last item conjures up a picture of somewhat haphazard methods of fitting, nevertheless within a short time the Eastern Union company possessed a very well equipped locomotive works at Ipswich (see Appendix four).

A few days after the E.U.R. contract had been signed, Sharps offered to supply identical locomotives to the Ipswich and Bury St Edmunds company on the same terms, but it was not until 25th November that the arrangements were completed, by which time the price had risen to £1,610 for an engine and £430 for a tender, with delivery charges as before. Six were ordered (Sharp Brothers' Order No 170), to be delivered in pairs in February,

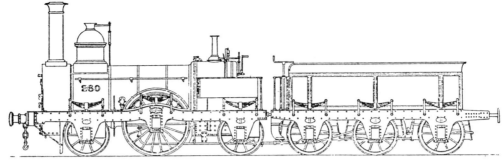

March and April, 1847. The builders managed to deliver the first pair in December, 1846, and the next pair arrived as scheduled in March, 1847. After that, no more locomotives for either of Bruff's railways arrived from Sharp Brothers until the early part of 1849.

All were typical "Sharp singles" of the period; all except one were later re-boilered by the G.E.R. during the regimes of Sinclair and Johnson, and all were scrapped between 1867 and 1880. E.U.R. No 3 *City of Norwich*, later re-numbered 262 by the E.C.R., was at one time fitted with a short Sinclair-type chimney for working on the Woolwich branch. Further details of these, and the other E.U.R. engines, are given in Appendix two.

The I.&B.R. had been seeking locomotives from other suppliers as well; in October, 1845, Bruff managed to get an order for three 2-2-2 tender engines accepted by R.&W. Hawthorn of Newcastle. Although this firm could not promise delivery in April, May and June, 1846, as Bruff wished, they did offer to supply an engine a month from August to October. The specification was as follows:

> Cylinders: 15 inch bore × 21 inch stroke
> Boiler: 11 feet 6 inches long × 3 feet 7 inches diameter, with 120 brass tubes of 2 inches internal diameter.
> Copper firebox, 3 feet 3 inches long × 3 feet 5 inches wide × 3 feet 10 inches high.
> Driving Wheels: 6 feet diameter
> Fore and Hind wheels: 3 feet 6 inches diameter.
> To be similar to engines recently supplied to Croydon, Brighton and Dover Railway Companies, and fitted with their patent expansive valve* and gearing.
> Tenders: 6 Wheels, 3 feet diameter.
> > Tank: 1,000 to 1,200 gallons
> > With brake acting on both sides of the wheels.
> Price: Engine £1,750 Tender £375
> Payment: ⅓ on confirmation of order
> > ⅓ when shipped or delivered at Gateshead Station
> > ⅓ when proved upon the line, say, after each engine shall have run a fortnight.

These Hawthorn engines were numbered 11, 12 and 13 by the E.U.R. — whether they were ever separately numbered by the

*See Appendix three.

I.&B.R. is doubtful — and were typical of the single-drivers built by the firm at that period. They may have been delivered in October, 1846, when the *Ipswich Journal* reported the arrival of three engines "for the Bury Railway" at Ipswich station. The first Sharp-built locomotives for the I.&B.R. were not delivered until December.

There was close collaboration between the two companies over the purchase and use of locomotives and rolling stock. Bruff suggested that perhaps everything should be purchased by the E.U.R., and the I.&B.R. should hire what it required, but the directors mutually agreed that some should be charged to the accounts of each company, although all items were pooled for working both lines, and amalgamation seems to have been understood almost from the outset. When the first general meeting of the united companies was held in June, 1848, it was reported that up to 31st December, 1847, the E.U.R. had expended £17,224 8s. 3d. and the I.&B.R. £20,213 0s. 8d. on locomotives.

In April, 1846, the Eastern Counties company offered to help the Eastern Union with the temporary provision of engines or rolling stock, if required, before their own were delivered and this offer must have been accepted.

Early in September, nearly three months after the line had been opened from Colchester to Ipswich, we find Bruff reporting that the company was hampered by having only three locomotives. These were the ones which Sharp Brothers had diverted from the Blackburn and Preston Railway. Three more should have arrived from Hawthorn's in July (evidently he had cajoled them into promising quicker delivery) but unfortunately in February there had been a serious fire at their Forth Bank Works in Newcastle. However, delivery was then expected soon, together with another trio from Sharps' Atlas Works at Manchester but, he added, had everything gone according to plan the company would at that time have had eleven locomotives instead of only three. Sharps' had evidently not managed to deliver their second batch of three in July and the remaining two engines mentioned were probably on order from Stothert and Slaughter of Bristol, later the Avonside Engine Company.

Eastern Counties Railway No 272, originally supplied to the Ipswich and Bury St Edmunds Railway by R. & W. Hawthorn in 1846, and numbered No 13 in the E.U.R. stock list.

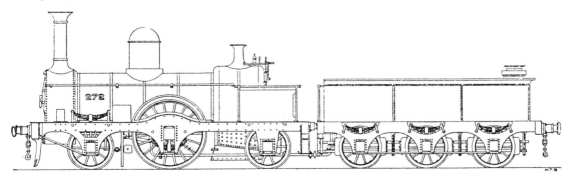

Information on the locomotives supplied by Stothert and Slaughter is sparse. I have been unable to locate any of their records, if any still survive, and the records of the E.U.R. and I.&B.R. do not mention the Bristol firm until June, 1846, when the E.U.R. directors resolved to "order from Messrs Slaughter two Passenger Engines and two Goods Engines for delivery as soon as possible in accordance with their offer". No specification of the engines was recorded in the minutes, but the two railway companies purchased a total of four 2-2-2 tender engines, numbered 7, 8, 20 and 21; and six 0-4-2 tender engines, which were numbered 9, 10, 22, 23, 24 and 25. All had inside cylinders and outside frames. The front-coupled engines were, of course, for goods traffic (the E.U.R. never possessed any six-coupled goods engines), and they seem to have been regarded as being a very powerful class at the time they were built.

In August, 1847, a local newspaper reported that one of Slaughter's engines named *Essex* had arrived one day at Ipswich from Stowmarket with "the amazing number of 149 loaded waggons at one time". The train was alleged to be nearly a mile long (which was certainly an exaggeration) and to be a record load, although it was said that there had once been a train of 192 empty waggons on the former Manchester and Birmingham Railway.

The Slaughter singles, on the other hand, seem not to have been entirely satisfactory. In his report to the company's general meeting in August, 1852, Bruff said, "Two of your heaviest and most powerful passenger engines, found to be more expensive with fuel than necessary, have during the past half year been converted into coupled goods engines by the makers. Two more engines of the same class are to be similarly altered".

By February, 1847, Bruff was able to report to the Eastern Union directors that twelve locomotives had been received since the previous general meeting in September. These must have been E.U.R. Nos 4 to 6, from Sharps, and the first two similar engines ordered in the name of the Ipswich and Bury company, together

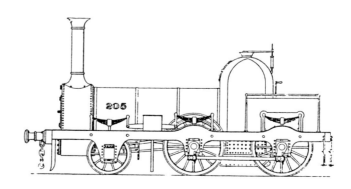

Eastern Counties Railways No 205, originally E.U.R. No 7, built by Stothert and Slaughter in 1846 as a 2-2-2 and rebuilt as a coupled engine in 1852. The tender is not shown.

with the three from Hawthorns and four from Stothert and Slaughter. It seems likely that these last were Nos 7, 8, 9 and 10 — two passenger and two goods engines ordered in the previous June — two of which Bruff had hoped would have been delivered in September, 1846.

In November, 1846, Stothert and Slaughter wrote to Bruff saying that they were able to offer twelve engines at £2,500 each. The directors tried to snap them up, but only a week later Bruff was reporting that he had had a reply from Bristol saying that the engines had already been sold.

Hawthorns also wrote at this time to say that they could offer four passenger locomotives. Bruff inquired the price, but heard nothing more.

In spite of the terms laid down by the locomotive builders they often had great difficulty in obtaining payment. For example, Sharp Brothers' terms were "nett cash on delivery", yet although they had supplied three engines with tenders during May, 1846, the E.U.R. paid them only £4,000 at the end of the month. Following receipt of "a letter" from Manchester, the company handed over an extra £50.

On the other hand, Hawthorns required a third of the contract sum to be paid upon confirmation of the order, and a payment of this amount is clearly identifiable in the accounts presented to the shareholders of the I.&B.R. As the company paid nothing for locomotives between 1st June and 30th November, 1846, and then £13,000 in the ensuing six months, it seems probable that the Newcastle firm obtained settlement in full before the end of May, 1847.

After these transactions many of the payments made to the suppliers of locomotives and rolling stock were not recorded in the directors' minutes, and such references as there are indicate that the firms were content with a series of accepted Bills of Exchange, payable three or more months later.

In July, 1848, Stothert and Slaughter served a writ on the E.U.R. Company for breach of contract over the supply of engines. The directors passed it to their solicitors, who negotiated a settlement out of court and reported back to the board the following month:

> The defendants agree forthwith to take possession of the four engines and tenders at the invoiced price of £10,120 . . . to be paid as follows:
>
> £120 in cash down and the usual costs of the delivery of the engines as on former occasions.
>
> £1,500 to be secured by Bill or Pro. Note payable at 3 months
> £1,500 to be secured by Bill or Pro. Note payable at 6 months
> £3,000 to be secured by Bill or Pro. Note payable at 12 months
> £4,000 by debentures at 2 years bearing 5% interest . . .

Trouble was brewing with Sharp Brothers, too, over the

remaining four locomotives which had been ordered from them back in 1845. Three were ready for delivery, and the builders were insisting that the company should accept them and settle accounts. Bruff went up to Manchester to negotiate terms, and reported the results to the directors in January, 1849. Sharp Brothers had agreed to

> draw upon the Company at six months from this time for the amount of three engines and tenders as below — the whole or such portion of the amount as the Directors consider absolutely necessary to be renewed for a further period of six months. The fourth engine and tender to be postponed until required . . .
>
> Two Engines & Tenders including delivery   £4,100
> One Engine & Tender including delivery   £2,090
> ————
> £6,190

The two must have been ordered in the name of the E.U.R. and the one by the I.&B.R., and yet the price of each had risen by only £5 over a period of more than three years, including credit charges.

Just before Christmas, 1848, despite the recession after the "Railway Mania" (or, perhaps, because of it), Sharp Brothers, Hawthorn and Slaughter jointly entertained the men of the Eastern Union locomotive department with a social evening at the *Sea Horse* public house in Ipswich. Robert Taylor, the locomotive superintendent, presided and among those present were J.S. Martin and Mr Dent, the goods superintendent. This must have been a very early example of sales promotion on the expense account.

In addition to locomotives, Sharp Brothers in 1847 also supplied a number of machine tools for the Eastern Union motive power depot in Ipswich. The original building erected for this was still in use as the smith's shop when British Rail closed the depot in 1968. When the Eastern Union Railway was taken over by the Eastern Counties company in 1854 some of these tools were removed to the locomotive depot at Norwich.

On 12th February, 1849, a party of directors from the E.C.R.

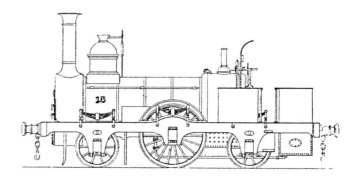

Eastern Counties Railway tank locomotive No 16, originally E.U.R. No 27, built by Sharp Brothers in 1849.

Company travelled down to Manningtree to inspect the work which had been started on the branch to Harwich. They rode in what the *Suffolk Chronicle* called a "Lilliputian Steam Engine and Carriage". This was an engine and carriage on one frame, an idea which had first occurred to James Samuel, the engineer of the E.C.R., a few years before, for inspection or branch line use, and a few had been built by W.B. Adams of Bow. The vehicle used for the Manningtree trip was probably the *Enfield,* a 2-2-0 locomotive combined with a four-wheeled carriage.

There was certainly not much to see of the Harwich branch, so the little engine was put through its paces with a run to Finningham for the benefit of the E.U.R. representatives who were present. Bruff's directors were evidently impressed: shortly afterwards they approved his suggestion that the last locomotive then outstanding for delivery from Sharp Brothers should be converted to a tank engine for working between Haughley and Bury St Edmunds. The work was carried out at a cost of about £150, and the engine delivered in the following November. It entered service on the 21st of that month and for the first two days, at least, worked trains right through from Colchester to Bury.

As this was the first tank locomotive belonging to the company, the *Suffolk Chronicle*[37] published the following quaint description for the benefit of its readers:

> The tank engine consists of the ordinary locomotive, with the addition of the usual requisites of the tender — the tank and the coke box — so as to combine in one machine both engine and tender, but on a smaller scale as regards the latter. In order to ensure a due equilibrium of the parts, the driving wheels are fixed to the middle of the machine, and the weight of the tank, when full, is made exactly to counterpoise that of the cylinder and chimney at the other end.

This locomotive became No 27 in the company's stock list.

Oddly enough, the balance sheet of the company's assets as at 31st December, 1850, records the stock as twenty-one passenger and six goods locomotives — all with tenders. Someone in the office must have blundered.

On 30th December, 1851, Sharp Brothers recorded an order from the E.U.R. for a second tank engine of this type, having 15 inch by 20 inch cylinders, and three tank engines with 14 inch by 18 inch cylinders. Shortly afterwards the order for the first of these was cancelled; it eventually found its way to the Demerara Railway in South America. The latter trio were the last locomotives ordered by the E.U.R. and were intended to be numbered 29, 30 and 31, but as the first two were not delivered until 14th February, 1854, and the third six days later, by which time the Eastern Counties company had taken possession of all the E.U.R. stock, it is unlikely that they ever carried those numbers.

According to the specification, they were to be fitted with

"Brown's conical spring buffers" [38] and were to be delivered to the Eastern Union system at Norwich, via Peterborough.

So far as the livery of the company's locomotives is concerned the evidence is scanty. I know of only two coloured pictures and in each an engine is shown only as an incidental feature. The livery seems to have been green, with polished brass domes, chimney caps and beading. The under-frames were a dark colour — black or brown — and buffer beams likewise.

It is said that all the locomotives had names. As we have seen, those given to the first six, built by Sharp Brothers, were recorded in the order. Some of the other names are known, but it is now, in most cases, impossible to say which engines carried them.

However, we can be certain of one engine name. This was *Ariel's Girdle*, carried by another of W.B. Adams' patent light locomotives permanently close-coupled to a coach for push-pull working (the original long rigid wheelbase of the E.C.R.'s *Enfield* had not proved satisfactory in service, and it had been converted into an articulated vehicle).

The locomotive part of the unit was built by the Leeds firm of Kitson, Thompson and Hewitson, and exhibited by Adams, with one of his coaches, at the Great Exhibition of 1851. The E.U.R. subsequently purchased the unit for working the Hadleigh branch; hitherto, the company must have worked this line with its main-line tender engines.

Ariel's Girdle became No 28 in the E.U.R. stock list, and was the company's only locomotive to have outside cylinders. It was a 2-2-0 well tank, with the 304-gallon tank occupying almost the entire space between the axles. The coke bunker held 6 cwt and was located above the firebox so that the driver could see over the top of it. It was unlikely that there was much obstruction to his vision, as the boiler had a diameter of only 2 feet 6 inches and, with its centre a mere 4 feet 3 inches above rail level, it gave the engine proportions much like those of a broad gauge locomotive.

As was almost universal at the time, all Eastern Union locomotives used coke as fuel; indeed, the company's Act of

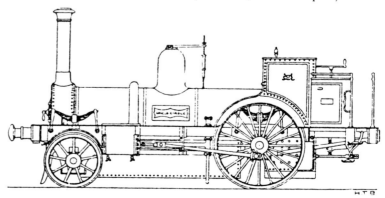

Ariel's Girdle as originally built. There are no buffers at the trailing end as it was intended to be worked with a close-coupled carriage.

112

Incorporation laid down that the engines were "to consume their own smoke", and there was to be a penalty of £5 per day for any infringement.

In April, 1846, the directors accepted an offer from Frederick Ransome of Ipswich to supply coke at twenty-eight shillings per ton for a period of three months. Ransome's coke ovens were near the railway company's quay at Griffin Wharf, and the fuel was to be delivered there in bags. There was no rail access to the quay at that time.

A little later, the company was paying some supplier twenty-two shillings per ton. In 1849, the directors reported that they had recently begun to take delivery of seaborne coke supplies at twenty-six shillings per ton; this represented a considerable saving, as only 27 lb per mile were required, compared to 42 lb per mile with the previous type. In view of the lack of any other data, the only conclusion which the shareholders can have reached was that the previous fuel was pretty poor stuff!

Water for the locomotives was sometimes a problem, too. At Colchester only a very limited supply was available, apparently from the E.C.R., and the situation was not improved when relations with that company deteriorated. In the very early days trains would stop in the cutting at Lawford so that the engines could replenish their tenders from the springs which issued there. This water was soon piped down to a cistern at Manningtree station and pumped, apparently by hand, into a raised tank. But the supply was sometimes unreliable, and in 1851 the directors accepted Taylor's recommendation that it should be abandoned and a proper supply obtained at Colchester from the local water

Ariel's Girdle as shown *in* The Illustrated Exhibitor, *1851. It was much smaller than is suggested here, as the driving wheels were only 5 ft diameter. It is not known for how long it was operated with the attached carriage, under which there was a second water tank containing 533 gallons.*

Science Museum

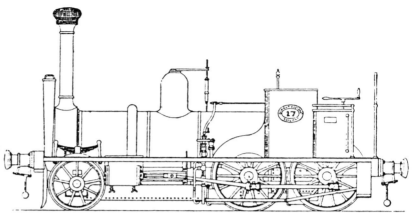

Ariel's Girdle as rebuilt at Stratford in 1868 with 4 ft driving wheels. The long pipe in front of the smokebox was the water inlet, so that the ordinary water columns could be used to replenish the tank beneath the boiler. The spark arrester on top of the chimney was fitted for working on the Millwall Extension Railway, in London's dockland.

undertaking. The services of two men were no longer required for pumping.

At Ipswich there was an abundant supply of free water; some of the copious springs in Stoke Hill, above the tunnel, were drained down to the locomotive depot.

Tenders for the first batch of carriages for the Eastern Union were invited in September, 1845 — eight 1st class, twelve 2nd class, eight 3rd class and three composites — all to have six wheels and to be delivered to Ipswich by 25th March following. Three firms tendered: Dunn and Son of Lancaster, Adams and Co of Bow, and Quadling of Ipswich.

The contract was awarded to Dunn, whose prices were the lowest, viz:

1st class carriages	£387 10s. each
2nd class carriages	£245 each
3rd class carriages	£220 each
Composites	£287 each

"If breaks are attached, £30 extra per carriage. Guard boxes are included."

The railway company was to retain twenty per cent of the price until the vehicles had run 1,000 miles, and they later agreed to accept delivery at Colchester.

The local press commented at once on the comfort and steadiness of the vehicles. At least one journalist claimed to have travelled on railways in all parts of the country and to have had no smoother ride anywhere than on the well-laid permanent way of the Eastern Union. In the weeks that elapsed before the line was opened, many Ipswich people visited the station to see for themselves what the company's carriages were like. According to the *Suffolk Chronicle*:

> They are of a size larger than generally found upon the narrow gauge lines, each carriage being divided into five compartments; but excepting the first class, the seats of which are cushioned, and separated in the usual luxurious manner, they are somewhat superior in point of comfort

and accommodation. The second class are closed up the sides, and have glass windows at the doors, so that the wind and rain can be entirely excluded; but ample provision is made for ventilation by means of perforated openings in the roof and sides. The interior of the carriage is open from end to end, the divisions being effected by a slightly raised backboard. The seats, however, are not covered; and in this respect they are scarcely one whit more comfortable than the third class vehicles, which are equal to the second on most other lines, having sides and a roof to keep out the weather. The interior is also conveniently seated, so that this class of passenger will not as heretofore have to stand like so many sheep in an open truck, a circumstance that once occasioned a Scotch minister, when travelling in this fashion, wittily to exclaim that he had "joined the congregation of the upright". Accommodation has also been made for the guards, for whom sheltered and convenient berths have been erected in front of the first class carriages.

The *Chronicle* was wrong, of course, to suggest that the Eastern Union was ahead of other railway companies in providing covered carriages, with seats, for its third class passengers. The Railway Regulation Act of 1844 had specified that all railways were to provide at least one train a day in each direction, at a speed of at least 12 m.p.h., including stops at every station, carrying passengers in such carriages at a fare of one (old) penny per mile. These were the so-called "Parliamentary" trains.

Tenders for goods rolling stock were invited by the Ipswich and Bury Railway in February, 1846. There were to be "50 Coal Waggons, 30 Goods Waggons, 12 Luggage Vans, 10 Ox Waggons,

Griffin Wharf, Ipswich, about 1859, seen in a photograph by Richard Dykes Alexander. Note the "drop", from which coke from the adjoining ovens was loaded into barges. The paddle tug Amazon *was not owned by the railway.*

Suffolk Record Office

10 Sheep Trucks, 8 Carriage Trucks and 6 Horse Trucks". Bruff knew exactly what he wanted and drew up his own plans and specifications.

It is interesting to note that he proposed from the outset to provide special stock for cattle; no doubt he was mindful that the line ran through an agricultural region. Most railways at that time carried cattle in open waggons, and some were still doing so in the 1870s.

Seven firms made offers, including Dunn, Adams, Quadling and also Ransomes of Ipswich. Dunn's was again the lowest, and was accepted:

Luggage Vans, "besides the two already ordered", £195 each
Horse Boxes and Sheep Trucks, all with "breaks", £130 each
Carriage Trucks,[39] with "breaks", £105 each
Cattle Waggons, and Goods Waggons, with "breaks", £95 each
Cattle Waggons, £59 each, or £5 extra if fitted with "breaks".

All were to be fitted with Losh's Patent Wheels (the spoked type, patented in 1830, and widely used until quite recently), and the axles were to be of Low Moor Iron or "from the Patent Axle and Shaft Company's Works". The terms were nett cash on delivery, at Colchester.

Judging by the relative prices, we can only assume that the sheep trucks were fairly elaborate, probably double-decked with roofs (as depicted in a well-known print of the Liverpool and Manchester Railway); while the cattle and goods waggons were probably provided with canvas covers, like American "prairie schooners". Unfortunately goods trains did not often appeal to early artists, and little is known of the vehicles.

Cattle and sheep trucks on the Liverpool and Manchester Railway.

A report dated 27th June which Bruff presented to the board of the Eastern Union company was passed on to the Ipswich and Bury directors a few days later.

Your Carriage Department when Messrs Dunn's contract is completed will consist of:

8 1st Class Carriages, 12 2nd Class Carriages, 8 3rd Class Carriages and 3 Composite Carriages. All upon six wheels and 16½ feet between extreme axles.

For working the Bury Line an increased carrying stock is required but the increase perhaps will be more advantageously made to your stock rather than for them to procure stock for themselves. The gross Capital expended in carrying stock could afterwards be divided between the two Companies if thought desirable and the expenses arranged either on the principle of each Company paying according to mileage run or an equitable rate of charge for power and carriages could be made by this Company to the Ipswich and Bury Company.

The principle of Adams' Bow Springs appears to me peculiarly adapted for our Carriages, and the working of the single Carriage which we have running confirms this opinion, much wear and tear will, I believe, be saved by their adoption, to the Carriages, Engines and Road.

If you thought well of it, I should recommend an arrangement in any Stock which you order to adopt Adams' Bow Springs for a portion of the Carriages, upon Terms that should ensure the Company against loss provided the extended working of them should not prove satisfactory.

The additional Stock of Carriages that as far as I can judge will be required for working the Bury Line in addition to your own Stock will be: 6 1st Class Carriages, 12 2nd ditto, 6 3rd ditto, 5 Composite ditto and 6 Luggage Vans.

And I should recommend that you arrange for building them without advertising — say, offer one third to Messrs Dunn, one third to Messrs Adams and one third to the Carriage makers of Ipswich; you will then get the benefit of competition in quality if not in price.

The provision that has been made for Goods Traffic consists of 30 Goods Waggons, 6 Horse Boxes, 10 Sheep Trucks, 12 Luggage Vans, 8 Carriage Trucks, 50 Coal Waggons and 10 Ox Waggons. In addition to these, I should strongly recommend that you order 50 Coal Waggons, 30 Goods ditto, 6 Horse Boxes, 5 Sheep Trucks, 8 Carriage ditto, 20 Ox Waggons, and in arranging for the building of these I should advise you to offer them to parties in the same manner as the Coaches.

I beg in conclusion to impress upon you the necessity of an early decision in order to secure delivery in time, as well as to give the parties employed a fair chance of doing their work creditably, for which there is scarcely time if the Bury Line is completed as early as I anticipate.

I remain, Gentlemen, your obedient Servant,
Peter Bruff.

An eight-wheeled carriage built by W. B. Adams for the E.C.R. in 1847, showing his Bow Springs. Each single-leaf spring was in two sections, shackled to the axle box, and there were no horn-plates to guide the box. Each section was elliptical in plan view, with a maximum width of about ten inches. Not surprisingly, there was an alarming motion with four-wheeled carriages at speeds above 20 m.p.h., and as most British railways used this type of vehicle the Bow Spring never caught on in this country. Where there were three or more axles, however, mutual damping occurred. The spring is said to have been widely used in Germany. From the Illustrated London News.

The recommendations were accepted and it was resolved to issue the orders as soon as possible. The report clearly shows that the rolling stock purchased by either company was intended for use on both railways.

Adams and Co had already delivered goods waggons to the value of at least £1,000 to the E.U.R. by August, 1846. It was at about this time that the firm produced — for the E.C.R. — the first smoking saloon, in which, according to the *Suffolk Chronicle*, "lovers of the weed may enjoy the delusion of smoking a rolled rhubarb leaf, under the impression that it is mild Havannah" (whatever that may have meant!). The idea caught on. The E.U.R. appears to have borrowed the smoking saloon for the trial run to Bury St Edmunds

in November, 1846, and by the following August there seem to have been at least three available for the opening of the branch to Hadleigh. In 1868 Parliament decreed that there should be accommodation for smokers on every train in the land.

The "Carriage makers of Ipswich" mentioned by Bruff in his report were Messrs Catt and Quadling, a firm established very soon after the Eastern Union Railway Company by two coachbuilders in the town, William Catt and Edwin Parke Quadling. New premises specially for building railway rolling stock were opened in Handford Road; the works had no siding access to the railway and must have been at least half a mile from it. The partners must have been disappointed when they failed to secure either of the first local contracts by competitive tendering, but having received a later order in accordance with Bruff's recommendation they soon showed what they could do.

The local press enthused about a batch of second class carriages which they completed in December — "The seats and backs are covered with leather cushions, and the doors and side openings furnished with glass windows". These were luxuries indeed for second class travellers at that time, and the E.C.R. promptly banned these carriages from running through to Shoreditch lest, it was said, their own first class traffic should suffer. The *Ipswich Journal* warned its readers that second class travellers would have to vacate their comfortable carriages at Colchester and continue their journey in E.C.R. "tumbrels".

The firm of Catt and Quadling had a brief but not uneventful life. In February, 1847, one of their carriage-building shops, a brick building, collapsed during a gale. Inside, fifteen men were at work on eight carriages for the E.U.R., five of which, with gleaming paint and varnish, were all but ready for delivery. Only two of the men were injured — the others saved themselves by diving under the carriages — but the damage was estimated at about £700 and seems to have fallen entirely upon the partners. Quadling wished to move to new premises and expand the business, but Catt preferred to write off his losses and withdraw.

In the meantime, the E.U.R. had taken a lease of an area of riverside marshland from Ipswich Corporation, land needed not only for a tramway to the dock and for future shunting yards but also for roads to give access from the town to the proposed permanent station at the northern end of the tunnel. J.C. Cobbold and John Footman with a friend of theirs then formed a syndicate known as "the Little Company" and, being astute speculators well aware of the potential value of the adjoining land, they obtained a lease of a further area of the Corporation marshes. Upon this they were to lay out streets, and either develop sites themselves or, jointly with the Corporation, lease them to others.

By November, 1847, Quadling had agreed with Cobbold and his associates to take a site at the corner of the street which now

The present building on the site of Quadling's second works in Ipswich has its entrance in the same position as that of the carriage works. The alignment of his siding, in the foreground, could be traced until the 1980s.

bears his name. The Little Company was to lay a siding from the E.U.R. dock tramway and Quadling would have the right to connect a line to it and so be able to move rolling stock directly from his building shops to the railway. At that time he had already put up some buildings, and as early as September he had been able to accept an order from the E.U.R. for fifty coal waggons, but whether these were to be built here or back at Handford Road I do not know.

On New Year's Day, 1848, the partnership with William Catt was formally dissolved. Catt took over Quadling's road carriage business and the latter devoted himself entirely to railway rolling stock. His lease of the new site from the Corporation, for the remainder of the Little Company's tenure, was completed in April, 1849. By its terms, he undertook to complete within a year buildings to the total value of £2,650, erected in a "good substantial and workmanlike manner", and to insure them against fire for at least £1,000. At the same time he was bound to make good all damage, *however caused*, within three months.

His new premises included a foundry and spring-making shop.

Alas for Quadling, his buildings were not substantial enough, for three years after the collapse at Handford Road, almost to the very day, another great gale blew up.

Over the Marshes, the wind swept with prodigious power. At Mr Quadling's manufactory, between 300 and 400 feet of 9-inch wall, with the entire roof of one of the carriage sheds, were blown down, the bricks and rafters falling upon a number of new first and second class carriages, manufactured for the Eastern Union Railway Company. The damage is said to amount to several hundred pounds, though fortunately the carriage stock has not been injured to the extent that was at first anticipated.

The carriages were actually blown several yards along the rails on which they stood. Of course the damage was not covered by insurance, and in view of the terms of his lease it is not surprising that he was declared bankrupt a few months later.

At the bankruptcy hearing it was stated that Quadling had "extensive transactions" with the E.U.R. and had been in the habit of drawing on the company whenever he needed cash. He had been "greatly inconvenienced by the Company not fulfilling its pecuniary engagements". This we can well believe, but the railway company claimed that he was actually their debtor. In closing the hearing, the Commissioner remarked that it was strange that the bankrupt's premises had blown down twice.

> Either he must have been a very odd kind of builder, or Ipswich must be a very stormy place (laughter).

To conclude the story of Quadling's premises, known as Greyfriars Works, they were used next for a flaxworks, but the winds had not yet finished with them. Incredibly, more roofing blew away in a gale in 1860 and workers had to fling themselves down spreadeagled upon the flax to prevent it following. Shortly afterwards the Corporation decided that the stench of rotting flax could no longer be tolerated in an urban environment and ordered the business to move. The site was then taken over as an engineering works.

It is strange that on each occasion when Quadling's buildings blew down carriages for the E.U.R. were being built inside. Presumably the firm supplied rolling stock to other railways, but I know of only one instance. In his *History of the Great Western Railway*, E.T. MacDermot lists Quadling — and Adams, too, incidentally — among builders "not so well known" who supplied carriages to either the Shrewsbury and Chester or the Shrewsbury and Birmingham Railways; these carriages were thus among the first narrow gauge coaches to be acquired by the G.W.R. when it absorbed the two Shrewsbury lines in 1854.

One of Quadling's quotations survives, giving an insight into the production capabilities of the firm in its heyday. For supplying a hundred coal waggons to the E.U.R., it was accepted in February, 1848. The waggons were to be

> similar in size and construction to those now in use.
>
> The Frame Work to be of the best English Oak and the sides and ends of Red Wood battens. The Draw Bar at each end to be fitted with patent India Rubber Draw Springs . . .
>
> The ends to be circular as proposed for the Company's future waggons rising to about 2′ 6″ in the centre, the end boards to be 1½ inches thick . . .
>
> The springs to carry from 6 to 8 tons without injury . . .
>
> The price to be £80 per waggon delivered on the line painted (and numbered, if required).

A circular-ended waggon, perhaps built by Quadling, on the quayside at Ipswich about 1858. Photograph by Robert Burrows.

Suffolk Record Office

To be delivered		Terms of Payment				
25 in September 1848	Sept 15th	Bill at 4 months for £1,000				
20 in October „	Jan 15th	„	„ „	„	„	„
15 in November „	Feb 15th	„	„ „	„	„	„
15 in December „	March 15th	„	„ „	„	„	„
15 in January 1849	April 15th	„	„ „	„	„	„
10 in February „	May 15th	„	„ „	„	„	„
	June 15th	„	„ „	„	„	„
	July 15th	„	„ „	„	„	„

As there is an abundance of time, you may rely upon having a very superior article.

An interesting glimpse of how the payments were made (in effect, by post-dated cheques) is given by the following letter from Bruff to Saunders, who was in London:

To J.F. Saunders Esq
25th Nov 1849
My dear Sir,
    I am in receipt of your note this morning and send you on other side certificate in favour of Messrs Quadling for five hundred pounds with a new Bill for £1,000 and checks for £500 in part payment of the bill due on Monday.
    Messrs Quadling would feel obliged, and in fact I all but promised, that the large check should not go into your Bankers until Tuesday and the other, which is dated I see a week on, at the time at which it is dated. They also wish most particularly to have the new Bill back on Tuesday morning so that they get it in to their Bankers before the check gets paid in. They also say that if you could pay the checks through any other than the Commercial Bank they should like it all the better for reasons which will occur to you.

Yours etc,
Peter Bruff.

The only reason which could have occurred to him was that Quadlings were suffering from what are now termed "cash flow problems". The cheques must have been drawn by Quadlings themselves upon the Commercial Bank; there was no branch of this in Ipswich — a fact which normally guaranteed a precious delay in presentation.

At the end of 1850, the company's carrying stock consisted of the following vehicles:

First class carriages	14
Second class carriages	22
Third class carriages	18
Composite carriages	8
Luggage vans	15
Carriage trucks	13
Horse boxes	13
Sheep and cattle trucks	74
Goods waggons	79
Coke and other waggons	700
Waggon and carriage "breaks"	144

121

These, together with the twenty-seven locomotives already mentioned, represented a total outlay of £169,303 9s. 7d.

The E.U.R. was probably the first railway to experiment with a communication cord on a train, so that the guard could attract the attention of the driver, when a device invented by Edmund Tattersall, a Newmarket auctioneer, was tried out in 1848.

The cord was contained in a spring-loaded drum, mounted like a carriage pot-lamp on the roof of the guard's van, and was carried forward to the engine through rings attached to the roofs of the carriages. Tattersall's idea was to have it arranged to ring a bell or gong on the tender, but Martin, the traffic superintendent, suggested that the locomotive should be fitted with a special alarm whistle, in addition to the normal one, and that the cord should operate this. Such alarm whistles had been adopted on the Great Western, where Martin had previously been employed; according to one account, he may have introduced them on the E.U.R. immediately before Tattersall came along.

The "Signal" was demonstrated to the press on a train between Bury and Thurston in February, 1848. The *Norfolk Chronicle* informed its readers that the sound of the alarm whistle would be continuous "till all the steam in the engine should be exhausted", inferring that the train would eventually be brought to a stand even if the driver took no action!

According to the *Suffolk Chronicle*:

> As a proof of the power of this instrument, on one or two occasions when tried at Ipswich, it has been distinctly heard at Bramford, a distance of three miles, and the effect it produced on Wednesday on some of the natives in the vicinity of the line was quite ludicrous; uplifted hands, gaping mouths and electrified rustics were continually presented to the view of the experimentalists. We believe the ingenious inventor of this signal has it in contemplation to introduce one for the use of passengers, but the plan is not sufficiently matured to make it public at present.

The whistle may have been adopted, but the cord seems not to have been; probably because it ran centrally along the roofs, to minimize the effect of curves and to prevent passengers grabbing it, and would thus have precluded the carriage of luggage on the roofs.[40] Certainly it did not survive into the regime of the E.C.R., after 1854.

Permanent Way, Stations, Etc.   10

MOST of the rails came from the Coalbrookdale Company in Shropshire. The initial order was placed in August, 1844, for 2,300 tons at £6 15s. per ton, delivered on board ship at Newport (now in Gwent).

This quantity was enough for a single line from Colchester to Ipswich; but as J.C. Cobbold and his colleagues on the E.U.R. board were thinking that the line should be doubled, they tried to delay their option on a further 1,900 tons at the same price so that they could take advatage of an offer made to Joseph Locke of 1,000 tons at £6 10s. per ton. By delaying, they seem to have lost both chances and, as the "Railway Mania" gathered impetus over the next two years, so the demand for rails rose, and the price with it. The bargain offer which Locke just missed was of material "originally designed for Mr Attwood's Harwich line". Parliament had thrown the scheme out, but the rails had been on order.

A year later Cobbold and his friends were buying rails for their line to Bury. This time, they had been considering the matter as members of the "Committee of Management" before the new company had been incorporated, and had authorised their representatives to order 2,000 tons at any price up to £9 10s. per ton. They were lucky. Ten days after the Bury line had been authorised, it was reported at the first board meeting that the order had been placed with the Coalbrookdale Company at £9 per ton.

At that booming time of railway building the national capacity for rolling rails must have been under considerable pressure, and it might well be that there were entrepreneurs speculating in such a vital commodity. Who was Mr Uzielli, to whom the E.U.R. paid £4,056 for rails in October, 1845? As late as March, 1846, the company's directors were authorising payment to a Mr Hemingway for 1,000 tons at £10 per ton; the goods had not even been delivered, for it was reported at the same board meeting that "500 tons had been ordered to be forthwith shipped from Newport, at Mr Bruff's request".

Although it was Brassey's responsibility to provide the sleepers, the Ipswich and Bury company was inviting tenders for "70,000 Larch, Oak or Fir Sleepers, or any part thereof" at the same time as the rails were being ordered. Negotiations were still going on with the contractor over the relative prices for English and Baltic timber, but the price of timber generally could be expected to rise rapidly at that time and the company wished to be sure of supplies. Brassey could always be paid his profit separately. Early in September, 1845, Bruff was instructed to write to him again, as the company had heard nothing on the subject since a meeting on 19th July and they wished to have Baltic triangular sleepers, if the

Eastern Union Railway chairs. Left, a well-preserved Ransomes Patent, right, a rail-joint chair; both found deep under the track-bed at Finningham in 1972. Microscopical examination of an associated fragment confirmed that the rail-bearing surface was unchilled, i.e. according to the 1847 patent. The chair in the middle is probably a joint-chair for the contractor's temporary track, found under Belstead Bank. The spike was found in the same place, although the two were not together.

price was right. It was found that the tender price allowed for the use of "common" sleepers at 5s. 3d. each; Baltic ones would cost 6s. 6d. The company opted for the latter.

Judging by the increase in the number of timber shipments into Ipswich from Scandinavia and the Baltic as soon as construction began on the line from Colchester, it seems that much of the original E.U.R. was also laid with imported sleepers. Other timber, described as "fathom wood for railway purposes", arrived from Chatham Dockyard; some of these offcuts may have been used for permanent sleepers.

Although on some railways triangular sleepers were produced by sawing large square baulks of timber diagonally, providing four sleepers from each length, there is evidence to suggest that on the Colchester to Ipswich line (and certainly on the East Suffolk Railway fifteen years later) the sleepers were made in pairs, from logs sawn lengthways. Triangular sleepers were laid with the broadest face uppermost; the raking lower faces facilitated the ramming of ballast underneath to maintain the level. Half-rounded sleepers could be similarly laid, although at least one contemporary text book illustration shows them with the chairs fixed to a narrow face cut on the rounded side. There was no such thing as standard practice in those early days.

The chairs for the E.U.R. and the I.&B.R. lines were of a special design manufactured by the Ipswich engineering firm of J.R.&A. Ransome, having been patented by James Ransome[41] and Charles May, one of his partners, in 1841. In 1846 the firm's title was changed to Ransomes and May.

May, a Quaker like the Ransomes, was another of those remarkable engineers who have been associated with the firm during its long life. Born in Hampshire in 1800, he was trained as a chemist but soon turned to inventing and making machines for grinding drugs. Like William Cubitt, he also took up millwrighting and later became a partner with Ransomes — in 1836. His interest in astronomy brought him into contact with Sir George Airy, the Astronomer Royal, who had Suffolk connections, and this resulted in Ransomes building equipment for Greenwich Observatory. For his part in this, May was elected a Fellow of the Royal Society. In 1844, in conjunction with James Nasmyth, of steam-hammer fame (and another amateur astronomer), May proposed the principle of the continuous vacuum brake, for every vehicle in a train; but it would not have been "automatic" i.e. fail-safe. He left Ransomes in 1851, and set up as a consulting engineer in London, where he died in 1860.

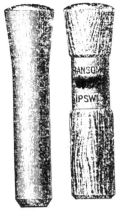

A Ransomes treenail.

To return to the Ransome and May chair, an important feature of the design was the use of stout oak pegs or treenails to secure it to the sleeper. Iron spikes had long been a recognised source of weakness, when so used, as they rusted and worked loose. The treenails and keys made by Ransomes were compressed by being forced by hydraulic rams into moulds, in which they were retained and heated in a steam chest for about fifteen minutes to maintain the compressed state. Upon exposure to the elements they swelled to their original size and tightened. Two treenails secured each normal chair.

The chairs themselves were cast in moulds in which side plates of iron formed part of the moulding surface; and a cast-iron core, supported between these plates, was used to form the surface upon which the rail actually rested. The object was to produce accurate and uniform castings, and a chilled, hardened surface upon which the rail rested. In practice considerable skill and dexterity was required to dismantle the moulds as soon as the castings had solidified and knock out the iron cores before they were gripped too tightly by contraction as the temperature fell further.

Modifications to the process were patented by May alone in 1847. The iron core was faced with sand, compressed round it by hydraulic pressure in a special machine; the treenail holes were formed with iron cores and the treenails themselves were impregnated with creosote and also coated with resin to retard expansion during storage.

With all the uncertainties that he faced with supplies of rails and sleepers, Bruff was fortunate to have at least one manufacturer of permanent way components on his doorstep. The companies provided the chairs, but Brassey and his partners supplied the treenails and keys. It was specified that these should be obtained from Ransomes, but it was not long before the firm complained that supplies were being obtained from elsewhere. Allen Ransome, one of the partners, personally attended an E.U.R. board meeting to assure the directors that his firm was well able to maintain deliveries at the required rate; the complaint was referred to Locke, and Brassey himself made a rare visit to Suffolk to investigate and have the matter rectified.

For the Bury line the price of the chairs was £7 15s. per ton, delivered to Bury. The West Suffolk town at that time received most of its coal by way of King's Lynn and thence by barge up the rivers Ouse and Lark. It is probable that permanent way material went by the same route — certainly several shipments of "iron" left Ipswich for Lynn at that time.

Ransomes' patent chairs were widely used. They were to be found on parts of the Eastern Counties and South Eastern Railways and extensively on the Great Northern, where the railway company cast them themselves under licence at a foundry in Lincoln. Many were used in Germany and Italy.

But the ever-increasing weight of trains soon revealed the inadequacy of a chair held down by only a couple of wooden fixings. On some lines there were derailments when the treenails sheared and the track spread. By the end of the 1850s the Inspecting Officers of the Board of Trade were refusing to approve new lines using only two treenails for each chair and were requiring iron fastenings to be substituted. The patent chair itself rapidly became too small for main line use; it weighed a mere 22 lb or so (barely half the weight of chairs used when British Rail finally abandoned the bullhead rail) and it was obsolete at the same time as its pair of pegs.

What may have been one of a final batch came to light not long ago in Suffolk. Larger than earlier specimens, it is of the same basic shape, pierced for only two treenails; but on the underside it carries the initials "R & S" and — remarkably — the precise date "12th Sept 1862". The firm was at that time known as Ransomes and Sims.

On the E.U.R. the ends of each successive rail were held together in a special and larger "joint chair" fastened by three treenails. This was the method employed at that time on every British railway which used transverse sleepers, and it was a source of great weakness. As a wheel approached the joint, the end of the rail tended to rise as the adjacent part sagged; the wheel then thrust the end down. The wooden keys worked loose. The soft wrought iron rail was hammered and flattened underneath by the supporting chair, giving more play, and it was never very long before the rail-ends worked loose; often the rails broke.

The fishplates which were universally used later, until the advent of welded rail joints, were so simple a solution to the problem that it is surprising that they were not thought of earlier, or immediately adopted everywhere when they were. They were patented in 1847 by William Bridges Adams, the rolling stock builder, and Robert Richardson, who was one of Bruff's assistants.

Richardson's name has often been merely mentioned in this context before, so perhaps we should look further into the subject.

Richardson was born in 1812 and began his engineering training under Henry Palmer, whose unfortunate experiences at the hands of John Wilks we have already noted. In 1837 he entered the service of the E.C.R. as a draughtsman, later becoming an assistant engineer under John Braithwaite on the construction of the line. Richardson then worked with Bruff on the E.U.R. from Colchester to Ipswich, on the Hadleigh branch and on the Stour Valley line. He set up on his own in London in 1851, laying out a number of other lines, and becoming particularly associated with permanent way patents. He died in 1891.

In 1857, W.B. Adams presented a Paper to the Institution of Civil Engineers on the subject of different types of permanent way which had been actually used on railways.[42] He stated that he had "specified" fish-joints on the E.C.R. in 1847 as a repair for damaged rail-ends. A chair was located about three inches on each side of the joint, with iron fishes passing through both chairs like elongated keys (this was the arrangement shown in the patent). To avoid the need for special castings, the chairs were later moved about 20 inches apart and the fishes were fixed with four bolts to the rails.

Some of the engineers in his audience did not agree with this account of the invention, and the discussion after the lecture was somewhat lively. Robert Richardson "asserted his claims as the joint inventor" and produced correspondence which he had had with Adams in 1846/47, although what he said or had written down we do not know. Charles May said that the joint "was published as the invention of Messrs Adams and Richardson, and therefore, he thought, it should have been so stated in the Paper, instead of the former gentleman claiming all the merit".

Bruff bluntly asserted that

he believed that Mr Adams had nothing whatever to do with the invention, beyond giving it a name. The invention, as patented, was taken by Mr Richardson to Mr Adams, who had the far-sightedness to perceive that it would become valuable. At the same time, he felt it incumbent on him to state, that the fish-joint was laid down by himself prior to that period, whilst Mr Richardson was his Assistant, in order to overcome a difficulty. A timber bridge, of about 50 feet opening, was considered too weak for a locomotive to run over it safely, at high speeds. After some consideration, it occurred to him, that the simplest mode of imparting strength, was to connect, or "fish" the rails, thereby converting them into a tension bar across the bridge. That had the effect of rendering it temporarily safe, until a stronger structure could be erected, and as far as he knew, that was the first application of the "fish-joint" to the railway system. Mr Richardson improved upon the idea, and then went to Mr Adams, and conjointly they brought it to its present state. He had subsequently applied it, in a similar manner, to impart rigidity to timber bridges.

In his reply, Adams said that the idea had not come to him from either Richardson or Bruff; the former had merely said that he had an idea for an improved rail joint, and suggested that they take out a patent together. He (Adams) had declined, due to all the paperwork involved. Later, Richardson approached him again, and said that Bruff would use the invention on the E.U.R. It was

127

only then that Richardson revealed that his idea was a scarf, or half-lap, joint.

Adams claimed to have pointed out that a fished joint was much stronger than a scarfed one, which was agreed, and "this consideration led to the invention", and they both took out a patent. This, however, "remained in abeyance for some time, as Mr Bruff would not lay it (the fish-joint) down on the Eastern Union".

It is unlikely that we shall ever learn more of this matter, but it would seem perhaps that Richardson's claim was stronger than the surviving account indicates. At that meeting in 1857, however, the matter was finally put in perspective when another speaker said that there was "no novelty whatever in the fish-joint". He had seen "hundreds of tons of fish-plates, at Liverpool, twenty-two years ago", and quoted from a book published in 1838 that they were used throughout the length of the Camden and Amboy Railway in the United States.

Ten years after Adams and Richardson took out their patent, a bewildering array of different types of rail, chair and sleeper was in use, and the fishplate was only to be found to a limited extent. They were not generally used.

Bruff's expedient of strengthening a weak bridge by fish-jointing the rails together sounds quite incredible today. A timber bridge, particularly one with an opening of as much as 50 feet, sounds like a river crossing. For the rails to form "a tension bar across the bridge" presupposes trusses which extended to some

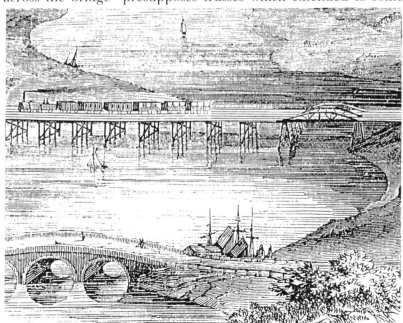

Cattawade viaducts, from the Illustrated London News, *1846, showing the bowstring truss over the navigable channel. This might well have been the location of Bruff's pioneer use of fishplates.*

height above the line, probably above the tops of the trains. This bridge must have been constructed no later than 1846, and, for Richardson to know about it, it was probably not on the Bury line.

We can only guess where it might have been, but the most probable location is at Cattawade, where the E.U.R. line crossed the Stour, the boundary between Essex and Suffolk. The illustration of these viaducts shows one span with a bowstring truss, carrying the line over the navigable channel used by the Sudbury barges. Bruff said that his measure was only a temporary one "until a stronger structure could be erected"; the Cattawade viaducts were extensively rebuilt in 1851 (and remained of timber until 1904). The *Ipswich Journal*, describing the features of the line a few days before it was opened, referred to these viaducts as "substantial and scientifically constructed". Were these words suggested by a handout from a proud Bruff?

In 1850, the Chappel viaduct, on the Stour Valley line, was the subject of a Paper presented to the Institution of Civil Engineers[43] by Bruff himself, in which he said:

> The permanent way consists of longitudinal timbers 14 inches by 7 inches scantling, with cross pieces to tie them together, and jointed over each pier with timber of similar scantling, secured by bolts. Upon these timbers Ransome and May's cast-iron chairs are fixed, with compressed oak treenails, which carry a double-headed rail, weighing 75 lbs per yard, whose joints, instead of abutting in a chair as usual, are secured by two wrought-iron cheeks with four bolts, the chairs being placed at a distance of 9 inches on each side of the joint, so that in the event of the fracture of either chair, the continuity of the rail would be preserved, the length of bearing between the other chairs being increased only 18 inches.

Bruff seems to have used fishplates here more as a precaution against fracture of the light-weight chairs than to avoid loose rail-ends; it is understandable that he should take special measures to guard against a derailment on the viaduct. Elsewhere, at least part of the line to Sudbury was laid with single-headed rails, which must have precluded the use of the Ransomes chair, of which he was usually a staunch advocate. Even these flimsy rails were not fished.

Fishplates were not generally used in East Anglia, apart from repairs or in special circumstances, until 1863.[44] A notable exception was the East Suffolk Railway, often criticised as a line cheaply built.

The plans which accompanied the company's Bills for new lines did not show any proposed stations. It was not until September, 1845, when construction of the line from Colchester to Ipswich had been in hand for a year, that Bruff asked the E.U.R. directors to approve locations for the intermediate stations. Early in the following year he was instructed to arrange for the contractor to build the Ipswich terminus, and to proceed with designs for other stations at Ardleigh, "Cattawade Bridges" and Bentley. All were to be of wood.

Ogilvie put in a price of £1,740 for the Ipswich station, but this was considered so high that other tenders were invited from local builders. The work was carried out by Samuel Baldiston of Ipswich, whose bid was only £1,340. Baldiston designed the buildings at Bentley, and probably the others as well as there was a similarity between them.

A journalist, having seen drawings of the stations displayed at a meeting, criticised the architectural contrast between the station building at Bentley, "in the modern villa style", and the adjacent level crossing gate keeper's lodge which had an Elizabethan appearance. This lodge may have been from the drawing board of Frederick Barnes, whose stations in that style were so notable a feature of the Ipswich and Bury line.

The station at Ardleigh — and probably that at Manningtree, too — had a subway for passengers to cross the line, and must have been among the very earliest to be so equipped. The E.C.R. was at this time introducing footbridges at some of their stations to prevent the accidents which so often occurred to both railway staff and the travelling public, but such amenities seem to have been all too rarely provided on contemporary railways. By 1849, if not from the outset, Bentley station had a footbridge.

Manningtree station, which had assumed its present name by the time the line opened, was rebuilt in later years, but the original buildings at Ardleigh and Bentley survived until those stations were closed in the 1960s.

Ardleigh station, now demolished, looking towards Colchester. The entrance to the subway can be seen on the right, and a window under the opposite platform gives light to the subway.

At Colchester, the E.U.R. at first shared the facilities of the E.C.R. station, but the rent charged was so high — according to one account it was £2,000 per annum — that in 1848 the Ipswich company constructed their own platforms and offices about 100 yards from the junction of the two systems, adjacent to E.U.R. engine and carriage sheds. As the E.C.R. would not allow an E.U.R engine to run upon their tracks, it was customary for the latter company to detach their locomotives at their station and for trains to be drawn forward by E.C.R. engines so that passengers could change to continue their journey. It was then but a short step, when hostilities over the Norwich traffic began, for the E.C.R. to compel the E.U.R. to close their upstart station, or have their passengers walk between the two systems! Its reopening was one of the measures considered when the E.C.R. cancelled the traffic agreement in 1852.

The original terminus at the Croft Street site in Ipswich was always regarded as being only temporary. At the time the line from Colchester was opened, the building comprised a simple rectangular train-shed, open at the sides, with four tracks; the outer tracks extended down on each side of a central block of offices for almost the full length. A platform extended along the western side of the train-shed, and out beyond, with three tracks between it and an island platform on the eastern side. The western platform, slightly longer than the other, was used for all trains to or from Norwich. At some time after 1850 the northern end of the building, facing the street, was altered, with a new entrance and short wings on each side.

Trains ceased to run to the station when the present Ipswich station was opened in 1860, but the old building was apparently

A 1968 view of the criticised architectural contrast at Bentley. The "modern villa" style station house has since been demolished, and the chimneys of the lodge have been cut down.

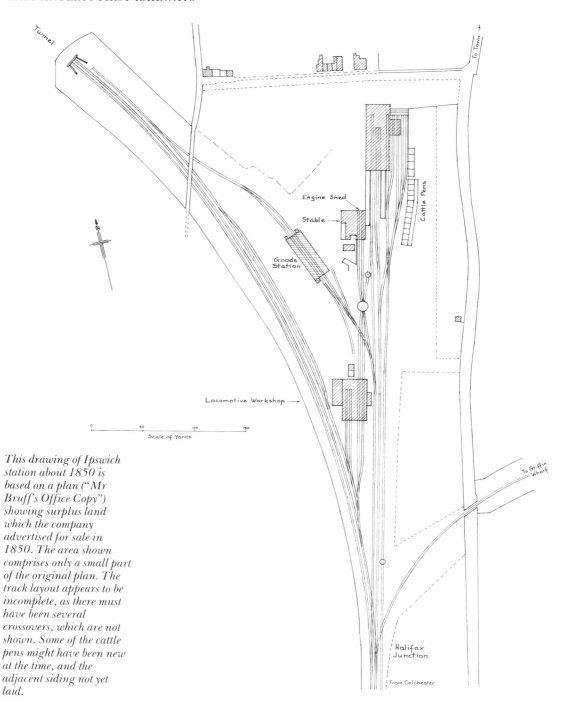

This drawing of Ipswich station about 1850 is based on a plan ("Mr Bruff's Office Copy") showing surplus land which the company advertised for sale in 1850. The area shown comprises only a small part of the original plan. The track layout appears to be incomplete, as there must have been several crossovers, which are not shown. Some of the cattle pens might have been new at the time, and the adjacent siding not yet laid.

132

still in use as a store in 1878, when the original goods station nearby was burned down. Four years later the old passenger building had disappeared, but traces of the platforms survived until about 1950.

Designs for a permanent "joint" station at Ipswich, for both the E.U.R. and the I.&B.R., were invited early in 1846. Nineteen entries were received and the winning design was that of Sancton Wood.

Wood (1816-1886), who had only the one unusual Christian name, was articled to Sir Robert Smirke, architect of the British

The original terminus at Ipswich, showing alterations made after 1850 Paul Fincham

The present Ipswich station before the down-side island platform was built.
Suffolk Record Office

This drawing of Bury St Edmunds station in 1851 is based on the Parliamentary Plans of the Newmarket Railway Company's proposed extension to Bury. The station is only a small incidental feature of the original plan and no track layout appears, apart from what is shown. Perhaps there was a short siding to the cattle pens, enabling single trucks drawn by horses to reach them via the turntable; but a siding to the goods shed was mentioned as an apparently new amenity when the Newmarket line was opened in 1854. The goods and maintenance facilities must have been very cramped in the early days, when the station was a terminus—the bank behind the engine shed was 16 feet high. How coal traffic, for example, was handled is not clear.

Museum, and completed his training under Sir Robert's brother Sidney. The new railways soon offered an outlet for his talents. He designed Cambridge station and others on the Midland Railway branch from Syston to Peterborough; much of his work was in Ireland, notably the Kingsbridge terminus in Dublin.

He submitted his Ipswich entry in two alternative styles, Italian and Elizabethan, and it was the former which was preferred by a joint committee of directors from the two companies. However, due to severe financial restrictions, the erection of the station was not undertaken until 1858. Wood also designed the station at Bury St Edmunds, in an Elizabethan style, and he seems to have been awarded the commission without a competition, probably as a result of his success at Ipswich.

For nearly a year the trains ran to a temporary Bury station on the Ipswich side of the bridge until the permanent station was brought into use, still incomplete, in November, 1847. Unlike any of the other stations on the line until then, the main structure was built by Ogilvie, as part of Brassey's contract.

Four lines of rails ran between the platforms, although only one platform was used before the line to Newmarket was opened in 1854. There was an overall roof in three spans, with the middle one covering the two central tracks, on either side of which the roof was carried on rows of twelve iron columns. This roof, sub-contracted to a Bury builder named John Trevethan, covered a space 260 feet long by 84 feet wide. With its twin towers, it must have been an impressive station when new; but unlike most covered termini, the lines ran through to a turntable and engine shed beyond.

This shed, of course, was demolished when the line arrived from Newmarket; it was a single line, and remained so until some time after 1883. The train shed roof was removed in 1893; the elaborate Tudor-style brick chimneys were cut down and the

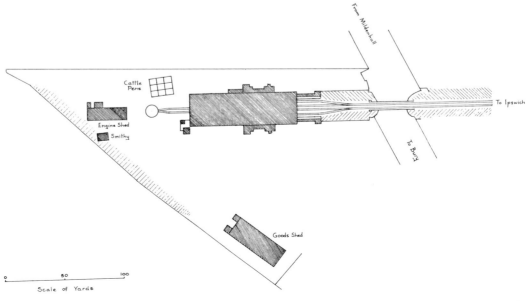

Cattle Pens

Engine Shed

Smithy

From Mildenhall

To Ipswich

To Bury

Goods Shed

0   50   100

Scale of Yards

Above: *This photograph of Bury St Edmunds station dates from before March, 1854.*
Mr O. G. Jarman

Right: *The same station about 1875, by which time there was a roof on the nearer part of the station.*
Mr O. G. Jarman

Below: *The station about 1900, after the train-shed roof had been removed.*
Mr O. G. Jarman

Needham station as it was about 1970 and, right, as it was originally built. The original Dutch gables and ogee caps on the towers remained until at least 1912. Suffolk Photographic Survey, Suffolk Record Office

platforms lengthened in a westerly direction at about the same time. In recent years, the two central tracks in the station have been lifted.

The Bury line is, however, best known for its delightful intermediate stations, which were from the drawing board of Frederick Barnes. Barnes was born in Hackney in 1814 and was educated at Christ's Hospital School, where his father was Master. Like Sancton Wood, he received his architectural training under Sidney Smirke, one of the leading practitioners of the time. In 1843 he moved to Suffolk to work in association with his friend, John Medland Clark, who had distinguished himself by winning

the competition for the design of the Custom House by the new Wet Dock at Ipswich. Bruff employed him to design the stations on the Bury, Hadleigh and Norwich Extension lines, and upon the completion of that work he set up in general practice in Ipswich. Most of his work was in the Eastern Counties, including many churches, chapels and schools; but he was also responsible for some classrooms and boarding houses at Harrow School. He died at Ipswich in 1898.[45]

Frederick Barnes' station building at Elmswell, looking towards Bury. It was demolished in 1974.

None of the stations between Ipswich and Bury was complete at the time the line was opened; most of them had hardly been started. All were erected by local builders.

By the end of 1846, the work at Needham was the most advanced, and even there the walls were only about half way up. That September the contract had been awarded to Daniel Revett of Stowmarket; a month later he also began constructing the station in his home town.

Barnes exhibited a perspective drawing of Needham Station at the Royal Academy. It showed the building with ogee caps on the towers and with curved Dutch gables, features which it retained until this century. This station, also, had a subway for passengers.

The work at Stowmarket was delayed, after about a year, by the death of Revett; due to the need to appoint a fresh contractor it was not completed until July, 1849. Passengers here were provided with a covered footbridge[46] to reach the up platform, according to the *Norwich Mercury*, which added, "This station is one of a series upon the expensive erection of which considerable blame has been cast by the Shareholders on the Directors, and it is wanting in good taste as well as economy". The people of Stowmarket, however, had

137

been determined to have a station worthy of their town; according to the *Ipswich Journal,* the parish authorities had contributed £1,000 towards the cost of the new approach road from the town, and had also advanced a low-interest loan of £3,000 to the company towards the cost of the building itself, which financed the larger part of the work.

At Thurston the station was located on an embankment about 20 feet high; access to the platforms was from the upper floors of the buildings on each side. Elmswell and Claydon stations were smaller, and particularly charming with their Dutch gables and high brick chimneys. Alas, at Elmswell Barnes' buildings have been completely demolished, while at Thurston the original structure on the up (southern) side of the line[47] has also disappeared since these stations became unmanned halts in 1967. Claydon closed completely in 1963, and now stands forlorn and covered with dust from the nearby cement works.

Bramford station featured in the timetables from the opening of the Ipswich and Bury St Edmunds Railway, but remained of timber construction for most of its life. Like Thurston, it stood upon an embankment, but its proximity to Ipswich probably deterred the company from providing elaborate buildings.

Frederick Barnes'
masterpiece at
Stowmarket, said at the
time of its building to be
"wanting in good taste as
well as economy". The
writer was apparently
unaware of the
determination of the
townspeople to have a
station worthy of their
town.

Elmswell station from the yard.

This station had more than its fair share of mishaps. On 28th February, 1860, a great gale which also unroofed the Ipswich flaxworks, formerly Quadling's carriage works, demolished a large part of the buildings and they collapsed across the permanent way. Fortunately the telegraph was available to prevent trains ploughing into the debris; and a large gang of repair workers was immediately dispatched from Ipswich to clear the tracks and shore up the rest of the buildings. First reports indicated that complete rebuilding would be necessary.

Bramford station was still of timber when it was burned down in 1912. The G.E.R. then had a rail-borne fire engine at Ipswich which was sent to fight the flames. Several adjoining cottages were consumed in the conflagration. The station was then rebuilt, in red brick, on the opposite (southern) side of the road bridge. Oddly enough, the goods shed — "the last part of the original station" — was destroyed in another blaze in 1919. The station was closed in 1955.

The first station at Haughley — known as "Haughley Road" — was sited by the first overbridge on the Bury side of Haughley Junction. It was closed when the station at the junction, about a mile away, was brought into use on 9th July, 1849, the platforms being immediately demolished; but the "cottage", together with a small structure by the lineside which might have been a shelter for the use of passengers, was retained. H.F. Hilton in his booklet on the E.U.R. wrote of the site being distinguished by the levelled area of the station sidings, but any such area is several feet above the level of the permanent way. The cutting at this point seems to be substantially as it was excavated in 1845/46. In recent years, the cottage has been razed to ground floor level, and the lower part now appears to serve as a basement for a large modern house. Some of the original outbuildings still stand at the time of writing.

The Haughley Junction station was almost certainly also designed by Barnes, who was responsible for the others on the line

Above: *Forncett station, looking towards Norwich, about 1910.*
Lens of Sutton

Left: *Haughley station at the same period, showing the original timber footbridge, soon to be replaced with a steel one.*
Lens of Sutton

Below: *Elmswell station, also about 1910.*
Lens of Sutton

to Norwich and remained in the company's service until about a month before the new station was brought into use. It was a much less characterful building than his earlier ones, and resembled in style almost any contemporary villa. From the beginning, it boasted a bay for trains on the Bury St Edmunds line, reduced to the status of a branch, and was provided with "commodious platforms, partially roofed across" and "an elevated footbridge across the line, similar to the one at Bentley".

Haughley station, as it was later called, was closed in 1966, and at the time of writing only a very small part of the original building survives, serving as a shelter for the level crossing gate keeper.

Barnes' other stations on the Norwich line were much more subdued in style, reflecting the harsher economic climate of that time and the protests over the flamboyance of his earlier buildings. All were built by Brassey and Ogilvie as part of their main contract.

Mellis was "in style partaking something of an Elizabethan character, built of red brick, pointed with black mortar", according to the *Suffolk Chronicle*. Flordon was very similar. Diss was more Gothic, but at Tivetshall the stationmaster's house, at least, echoed even more strongly the neo-Tudor glory of Barnes' earlier work.

We have already noted the origins of the Victoria Station at Norwich. Here, the building which had formerly been used for public entertainments stood on the base of what was essentially a large open triangular platform with its apex pointing up the line. Parallel to the departure platform on the side nearer to Queen's Road (known as Lame Dog Lane in 1851) were carriage sidings and a large goods shed. Photographs taken early in this century show train sheds over both platforms and the adjacent tracks, but these structures seem to have been later additions.[48]

Originally there was no station at Swainsthorpe, but in March, 1850, the company announced that certain trains would stop at the level crossing there "when required".

The construction of permanent stations at Finningham and Burston was postposed until it was ascertained what traffic would

An up express headed by Britannia class No 70008 John of Gaunt passing through Tivetshall on 5th January, 1953, the day the Waveney Valley line closed to passenger traffic. The timber buildings are similar to those at Forncett.

Ipswich station about 1910, showing the covered bay originally built for the East Suffolk trains.
Lens of Sutton

develop; but not until December, 1861, was it reported that the E.C.R. was considering replacing "the present unsightly and disconsolate-looking collection of old boarding yclept 'Finningham Station'." It was probably still there two years later, when a great gale unroofed some of the buildings and covered the tracks with the debris. On the same occasion at Forncett (apparently a permanent structure), "the entire down side of the station was blown down, completely covering the line". Presumably both were then replaced with the structures which survived until the stations closed in 1966. The platform buildings at Forncett resembled those at Tivetshall.

The original terminus at Ipswich soon became inconvenient, with the need to reverse at Halifax Junction, but the company's resources were severely stressed. After January, 1854, when the E.C.R. assumed responsibility for new work, both the townspeople and the E.U.R. shareholders began to press for a new station. The Town Council appointed a special committee to take the matter up with the railway company when it seemed that defective bridges on the Cambridge line might mean more trains through Ipswich (see Chapter fourteen), and as time went by the prospect of East Suffolk line traffic also having to reverse at Halifax Junction began to loom. Cornelius Welton, the surveyor to the E.S.R. Company, wrote to the *Ipswich Journal* to point out:

> We are to be shunted. I dislike that word above all others of recent coinage. We are all to be shunted on our way to the Metropolis; and by a gentleman whose name implies all the endearments of home and the family circle.

In response to pressure from the Town Council, Horatio Love, the E.C.R. chairman, and some of the directors visited the town twice in May, 1858.

Before the year was out building of the new station began. Oddly enough, it was carried out by the E.U.R., under the direction of Bruff, who had by then resigned from the service of the E.C.R. He assured the local authorities that public opinion would force the E.C.R. to use it, and in any case, the Board of Trade might not allow East Suffolk traffic to use the old station (in fact, Mr Welton had to put up with being shunted for the first thirteen months).

The new station, described by one local journalist as being reminiscent of a Tartar tent, was opened on 1st July, 1860. It had a single platform about 300 yards long, served by a loop from the up main line. East Suffolk line trains were accommodated in a covered bay, later used for Felixstowe traffic. The present down platform was added in 1883, and the up platform was lengthened in 1912.

The railway from Colchester to Ipswich was provided with the electric telegraph as early as November, 1846. It appears to have been of the Cooke and Wheatstone letter-indicating type with a revolving needle, and was installed by the newly-established Electric Telegraph Company, which had bought out the patents of the inventors. The equipment was fitted with a clockwork bell, which the operator had to wind up; it was released electrically by the operator at the other end of the line, to call attention.

A correspondent from the *Suffolk Chronicle* went to see the company's staff familiarising themselves with the use of the apparatus, and:

> The following colloquy was on Tuesday morning carried on between Ipswich and Colchester in the presence of the writer. The alarum having rung the operator signalised, "Go on". No answer being received, he enquired, "What did you ring my bell for?" In a few seconds the answer, "Do not understand", was recorded. The question was repeated, to which the Colchester official replied, "I was winding up the alarum". The whole operation was performed in about three minutes.

It must all have seemed quite remarkable.

The directors of the Ipswich and Bury company intended to have the telegraph on their line as soon as it was completed, but found themselves unable to proceed; money was in short supply. Early in 1849, a fresh quotation was obtained for extending the wires to both Bury and Norwich; but when it was found that the total cost would be £9,160 (with the Electric Telegraph Company's men and materials being carried free of charge) the company decided that the scheme was "inexpedient at the present time".

On 7th December, 1853, the *Bury Post* reported that arrangements had just been made to complete the telegraph to Bury and Norwich, which latter place had for several years been in communication with London by way of Cambridge. There is evidence to suggest that the wires reached Bury from Ipswich shortly before the opening of the line from Newmarket in March, 1854; the new line was equipped from the start.

Meanwhile, in the previous spring, the telegraph between Colchester and Ipswich had become part of the first link between London and the Netherlands. The wires were extended along the roads to Orfordness (for much of the distance underground, in cast-iron ducts supplied by Ransomes of Ipswich) to link up with a submarine cable to Scheveningen. However, this cable was so frequently damaged by the anchors of ships that in 1858 it was replaced by another from Dunwich, which was reached by using the route of the Woodbridge branch, and part of the East Suffolk Railway, then under construction.

In April, 1850, Bruff reported to the directors that when he had travelled up to London a few days previously he had discovered that information to this effect had been telegraphed on to stations ahead. At Manningtree he found that the clerk, one Bowler, had received a message and "was in attendance accordingly, although in his (the manager's) opinion, not in the regular discharge of his duties". Summoned to Ipswich shortly afterwards to explain, Bowler admitted that a message had been received, saying, "Tell Mr Bowler to meet the Up train". He had been unwell in bed and he produced a medical certificate to prove it. Scopes, the porter, said that he had received the message and another the next day which said, "The train is left. Is Mr Bowler up yet?" He maintained that it had never happened before.

In view of the medical certificate the directors decided to take no action against Bowler, but Scopes and the Ipswich porter who sent the messages were both suspended for a week. Bruff's investigation of the incident also revealed that clerks from several stations were accustomed to gather together "for an unknown purpose" and these unofficial meetings were immediately forbidden.

By September, 1854, only months after the E.U.R. had been taken over by the E.C.R., almost all the latter's system was equipped with the telegraph, with the exception of the East Anglian Railways, around King's Lynn, and a few other lines in the western part of its territory. The Harwich branch and the single line between Bury and Newmarket were worked on the telegraph and ticket system, while the Hadleigh branch appears to have been operated on the "one locomotive in steam" basis. Primitive block-working by means of bell-rings was used on the Trowse link and at Ipswich between the Halifax and Dock Junctions; but trains could be despatched, even through the curved Stoke tunnel, with a suitable warning to the drivers, if there was no reply from the other end of the section five minutes after they had been offered forward!

Thurston station about 1970. Above are the buildings on the down side and at right are the now-demolished buildings on the up side.

Elsewhere on the E.C.R. at that time, there was proper block-working through the Audley End tunnels on the Cambridge line, and also between Bishopsgate and Stratford. By 1865, the only other space-interval working outside the London area was to be found between Manningtree and Halifax Junction, with double-needle instruments.

Generally, as on most contemporary railways, the signalling was on the time-interval system, with signals put to "Danger" for five minutes after a train had passed, and then to "Caution" for a further five minutes. At night, or after the passing of a goods train, the "Danger" period was for ten minutes; in fog, defined as when signals could not be clearly discerned at a distance of 800 yards, a second train was not allowed to proceed for fifteen minutes. In all cases, there was a further five minutes of "Caution", after which the signals indicated "Line Clear", and the little brass-bound locomotives puffed past at full speed.

In foggy weather, too, and at all times to give emergency warnings, the E.U.R. used Cowper's patent detonators. Perhaps they were obtained from the E.C.R., which had its own factory for manufacturing the things at Stratford — until it blew up in February, 1857, killing three operatives and throwing passengers from their seats in a train standing in the station.

A down goods near Claydon in the last days of steam. The pine trees were an early example of industrial landscaping; and the 1846 overbridge in the background, like many others, has since been rebuilt as part of the electrification works.

H. N. James

The Railway at Work 11

A timetable published just before the line was opened from Colchester to Ipswich showed a service of six trains daily in each direction, with three each way on Sundays. All trains stopped at every station and the whole journey took an hour. There was apparently some through-carriage working to Shoreditch in the early days but by Christmas, 1846, the second class passenger, at least, bound for London was obliged to change at Colchester.

The fastest-timed train was the down "Quick", for first and second class passengers only, which left Shoreditch at 3 p.m. and reached Ipswich at 5.35 p.m. The up "Quick" departed from Ipswich at 8 a.m. and took three hours on the journey to the Metropolis. All connections at Colchester were good.

As had happened in other parts of the country, people — at least those who could afford it — quickly took to travelling by rail. In its first four days of working, the line carried 1,264 passengers in the up direction but, for some reason, only 584 down from Colchester. The company was agreeably surprised by the heavy local traffic which soon developed — sometimes over a hundred people would board a train at Bentley for the five-and-a-half-mile journey to Ipswich.

The Ipswich and Bury line opened with four trains each way on weekdays and two on Sundays. The fastest time was just over one hour and twenty minutes in the down direction, stopping only at Needham, Stowmarket and Elmswell and carrying no third class passengers. Every other train called at all stations on journeys which occupied about ninety minutes and, of course, always involved passing through Ipswich Tunnel and reversing between Halifax Junction and the station.

By this time weekday services between Ipswich and Colchester had been increased to seven trains in each direction. The down "Quick", by not stopping at Ardleigh or Bentley, reached Ipswich twenty-three minutes earlier. Even the timing of the stopping trains had been accelerated to fifty minutes between Ipswich and Colchester; perhaps the first timetable was unduly pessimistic until it had been found in practice that "the Company's powerful engines surmount the gradients without difficulty".

Within a very short time of the Eastern Union line being opened cheap excursions were put on, enabling even those of modest means to travel to Colchester to see the castle or to Ipswich for a steamer trip on the river, and these were very well patronised by people who had never before had the opportunity of travelling so far and back in a day.

It is ironic that almost within earshot of the railway lived Willy Lott, the East Bergholt farmer whose cottage has been immortal-

EASTERN UNION RAILWAY.

THE above RAILWAY WILL OPEN BETWEEN IPSWICH and COLCHESTER, for GOODS, CATTLE, PARCELS, &c. &c. on and after MONDAY, JUNE the 1st; and for the CONVEYANCE of PASSENGERS, on and after MONDAY, JUNE the 15th.

The following TIME TABLE will shew the ARRIVAL and DEPARTURE of the TRAINS, and the FARES, &c :

By Order,

Brook Street, Ipswich, May 29th, 1846.

JAMES F. SAUNDERS, Secretary.

EASTERN COUNTIES' AND EASTERN UNION RAILWAY,
ON AND AFTER JUNE 15th, 1846.

IPSWICH LINE.

UP TRAINS.

Distances from Ipswich.	FROM	WEEK DAYS										SUNDAYS						FARES			RATES		
		1st & 2d, 2dCl. & 3rd Morn. MAIL	1st, 2d & 3rd Cl. Morn.	1st, 2d & 3rd Morn.	1st & 2d & 3rd Quick Morn.	1st & 2d Class. Even.	2nd Class Even.	1st & 3rd Class. Even.	1st, 2d & 3rd Parl'm Even.	1st, 2d, 2d & 3rd Class. Even.	1st and 2nd Class. Morn.	1st, 2d, 2d & 3rd Morn.	1st, 2d, 2d & 3rd Class. Even.	1st, 2d, 2d & 3rd Class. Even.	1st, 2d, 2d & 3rd Class. Even.	Passengers. 1st. Class. s. d.	2nd. Class. s. d.	3rd. Class. s. d.	Horses. 1 s. d.	2 s. d.	3 s. d.
---	---	---	---	---	---	---	---	---	---	---	---	---	---	---	---	---	---	---	---	---	---
	Ipswich . .	1 45	—	—	8 0	10 0	1 0	—	3 30	5 0	1 45	7 30	—	—	4 45	—					
5	Bentley . .	2 0	—	—	8 15	10 15	1 15	—	3 45	5 15	2 0	7 45	—	—	5 0	—	1 0 0	8 0	4		
9	Manningtree	2 15	—	—	8 30	10 30	1 30	—	4 0	5 30	2 15	8 0	—	—	5 15	—	2 0	1 4	0 8	4 0	7 0	9 0 5 0
13	Ardleigh . .	2 30	—	—	8 45	10 45	1 45	—	4 15	5 45	2 30	8 15	—	—	5 30	—	3 0	2 0	1 0			
17	Colchester .	2 45	N B	7 45	9 0	11 0	2 0	—	4 30	6 0	2 45	8 30	—	—	5 45	—	4 0	2 6	1 4	6 0	10 0 15 0	8 6
21	Marks Tey .				9 10		2 10		4 42			8 40			5 55		5 0	3 1	1 8			
25	Kelvedon .	3 10	—	8 7	9 22	11 22	2 22	—	4 57	6 20	3 10	8 52	—	—	6 7	—	6 0	3 9	2 1	10 0 17 0 25 0 14 6
29	Witham . .	3 20	—	8 18	9 32	11 32	2 32	—	5 7	6 30	3 20	9 2	—	—	6 17	—	6 6	4 3	2 5	10 0 17 0 25 0 14 6
33	Hatfield . .			8 26	9 40				5 15	6 38		9 12			6 27		7 6	4 10	2 8			
38	Chelmsford .	3 45	—	8 43	9 55	11 54	2 49	—	5 32	6 52	3 45	9 29	—	—	6 41	—	8 6	5 8	3 1	13 0 22 6 32 6 17 6
44½	Ingatestone	4 3	—	8 58	—	12 8	3 6	—	5 53	7 6	4 3	9 44	—	—	6 59	—	10 2	6 6	3 8	
50	Brentwood .	4 23	8 20	9 15	10 20	12 23	3 19	5 30	6 11	7 20	4 23	10 0	1 0	6 0	7 15	8 30	11 6	7 6	4 1	17 0 29 6 42 6 22 6
56	Romford . .	4 38	8 35	9 30	10 35	12 39	3 34	5 45	6 29	7 35	4 38	10 18	1 15	6 15	7 33	8 46	12 6	8 3	4 7	19 0 33 0 47 6 25 0
61	Ilford . . .	4 48	8 46	9 42	—	12 49	3 46	5 55	6 45	7 47	4 48	10 33	1 26	6 26	—	9 0	13 3	8 9	5 0	20 6 36 0 52 0 27 0
	Forest Gate	—	8 50	9 47	—	—	—	6 0	6 50	7 52	—	10 38	1 31	6 31	—	9 5	14 3	9 6	5 3	
64	Stratford . .	4 54	8 59	9 55	10 50	12 58	3 56	6 8	7 0	8 1	4 54	10 48	1 35	6 35	—	9 15	14 3	9 6	5 3	22 0 37 6 54 6 28 0
67	Mile End . .	—	—	—	—	4	1 12	4 10	7 10	8 9	—	10 57	1 45	6 45	—	9 25	15 0	10 0	5 6	
68	London . .	5 4	9 7	10 5	11 0	1 12	4 10	6 21	7 20	8 20	5 4	11 5	1 50	6 50	9 30	15 0	10 0	5 8	6 0 40 0 58 0 30 0

On Wednesdays, the Train marked thus † stops at Mile End, to take up and set down Passengers.

N. B.—This Train starts from Colchester on Monday Mornings at 6, 45, calling at all the intermediate Stations, except Mile End.

DOWN TRAINS.

Distances from London.	FROM	WEEK DAYS										SUNDAYS						FARES			RATES		
		1st, 2d, and 3d Class. Parl'm Morn.	1st & 2d Class. MAIL	1st & 2d & 3d Class. Even.	1st & 2d & 3d Class. Even.	1st, 2d & 3d Class. Quick Even.	1st & 2d Class. Even.	1st and 2nd Class. Even.	1st and 2d & 3d Class. Even.	1st, 2d, & 3d Class. Morn.	1st, 2d, & 3d Class. Morn.	1st, 2d, & 3d Class. Even.	1st, 2d, & 3d Class. Even.	1st & 2d Class. MAIL Even.	1st. Class. s. d.	2nd. Class. s. d.	3rd Class. s. d.	1 s. d.	2 s. d.	3 Carriages. s. d.
---	---	---	---	---	---	---	---	---	---	---	---	---	---	---	---	---	---	---	---	---
	London . .	8 30	*11 0	1 0	2 15	3 0	4 15	5 30	6 30	8 30	7 0	8 30	9 45	2 15	6 0	8 30				
1	Mile End . .	8 34	—	1 2	2 19	—	—	—	—	—	7 2	8 33	9 48	2 18	6 3	8 40	0 4	0 3	0 2	
4	Stratford . .	8 41	11 10	1 11	2 28	—	4 26	5 41	6 41	8 40	7 11	8 45	9 58	2 28	6 13	8 40	0 9	0 6	0 4	3 6 6 0 9 0 4 6
	Forest Gate	8 45	—	1 15	2 32	—	4 30	—	6 45	—	7 15	8 47	10 2	2 32	6 17	—	1 0 0 8	0 5	
7	Ilford . . .	8 54	11 17	1 23	2 40	—	4 38	5 48	7 5	8 46	7 23	8 56	10 11	2 41	6 29	8 44	1 6	0 11	0 7	3 6 6 0 9 0 4 6
12	Romford . .	9 6	11 28	1 35	2 52	3 19	4 50	6 0	7 20	8 56	7 35	9 9	10 24	2 54	6 39	8 56	2 6	1 9	1 0	4 0 7 0 10 0 5 0
18	Brentwood .	9 20	11 45	1 50	3 7	3 31	5 5	6 15	—	9 11	7 50	9 25	10 40	3 10	6 55	9 11	3 6	2 6	1 6	6 0 10 0 15 0 7 6
24½	Ingatestone	9 36	—	2 6	—		5 21	—		9 35	8 1	—	—	—	7 12	9 45	5 0	4 3	2 3	
30	Chelmsford .	9 49	12 10	2 20	—	3 51	5 34	6 42	—	9 49	8 20	—	—	—	7 27	9 49	6 6	4 6	2 6	10 0 17 6 25 0 12 6
35	Hatfield . .	10 2	—	2 33	—	—	5 47	6 52	—	—	8 33	—	—	—	7 41	—	7 6	5 3	2 11	
38½	Witham . .	10 12	12 30	2 43	—	4 8	5 57	7 4	—	10 13	8 43	—	—	—	7 51	10 13	8 6	6 0	3 3	13 0 23 0 33 0 16 6
42	Kelvedon .	10 22	12 40	2 53	—	—	6 7	7 14	—	10 23	8 53	—	—	—	8 2	10 23	9 6	6 9	3 8	14 0 24 6 35 0 17 6
47	Marks Tey .	10 32	12 50	3 3	—	—	6 17	7 24	—	—	9 3	—	—	—	8 12	—	10 6	7 6	4 1	
51	Colchester .	10 50	1 5	3 20	—	4 35	6 35	7 45	—	10 40	9 20	—	—	—	8 30	10 49	11 0	7 6	4 7	17 0 30 0 43 0 21 6
55	Ardleigh . .	11 5	1 20	3 35	—	4 50	—	8 0	—	9 30	—	—	—	8 50	11 4	12 0	8 2	4 7	
59	Manningtree	11 20	1 35	3 50	—	5 5	—	8 15	—	11 19	9 45	—	—	—	9 5	11 19	13 0	8 10	4 11	21 0 37 0 52 0 26 6
63	Bentley . .	11 35	1 50	4 5	—	5 20	—	8 30	—	11 34	10 0	—	—	—	9 20	11 34	14 0	9 6	5 3	
68	Ipswich . .	11 50	2 5	4 20	—	5 35	—	8 33	—	11 49	10 15	—	—	—	9 35	11 49	15 6	10 0	5 8	23 0 40 0 58 0 30 0

* This Train calls at Ingatestone on Fridays.

BRANCH COACHES,
IN CONNECTION WITH THE RAILWAY, MEET THE FOLLOWING TRAINS FROM LONDON:

FROM MANNINGTREE STATION.
THREE P.M. TRAIN—Manningtree and Harwich.

FROM IPSWICH STATION.
HALF-PAST EIGHT O'CLOCK TRAIN—Woodbridge, Saxmundham, Yoxford, Wangford, Lowestoft, and Yarmouth.
Stonham, Seole, Harleston, Bungay, Beccles, Long Stratton, and Norwich.

Wickham-Market, Framlingham, Stradbroke, Fressingfield, Harleston, Bungay, and Norwich.
Needham-Market, Stowmarket, Woolpit, and Bury St. Edmund's.

ELEVEN O'CLOCK TRAIN—Woodbridge, Wickham-Market, Saxmundham, Yoxford, and Halesworth.
ONE O'CLOCK TRAIN—Needham-Market, Stowmarket, Woolpit, Bury St. Edmund's.

THREE O'CLOCK TRAIN—Woodbridge, Wickham-Market, and Saxmundham.
Stowmarket, Botesdale, Finningham, Becton, & Diss.
HALF-PAST FIVE O'CLOCK TRAIN—Woodbridge.
HALF-PAST NINE O'CLOCK TRAIN—Woodbridge, Saxmundham, Yoxford, Wangford, Lowestoft, and Yarmouth.
Seole, Long Stratton, and Norwich.

N.B.—The Coaches by the Train marked ‡ run also on Sundays.

FIRST & SECOND CLASS DAY TICKETS ARE ISSUED AT A FARE & HALF.

Return Tickets issued on Saturday are available on the Sunday or Monday following, and those issued on the Sunday are available on the Monday.

LUGGAGE to the following extent will be allowed to be taken by each Passenger, *free of charge*, viz :—FIRST CLASS, 112lbs. SECOND CLASS, 86lbs. THIRD CLASS, 56lbs. Any excess over this weight will be charged at the rate of ½d. per cwt. per mile, no less distance than twelve miles being charged. The Company is not responsible for any Luggage, unless it be specially booked and paid for. Passengers are particularly requested to have their Names and Destinations distinctly marked on their Luggage, and to see it deposited in the Train.

HORSES and **CARRIAGES** must be at the Station not later than 15 minutes before the time named for the departure of the Train by which they are intended to be sent. To prevent disappointment, one day's previous notice should be given at intermediate Stations. Passengers riding in their own carriages are charged Second Class Fare. Grooms riding in the Horse Boxes are charged Third Class Fare.

DOGS, for any distance not exceeding 12 miles, 6d., and for greater distances 5d. for every six miles.

CHILDREN under three years of age are conveyed free ; above three and under ten years, half price.

POST HORSES are in readiness at the London Terminus on the arrival of every Train. Charge to any part of London, including Post Boy, 10s. 6d. Post Horses, Flys, &c., may also be secured at any of the principal Stations by giving notice one day previously to the Chief Clerk of the Station where they are required.

ON SUNDAYS, Third Class Carriages are attached to all the Trains, except the Mail Train.

OMNIBUSSES, by way of Charing Cross and Fleet Street, and Oxford Street, and Holborn, meet Griffin's Green Man and Still, Oxford Street ; and Conveyance Company's Office, Paddington, one hour before the departure of every Train, calling at the Boar and Castle, Oxford Street ; George and Blue Boar, Holborn ; Universal Office, and Bull and Mouth, Regent Circus ; Golden Cross, Charing Cross ; Bolt-in-Tun, Fleet Street ; Cross Keys, Wood Street ; Spread Eagle, Gracechurch Street ; and the Four Swans, Bishopsgate.

PARCELS for conveyance by this Railway are booked at the following Offices :—Hatchett's, White Horse Cellar, Piccadilly ; Griffin's Green Man and Still, and the Boar and Castle, Oxford Street ; Bull and Mouth, and Universal Office, Regent Circus ; Golden Cross, Charing Cross ; Bolt-in-Tun, Fleet Street ; George and Blue Boar, Holborn ; Bull and Mouth, St. Martin's-le-Grand ; Cross Keys, Wood Street, Cheapside ; Swan with Two Necks, Lad Lane ; Spread Eagle, Gracechurch Street ; Blue Boar, and Bull, Aldgate ; Four Swans, Bishopsgate ; and at the Terminus, Shoreditch. (2407)

Passengers are recommended to be at the Stations Five Minutes earlier than the time specified in the Table.

• Post Horses are in readiness at the Ipswich Terminus on the arrival of each Train.

ised in the paintings of John Constable. When Lott died in 1849 it was stated that he had never been more than twenty-five miles from the house in which he had been born, and in all his eighty-eight years he had spent only one night under another roof. It might have been different if a railway had been available to him earlier.

The first day excursion was to Colchester on 29th June, 1846, when a special train left Ipswich at 11 a.m. The return fare from Ipswich or Bentley was two shillings first class or one-and-sixpence second class, and from Manningtree or Ardleigh one-and-six or a shilling respectively. As all these fares included admission to the "Botanical Gardens and Horticultural Show" they were considerably lower than the normal ones,[49] and for good measure "an excellent band" was provided on the train.

The public response took the company by surprise. The nineteen carriages provided were packed to capacity before the special left Ipswich; three hundred more people had to be left behind to follow on the next ordinary train, and many who had intended to join the excursion at the intermediate stations were unable to board even that one. In all, over 1,200 people visited Colchester in the day, and the catering resources of the town were severely strained by the unexpected scale of the "invasion of Suffolk borderers".

The homeward journey had been advertised to start at 7 p.m. and two trains had to be provided, one of twenty-four carriages and the other with six.

Encouraged by the success of this, the company organised an excursion to London on Monday, 27th July. A special train left Ipswich at 2 p.m. carrying nearly six hundred passengers in seventeen carriages and watched by nearly two thousand people who had turned up just to see the departure, "from the novelty of the circumstance". The travellers had the choice of returning by the 8.30 a.m. train from Shoreditch on any day up to the following Saturday.

A one-day excursion to the Metropolis followed on 14th September, leaving Ipswich at 7.30 a.m. and due to arrive three hours later, at a return fare of four shillings in open carriages or six shillings in covered ones. The train was double-headed and carried more than a thousand trippers, packed into thirty-one vehicles of one kind or another, and the day turned out to be not entirely uneventful.

After a late start, a coupling broke at Manningtree so that six vehicles became detached. This could easily have led to a hideous tragedy, in view of the primitive and feeble braking arrangements of the time, but it resulted in a delay of only ten minutes before the train was once more on its way. Martin and Taylor were on the footplate of the leading locomotive, while Footman, the managing director, rode on the second. At Colchester the two Eastern Union

Eastern Union Railway.

On and after June 15th, the Coaches

IN CONNEXION with the ABOVE RAILWAY, leave the following places, at the under-mentioned times, to meet the

UP TRAINS.

"The Old Blue."
From Yarmouth, at 9, a.m.; Lowestoft, at 10, a.m.; Wangford, 11 15, a.m.; Yoxford, 12 15, p.m.; Saxmundham, 12 45, p.m.; Woodbridge, 2 15, p.m.; arriving at Ipswich in time for the 3 30, p.m., Train.

"The Day."
From Norwich, at 10 30, a.m.; Long Stratton at 11 30, a.m.; Beccles, 10 30, a.m.; Bungay, 11, a.m.; Harleston, 11 30, a.m.; Scole, 12 30, p.m.; Stonham, at 1 45, p.m.; arriving at Ipswich in time for the 3 30, p.m. Train.

"The Union."
From Norwich, 9 30; Bungay, 11 30; Harleston, 12 30; Laxfield, 1 30; Framlingham, 2 15; Woodbridge, 3 30; arriving in Ipswich in time for the 5 o'clock Train.

"The Cambridge."
From Bury St. Edmund's, at 2, p.m.; Woolpit, 2 30, p.m.; Stowmarket, at 3 15, p.m.; Needham-Market, at 4 p.m.; arriving at Ipswich in time for the 5 o'clock Train.

"The Shannon."
From Halesworth, at 8 30, a.m.; Yoxford, at 9 30, a.m.; Saxmundham, at 10, a.m; Wickham-Market, at 11, a.m.; Woodbridge, at 11 30, a.m.; arriving at Ipswich in time for the 1 o'clock Train.

"The Regulator."
From Bury St. Edmund's, at 9 30, a.m.; Woolpit, at 10 20, a.m.; Stowmarket, at 11, a.m.; Needham-Market, at 11 30, a.m.; arriving at Ipswich in time for the 1 o'clock Train.

"The Retaliator."
From Saxmundham, at 7, a.m.; Wickham-Market, at 8, a.m.; Woodbridge, at 8 45, a.m.; arriving at Ipswich in time for the 10 o'clock Train.

"Wellington."
From Diss, at 6 15, a.m.; Botesdale, at 7, a.m.; Finningham, at 7 30, a.m.; Stowmarket, at 8 30, a.m.; Needham-Market, at 9, a.m.; arriving at Ipswich in time for the 10 o'clock Train.

"Quicksilver."
From Woodbridge, at 6 45, a.m.; arriving at Ipswich in time for the 8, a.m., Train.

"Yarmouth Royal Mail."
From Yarmouth, through Lowestoft, Wanford, Yoxford, Saxmundham, Woodbridge; arriving at Ipswich in time for the 1 45, a.m. Mail Train.

"Norwich Royal Mail."
From Norwich, through Long Stratton, Scole, Stoke, Stonham; arriving at Ipswich in time for the 1 45, a.m. Mail Train. (2498

"Defiance."
From Harwich, at 9, a.m.; arriving at Manningtree in time for the 10 30, a.m., Train.

When the railway first arrived in Suffolk it was the coaches which provided feeder services.

Opposite page: *The first Eastern Union Railway timetable, published in June, 1846.*

engines were replaced by a pair from the Eastern Counties Railway, but the three officials carried on at their posts. All then went well until the train reached Brentwood, when a platelayer's trolley was seen on the line ahead, at which "the feelings of those who had the superintendence of the engines were of the most painful and unenviable kind". Having shut off steam and put their locomotive into reverse, the leading driver and Taylor jumped off; the latter dislocated his ankle. Luckily the train was not derailed in the ensuing crash, which occurred on a 15-foot embankment, but there was a delay of about two hours so that Shoreditch station was not reached until after midday. Tempers were not improved by the fact that the barriers were manned by only three ticket collectors, who insisted on carefully examining every ticket.

The return journey had been advertised to begin at 7.30 p.m. but when the train appeared it was seen to consist entirely of open carriages, which did not please those who had paid to have a roof over their heads. The marshalling of the necessary rolling stock delayed the departure until 8.10 and the train had only reached Stratford when it was shunted into a siding for a time to allow the down Mail to pass. To crown everything the excursion train stalled on Brentwood Bank. Colchester was not reached until nearly midnight and the Ipswich contingent did not alight until two o'clock in the morning — three and a half hours late. The passengers "loudly exclaimed against the management of both the companies", but at least they did not wreck the carriages.

Some excursions were more than day trips. On 17th June, 1846 — only two days after the line had been opened for public passenger traffic — the Eastern Union directors organised a combined rail and steamer excursion from London to Rotterdam

Ipswich from Stoke Hill in 1851. The then E.U.R. offices in Commercial Road can be seen above the extreme left-hand tree. Better only a wisp of smoke from the tunnel mouth than the grossly inaccurate trains drawn by some other artists of the Illustrated London News!

Paul Fincham

to demonstrate the advantages of their line for the speedy dispatch of mails to the Continent.

A special train left Shoreditch Station at 5.30 a.m. and reached Ipswich in exactly two hours. The Ipswich Steam Navigation Company's iron steamer *Orwell*, which normally operated a twice-weekly service to and from London, had been specially chartered for the occasion; she sailed no more than ten minutes after the train arrived at the station. At 8 p.m. that evening the steamer picked up her pilot at Brielle, berthing at Rotterdam just before 10 p.m. The travellers had brought copies of that morning's London newspapers with them and these were distributed "to the great astonishment of many of the steadygoing Dutchmen".

The start of the return voyage next morning was delayed because the customs house at Rotterdam did not open as early as the party wished — "national habits were not easily to be accelerated" — but as the *Orwell* left at 10 a.m. her company was delighted to see the regular steamer from London just arriving with the previous day's mail and papers. Harwich was reached at 9 p.m. and, after a passage of an hour and half up the estuary of the Orwell, the London contingent joined a special train which delivered them back to Shoreditch at 1.10 a.m.

The party included the secretary of the embryonic Harwich and Eastern Counties Steam Packet Company. A railway to Harwich would have allowed an hour to be cut from the timings but, alas, Harwich was to see no trains for another eight years nor any regular steamers to the Continent until some time later.

The E.U.R. immediately proposed to charter the *Orwell* for fortnightly sailings if the E.C.R. company would agree to share any losses in a 2:1 ratio, but the latter declined. The owners of the steamer, however, ran a few similar excursions at irregular intervals.

To facilitate goods traffic on the line, the construction of a tramway to the waterfront at Ipswich was commenced as soon as the line was opened from Colchester. This extended from near Halifax Junction to Griffin Wharf, on the western side of the New Cut, where the company established its own wharf and where Frederick Ransome's coke ovens were located.

By the spring of 1847 Bruff was able to report that this siding had been completed, together with another to a quay on the Stour near Manningtree. The latter was probably never much used, although in 1849 there were "a warehouse, turntable and machinery" there (see Appendix five).

The Griffin Wharf line, on the other hand, carried heavy traffic. In October, 1847, the *Ipswich Journal* reported that no fewer than forty-seven vessels with coal had arrived in the port during the previous week, and "heavy trains of coal" had been dispatched to Bury, Hadleigh and elsewhere. The paper added, "So frequent are the arrivals at the Company's wharf that an extension is found necessary, which is now making". The total quantity of coal brought in — "upwards of 5,000 tons" — reminds us that the coasters of the period were only very small.

From the Bury line another tramway was laid to serve the quays round the Wet Dock at Ipswich; it was completed in 1848. Although there was speculation that locomotives would be used on this line, as they must have been on the Griffin Wharf branch from the outset, it was not until the mid-eighties that Ipswich Corporation agreed to the use of steam traction where the line crossed the highway near Stoke Bridge and ran along public quays. All waggons were moved along the dockside, as at most stations when there was no engine present, by means of horses; but even this simple method of haulage was not always uneventful.

There was one coalyard where the siding ran between bunkers or raised platforms on each side, and to avoid having the horses penned in by the trucks, the points were set for the yard and the procedure of "running the tip" was employed. The horses were urged forward at a fast trot and, as the waggons approached the switch, the traces were slipped and the trucks entered the yard by their own momentum. On one occasion, however, when a rake of three waggons was being drawn by two horses, the shunter failed to release the animals; the waggons entered the yard and the horses continued along the wharf until they were jerked round by the traces, which flung and crushed the unfortunate driver against the gatepost. The coal merchant said at the inquest that this method had always been used.

Long before the Bury line opened for traffic, agreement had been reached with the Trustees of the Stowmarket Navigation, who managed the navigable River Gipping from Ipswich, for their undertaking to be leased by the railway company. Experience

The head of the navigable River Gipping at Stowmarket; an etching by Henry Davy, 1838.
Suffolk Record Office

152

Even at larger stations like Ipswich horses were used for many years to move single vehicles on the railway. Here a van is about to be moved from the up fast line about 1910.

Lens of Sutton

showed that canals were poor competitors with railways, and the Ipswich and Bury Railway, for its part, was eager to monopolize all possible traffic. The lease was to be for forty-two years, at an annual rent of four per cent (£1,070) of the capital of the Navigation for the first half of the period, and three per cent thereafter. The Trustees obtained an Act of Parliament dated 26th June, 1846, which sanctioned the arrangement.

It is interesting to note that although the total tonnage of goods carried on the river rapidly fell to about twenty-five per cent of what it had been before the railway came, Cobbold was able to report to his shareholders in 1851 that the navigation tolls had always covered "working expenses". After five and a half years it was the fixed rental charge which resulted in a nett loss of £3,372. What maintenance work, if any, had been carried out is hard to say.

By 1868, the rail services offered by the then-struggling G.E.R. were so chaotic that the fertiliser manufacturers, Packards, entirely abandoned rail transport between their establishments in Ipswich and Bramford in favour of steam barges on the Gipping. This traffic continued until the 1930s.

In July, 1849, an irate traveller wrote to the *Ipswich Journal* complaining about the lateness of the last train of the day from Bury St Edmunds and blaming Bruff for taking the engine "for his private accommodation". The editor defended the engineer and pointed out that this train was really a goods train with a carriage attached, "and necessarily somewhat uncertain in its arrival". No description of the carriage survives, but it may well have been that passengers presenting themselves at goods stations were literally allowed to travel in a truck.

153

This would have been fourth class travel, which the company was certainly operating by the following March. Oddly enough, this facility seems not to have been mentioned in timetables, nor indeed even advertised, unless the term embraced all cheap excursions which were not part of the normal scheduled services. Covered carriages were mandatory on the Parliamentary trains, but railway companies were free to provide cheaper and more primitive travel, and many did so. The Eastern Counties, for example, certainly offered fourth class travel in open carriages, at a fare of ½d. per mile, which was probably the usual charge.

As we have seen, the early second class stock on the Eastern Union did not have upholstered seats, but by August, 1849, this defect had been remedied in at least some of the carriages. Those with hard seats were then little better than the third class carriages, and the demand for second class tickets dropped until the company took action. In the words of the *Ipswich Journal*:

> Some dissatisfaction has been expressed that covered third class carriages have been discontinued from all but the Parliamentary trains, and open trucks substituted. It appears it was considered that the notice affixed to the covered third class carriages, of their being intended "for the working classes", did not prevent many, whom the company thought qualified for second class, of availing themselves of the cheaper mode of conveyance.

One wonders what E.C.R. third class carriages were like. The company's Rule Book of 1854 contained the injunction:

> The use of Second Class Carriages or Passenger Luggage Vans for Goods Trains is strictly prohibited.

Then, as now, some passengers ended up in court. In 1851 a man appeared before the magistrates on a charge of travelling without paying the fare. He had bought a ticket from Finningham to Stowmarket, but fell asleep and did not awake until the train reached Bentley. He refused to pay the excess fare of 2s. 2d., saying that the company's servants should have woken him up. Not unreasonably, the latter took the view that trains could not be detained at every station while slumbering passengers were aroused in case they wished to alight; less reasonably, perhaps, they incarcerated him for the night in the station house at Bentley. However, this passenger was evidently a man of resource once he was fully awake, for in the morning he was found to have escaped! The Bench obviously had some sympathy for him, for he was fined only ten shillings instead of the full penalty of £2; nothing was said about any damage he might have done in breaking out of his prison.

On one rather foggy night just before Christmas, 1847, two men were walking home along the line near Bramford when one was struck by a train and killed. Neither was a railway employee, although one was said to have worked for the company in the past. At the inquest, a sergeant of the railway police who happened to be a passenger in the train gave evidence that it had been travelling at "the regular speed of about 25 miles an hour", the driver was perfectly sober, and the train came to a stand in "about 100 yards or so" after the whistle had sounded for the guard to apply his brake. Nobody mentioned the fact that the deceased should not have been there in the first place, although trespassing on railways was by that time forbidden by a general Act of Parliament. Whether or not the survivor (the ex-railwayman) was prosecuted, I do not know.

Among other trespassers on the line were poachers in Lord Henniker's woods, through which the railway passed near Mellis. They soon found that if they were pursued by gamekeepers they could "set them at defiance on arriving on the Company's property". His Lordship wrote to the directors and obtained permission for his staff to continue the chase along the line, although the company wisely refused to accept any responsibility for the consequences.

Horses were used for moving waggons at smaller stations so long as goods facilities remained. Here we see a pair in action at Woodbridge about 1965.
Suffolk Photographic Survey, Suffolk Record Office

We have seen that the usual speed of the trains was about 25 m.p.h. On one occasion a special ran from Colchester to Norwich at an average speed of just over 46 m.p.h., excluding a five-minute stop at Stowmarket, and this was considered to be quite remark-

able. Only on the Great Western, with its broad gauge and gentle gradients, were expresses timed to run at averages of over 50 m.p.h. in normal service; engineers on the standard gauge lines were haunted by the idea that a locomotive's centre of gravity was too high for safety at speed. Moreover, in most engines of the day, the moving masses were completely unbalanced and this, combined with a short wheelbase, imparted a lively yawing motion as speed increased which in turn punished the lightweight track, even if actual derailment did not ensue.

One factor which dictated low speeds was the feeble braking power available at that time. Hand brakes were customarily fitted on the tenders but not on the locomotives themselves because of the stresses set up in the crank axles when a retarding force was applied to the driving wheels. Most British railway companies in the last century favoured inside cylinders — the yawing forces at speed were less, quite apart from aesthetic considerations. But the forging of crank axles, necessarily from wrought iron, was one of the more difficult tasks which faced early Victorian technology; failures of these vital components occurred from time to time, often with the direst consequences, and it was essential to reduce the loads applied to them as much as possible.

Apart from the tender brake, there was another in the guard's van and the driver called for its application in emergencies by sounding the whistle — on the Eastern Union, the special deep-toned alarm whistle copied from Great Western practice.

The first accident to a passenger train occurred only the day after the Norwich line was opened. It was getting dark by the time the 2.15 p.m. from Victoria Station pulled away from Flordon and fortunately its speed was still low when it collided with a ballast waggon which the contractors were loading from a lineside pit about a quarter of a mile from the station. No one was seriously hurt, but the engine, tender and luggage van were derailed; as there was no telegraph, there was a two-hour delay before the passengers were able to continue their journey in a relief train. To avoid a recurrence the company decided to complete the ballasting and the remaining work with their own labour.

An accident involving injuries to passengers occurred in March, 1850, to a local train from Colchester to Norwich; it seems to have been the only serious accident on the E.U.R. The five-carriage train was crowded and already running late by the time it reached Diss, where so many people were waiting to join it that two more carriages had to be added. By the time everyone had taken their places there were some three hundred passengers on board. The driver, anxious to prevent further loss of time, asked the crew of a ballast engine to follow the train and assist it up the steeper gradients. This engine followed at a short distance, but on a 1 in 150 bank between Burston and Tivetshall it ran into the back of the train with some force. The rear carriage was slightly damaged and "the faces of the passengers, from being violently jostled together, received several severe contusions". Some first aid was rendered by the station staff at Tivetshall, and when the train arrived in Norwich doctors were summoned to attend to the more seriously shocked and injured cases. The crew of the ballast engine were subsequently dismissed and the train driver was fined £1.

An earlier case of impromptu banking in this way could have been attended with disastrous results. In October, 1846, the E.C.R. had forwarded an express cattle train, with one of their locomotives, from Colchester to Ipswich without previous notice, which in itself caused some consternation. But the crew of an E.U.R. ballast engine, who obligingly banked on that occasion, appear to have returned to Colchester on the same metals "which was against all the rules of the Company"; the driver was lucky to be merely reprimanded.

Cleaners returning to work after their midnight supper break discovered a fire in the company's engine shed at Colchester in January, 1850. The water supply from the tank was found to be partially frozen, and, as the resultant trickle was insufficient to combat the flames, the staff concentrated their efforts on trying to save the three locomotives in the building. Somebody ran to the E.C.R. station to ask for help with one of their engines, but "the answer received was that the Eastern Counties company had discontinued the practice of keeping an engine in steam through the night at this important station", according to a sceptical report in the *Ipswich Journal*.

Attempts to use horses were not entirely successful and one of the locomotives was considerably damaged, losing its wooden buffer beams and boiler cladding and even its brass dome casing. The building itself was severely damaged, together with the adjoining tank and coke houses; the total cost was estimated at £500.

We may note in passing that two years later the E.C.R. certainly had no spare engine in steam at Colchester. One February morning in 1852 an up train was standing ready to depart when the locomotive's boiler burst. Incredibly, no one was hurt — the crew were not on the footplate — but the glass and ironwork of the station roof were blown away and an adjacent wall demolished. The telegraph wires were brought down and a messenger had to be sent on horseback to Witham to summon another engine.

Ever since the E.U.R. had opened, the company had from time to time organised excursion trains to Ipswich for steamer trips down the river to Harwich in the Ipswich Steam Navigation Company's vessel, *River Queen*. Occasionally, the larger steamer *Orwell* ran excursions to other coastal resorts on which rail passengers were conveyed at special rates on production of their train tickets. One such trip was to Aldeburgh Regatta on Whit Monday, 1848.

Some two thousand people arrived in Ipswich from stations both up and down the line, some from as far away as London. There was a stampede to the quayside and about eight hundred hopefuls contrived to pack themselves into the *Orwell*; others boarded the *River Queen* which shuttled three times to Harwich. The deeply laden *Orwell* sailed at about noon but, alas, she ran aground at the mouth of the River Ore for an hour and a half until the flood tide lifted her over the bar. Aldeburgh was not reached until late in the afternoon, by which time the regatta was nearly over, and after but a short stay the return passage began.

An official of the shipping company disembarked at Orford on the way down the river and returned to Ipswich overland to allay anxiety should the falling tide trap the steamer again at the bar. As it happened, she managed to get out but a thunderstorm then broke, soaking many who were unable to get below. "The saloon, fore cabin and even the engine room were crowded almost to suffocation".

The steamer did not reach Ipswich until 10 p.m. Whether late trains were provided to take the trippers home was not recorded, but a journalist summed up with the delightful words, "The passengers bore the burthen of pleasure with becoming fortitude".

In the summer of 1849 regular rail/steamer excursions were introduced on Mondays and Fridays every alternate week. The *River Queen* sailed to Walton-on-the-Naze from the E.U.R. wharf in the New Cut at Ipswich, calling at Harwich in each direction. The service was advertised with the times of connecting trains from Colchester and Bury, and back, but there is no indication that trains actually ran to the quayside. The fares, to either Walton or Harwich, ranged from 8s. 6d. for first class travel from Bury to 1s. 6d. for third class travel from Claydon.

It would appear that the railway company was not satisfied with the arrangements for the sharing of receipts, however, for at the beginning of the following season Bruff reported to his directors that he had been able to arrange for a steamer to run to Harwich, with division of receipts on a mileage basis.

The vessel was the *Railway*, owned by the London and Blackwall Railway, a company with which the E.U.R. was beginning to foster amicable arrangements with a view to circumventing the E.C.R. line between Colchester and London; for the past year the *Orwell* steamer had been landing her London-bound passengers at Blackwall. The *Railway* entered service on 10th June, 1850, sailing to Harwich twice on weekdays and within a week on Sundays too. Fares ranged from nine pence single, a shilling return, in the saloon, to sixpence single, ninepence return, in the fore cabin. Oddly enough, ladies, as well as children, could make the round trip for sixpence — but only in the fore cabin.

The service was well patronised, and at the beginning of July a third sailing, in the evening, was introduced on five days of the week. On Tuesdays and Thursdays the steamer did not return from Harwich in the evening, but early the next morning. In one week about 2,400 passengers were carried, including the rector of Combs, near Stowmarket, "with a large party of friends, attended by the juvenile band from Semer Union House".

The Steam Navigation Company altered the times of sailing and reduced the fares in the *River Queen*; soon a fierce rivalry developed, with each company accusing the other of reckless seamanship.

In the middle of July the *Railway* was joined by a second vessel, the *Atalanta*, and an extra sailing was operated on four days each week, continuing on to Walton-on-the-Naze where trippers could stay for a couple of hours before returning. The Walton excursions were cut to twice weekly in September, being replaced by others to Aldeburgh and Mistley.

The *Railway* returned to her London owners and was replaced by the *Cardinal Wolsey*, which like the *Atalanta* was purchased in Bruff's name. It seems that the E.U.R. directors personally helped to provide the necessary capital, although when the two ships were re-registered at Ipswich in April, 1851, the engineer was the sole owner. The vessels were always regarded as "railway steamers", but the company itself was under great financial pressure, and in any case had no statutory powers to operate ships.

As the autumn approached the longer excursions were discontinued, but a winter service was maintained to Harwich, with two sailings on weekdays and one on Sundays. On the first Sunday in March, 1851, the *Atalanta* was returning from Harwich when she struck a submerged anchor as she approached the New Cut in Ipswich. She was severely holed and sank, but the water was only shallow and everybody on board was taken off safely. The next day the steamer was raised and docked for repairs, and she was back in service by the time the summer schedules were resumed in May.

This accident may have caused Bruff to reflect that another steamer was desirable and this time he had one built, by the Wivenhoe-based firm of Harvey and Son who had not long before expanded their business by taking over the Halifax shipyard in Ipswich. The *Prince*, as she was named, was launched from this yard in May, 1852, and towed to London to receive her engines. Remarkably for a wooden vessel, she was fitted with watertight bulkheads.

Probably the proudest day for the company was 3rd July, 1851, when Prince Albert used the line to travel to Ipswich to attend meetings of the British Association being held in the town, and also to lay the foundation stone of new buildings for Ipswich School.

A triumphal arch had been erected "between the two signal posts" at Halifax Junction. Anxious officials were gathered around the telegraph instruments in the station building when, at

10.07 a.m., news arrived that the royal train had passed Marks Tey. Just at that moment, a train of thirty carriages arrived and disgorged about 1,200 passengers from Norwich and Bury, giving the police and station staff some hectic minutes as they strove to clear the platform of the throng. They succeeded, and the civic dignitaries were all properly assembled by the time a distant whistle announced that the royal train was descending Belstead Bank.

The train, which consisted of the royal saloon belonging to the London and North Western Railway with one other coach for the Prince's entourage, arrived five minutes early, at 10.40. The engine was driven by Robert Taylor, the locomotive superintendent, and Bruff was on the footplate. The total journey time from Shoreditch had been an hour and three-quarters, and news that the Prince had arrived safely was telegraphed to Buckingham Palace by "special command" of the Queen. After spending the night at Shrubland Hall, near Claydon, the Prince returned to London by train the next day.

A century after Prince Albert's visit, B12 No 61562 heads an East Suffolk line train away from Ipswich. On the extreme left can be seen the incline originally constructed for the dockside tramway, and after 1866 leading to the lower goods yard.

H. N. James

Decline and Fall

The completion of the Eastern Union line to Norwich provoked bitter hostility from the Eastern Counties company, which was determined to maintain its traffic between London and Norfolk by way of Cambridge. The new route via Colchester was thirteen miles shorter, but the E.C.R. owned less than half of it — only fifty-one miles of the total 113. Before Bruff's new line was even opened they raised the rates on their Colchester line by eighteen per cent for passengers and by ten per cent for goods.

There were immediate criticisms in the press, as fares on the E.C.R. were already higher than on many other railways. The *Suffolk Chronicle* protested that the second class fare from Ipswich to London would in future be thirteen shillings, a thirty per cent increase in just over three years. The *Norwich Mercury* complained that people joining London-bound trains at Colchester were charged less than through travellers from the E.U.R. According to the *Ipswich Journal*, the second class fare from Norwich to Colchester was 8s. 2d., and from thence to the capital a further ten shillings, "but the Eastern Counties compel the Eastern Union to charge 21s. In order to make up the difference of 2s. 10d., the charges between Stowmarket and Norwich are most capricious; from Flordon to Norwich the charge for 6½ miles is 2s. 6d., whilst from Norwich to Flordon it is only 11d."

Later, the charges became even more capricious — at least in the down direction — with artificially low fares to Norwich subsidised by higher fares to intermediate stations as the E.U.R. strove to compete. And then there came the inevitable consequence.

In May, 1853, a certain Mr Frere, a respected J.P. of Roydon Hall, near Diss, was convicted by the Colchester magistrates of travelling on the railway without paying the proper fare. He had bought a second class ticket from Colchester to Norwich, costing five shillings, but had alighted at Diss, to where the fare was seven shillings. Not surprisingly, he appealed to the Quarter Sessions, where the case was adjudged to be so important and unusual that it was referred to the High Court. There, in due course, the fine of ten shillings imposed by the Colchester Bench was set aside. Although Counsel acting for the company argued that Mr Frere had obtained his ticket by false representation, the court decided that a passenger was entitled to alight at any intermediate point unless there were specific byelaws to the contrary. By that time the E.U.R. had been taken over by the E.C.R. and the matter was a dead letter.

Long before this, however, the E.U.R. directors had been striving to achieve some sort of agreement with the E.C.R. on the whole question of Norwich traffic and, in theory, accord had been reached. As early as 27th February, 1850, the two companies concluded a formal agreement to pool and divide the revenue from all traffic between London and Norwich on both routes; the E.U.R.'s share was to be twenty-five per cent, as they owned about this proportion of the combined route mileage. Mails and cattle traffic were excluded from the arrangement. But the E.U.R. continued to meet every kind of difficulty and obstruction.

One incident reported to the directors concerned some cattle trucks which had arrived at Colchester in good time to be forwarded to London by the scheduled E.C.R. cattle train.

> A Mr Simpson of the E.C.R. refused to allow the cattle trucks to be taken on, although the owner agreed to pay whatever was asked. Simpson would not for some time allow the cattle to be unloaded but ordered them to be taken on to the Eastern Union line, which was attended with considerable danger, as there was great risk of the cattle trucks running back a mile and a half.

Simpson also said that they should have been sent to London "by the other line". The directors decided to make a formal protest, as this was but one of a series of similar complaints "contrary to the spirit and tenets of the Agreement recently executed".

With cattle, such tactics were understandable, but it did not end there. Trains on the Cambridge line were speeded up, while those on the E.C.R. Colchester line were not; they were timed to give poor connections to the E.U.R., whose requests for improvements were either ignored or refused. According to the *Ipswich Journal*:

> On Monday last, passengers were informed at Shoreditch that they could not be booked beyond Colchester, the Company's servants affecting ignorance of the existence of the Ipswich line; and when the train arrived at Colchester the greatest care was taken that no passenger should proceed beyond or procure another ticket. Again, we are informed that this week, a carriage which was to be sent from Colchester to Norwich was despatched to London, to be thence forwarded on the Cambridge line.

The paper castigated the E.U.R. directors for allowing themselves to be so dominated and urged them to break the E.C.R. stranglehold by carrying their traffic between London and Ipswich by steamship. In the prevailing circumstances, even the Parliamentary fare from Norwich to the capital was 10s. 6d., whereas the maximum legal charge was 9s. 6d.

Even between Colchester and London the fares were higher than for comparable journeys elsewhere. In May, 1850, an enterprising Essex operator offered cheaper travel in "what at first appeared like a ponderous relic filched from a museum, an actual stage coach in all the glory of horseflesh and harness which belonged to ancient days". It was named the *Wonder*, but it must

First, second and third class carriages are clearly recognisable in this train, the heading to a newspaper advertisement of the 1840s.

have been of the nine days' variety, for we hear no more of it.

Meanwhile, the situation between the two railway companies continued to deteriorate and on 30th September, 1850, the E.U.R. board gave six months' notice of their intention to terminate the traffic agreement. In reply the E.C.R. suggested that the arrangement should be ended forthwith, but Cobbold and his colleagues declined to take so radical a step without having time to consider the consequences.

In November, they lodged a Bill in Parliament to give themselves running powers over the E.C.R. to London and, similarly, from Trowse to Yarmouth and Lowestoft over the tracks of the Norfolk Railway (already leased to the E.C.R.), in return for similar powers over their own metals. Traffic arrangements between the companies were to be properly co-ordinated, with disputes being referred to arbitration.

J.C. Cobbold and his fellow directors knew full well that even if Parliament granted them the powers which they sought it would not be until the summer of 1851. Before that, the notice which they had so defiantly served on the E.C.R. at Bishopsgate* would expire and no one knew what would happen then. Through bookings of any kind might be terminated and the E.C.R., assured of its Norwich traffic via Cambridge, could well initiate what would amount to a blockade of E.U.R. territory.

After reflecting on the subject for six nail-biting weeks, those E.U.R. directors who met as the company's Traffic Committee decided in November that they could no longer stand the suspense. They resolved that the E.C.R. should be asked what arrangements they would be prepared to make after the end of March, and that it should be suggested that differences should be submitted to arbitration. But the full board, meeting the following week, rejected the idea of any communication with Bishopsgate. Bruff was instructed to prepare plans to meet any eventuality.

There was, however, some communication between the two companies. Joseph Glynn, the vice-chairman of the E.C.R., and some of his colleagues were aware of their own financial problems; the chairman, Edward Betts, partner of Morton Peto, had been injured in an accident and resigned from the E.C.R. board about this time. Faced with the prospect of opposing the E.U.R. Bill in Parliament, they concluded a new agreement with the E.U.R. and also with the Norfolk Railway, whose shareholders had always been

* Shoreditch station had been renamed Bishopsgate in 1847.

163

resentful of the terms under which their line had been taken over and worked by their larger neighbour. This agreement, provisionally signed by the chairmen of the three companies in January, 1851, was as follows:

(a) The E.C.R. should take over the working of all lines belonging to the three companies and purchase the rolling stock of the E.U.R. and the N.R. for sums to be determined by independent valuers.

(b) After the E.C.R. had been paid its working costs, the surplus income was first to be applied to paying interest on the debentures and dividend on the preference shares issued by the three companies, with specified maxima in each case.

(c) The E.C.R. was to receive three-quarters of any surplus, and the others, an eighth each.

(d) The E.U.R. and the N.R. were each to nominate a director to the E.C.R. board, and application was to be made for a Bill to amalgamate the three companies.

Of course, the proposals had to be approved by the shareholders of the three companies; those of the E.U.R. and the N.R. ratified the agreement, but the E.C.R. proprietors rejected it (18th March, 1851). Glynn was replaced as chairman by the "hard-liner" David Waddington.

At last, on the very day that the E.U.R.'s notice to terminate the agreement expired, a letter arrived from Bishopsgate suggesting that the previous arrangements should continue on a temporary basis, subject to a week's notice of termination from either side. There must have been considerable relief in the E.U.R. boardroom!

The company's affairs were in a serious state, even without hostility and obstruction from its more powerful neighbour. Although the completion of the line to Norwich had brought a

The later E.U.R. office building in Commercial Road, Ipswich, shortly before it was demolished in the 1950s.

K. G. Leighton

considerable increase in revenue (£26,562 in the first half of 1850, as against only £9,926 in the corresponding period in 1849), the work had left the company with construction and land acquisition debts of about £350,000 and a bond debt of over £536,000 (in May, 1851, the board specially thanked Samuel Bignold for "having provided funds to pay for Miss Martineau's land, the want of which had held up the Works" on the Trowse link). The dividend on ordinary stock had been six per cent in 1847, but it had quickly disappeared after that. The capital had not all been called, but there were serious arrears on the calls which had been made. Now, there was no dividend for some of the preference shareholders and they were becoming restive. Even the company's solicitors were suing for £30,000.

The company again looked carefully at its internal organisation, searching for possible economies. In April, 1851, the wages of drivers were reduced from 7s. 6d. to 7s. per day, which was the highest rate paid by the E.C.R. A few men in various departments were made redundant, although manning levels had already been reduced in 1848. Surplus land was sold. The company's London office at No 32 Bucklersbury was closed. The Ipswich office was moved from its original location in Lower Brook Street to a newly-erected dwelling house in Commercial Road, adjacent to the land leased from the Corporation in 1846 for a future goods yard, and all part of the marshland development undertaken by J.C. Cobbold's "Little Company".

The secretary, J.F. Saunders, had been located in the London office and as a result of the business there being wound up he was accused of misappropriating over £5,000 of the company's money. The matter was eventually sorted out between solicitors, but Saunders left the company's service in September, 1851, and was replaced by Edmund Ayres, who had been assistant secretary since the company was first incorporated.

The work of the entire office staff was closely scrutinised and it was decided that "the practice of permitting the clerks to leave the office in the middle of the day for the purpose of dining be forthwith discontinued". The office hours were to be literally nine till five, with occasional overtime, if absolutely necessary, beginning at seven o'clock.

Meanwhile, the E.U.R. Bill had been progressing through Parliament, in the face of strong opposition from the E.C.R. It eventually passed, to become the E.U.R. Amendment Act dated 3rd July, 1851, but it had lost its sharpest teeth. The company was merely authorised to make agreements with the E.C.R., the London and Blackwall and the Norfolk railways about rates and through traffic; it had no running powers over lines which it did not own. Disputes could be referred to arbitration. The maximum fares which might be charged were firmly pegged at 3d., 2d. and 1½d. per mile respectively, for the three classes of travel.

Cobbold and his colleagues wished to convert their contract debts into a special creditors' stock, but in one of the company's Acts the Railway Commissioners, a special body set up by the Government to deal with the Board of Trade's railway functions during the "Mania", had inserted a clause empowering them to appoint their own auditor to supervise the company's financial dealings. This was almost unheard of, and the directors regarded it as an intolerable intrusion into their affairs.

This Government auditor, a certain Mr Quilter, was insisting that all available surplus revenue was to be directly applied to reducing the contract debts. To make matters worse, the E.U.R. board did not even regard him as an impartial authority; when he first notified his intention to come and see the books the directors resolved that "the Chairman see him and tell him that it would have been more satisfactory if the Auditor appointed by the Railway Commissioners had been unconnected with the Eastern Counties Company"! He was probably a shareholder.

The Commissioners, and presumably their auditor also, disappeared in 1851. In the following year the E.U.R. obtained an Act enabling them, subject only to the approval of the creditors and the shareholders, to create £250,000 of this stock at four per cent, ranking above everything apart from debenture and mortgage interest.

Brassey was the principal creditor, to the tune of £165,000, in addition to holding £60,000 of other stock. He had a greater stake in the company than the entire board of directors, which he joined in April, 1852.

We must now look at certain events which had been taking place far away from the territory of the E.U.R., in the fen country lying to the south of the Wash.

So far as railways were concerned, the ancient port of King's Lynn was in a similar situation to Ipswich. By 1848 small locally-promoted lines, extending from Lynn to Ely — with a branch to Wisbech — and to Dereham, had been amalgamated[50] to form the East Anglian Railways (note the use of the plural). This company was in a serious financial state, and the E.C.R. was trying to lease and work its lines.

Further to the west, Peterborough was already an important railway town. A branch from the London and North Western Railway linked it with the coalfields and industrial areas of the midlands. By 1847, the E.C.R. had reached out to it from Ely by way of March, from where a branch ran northwards to a second Wisbech station. Next, the Midland Railway built a line to Peterborough. Then came the Great Northern. From Peterborough, railway tracks owned by many different companies extended continuously throughout the North of England, and even to Edinburgh and the industrial regions of Scotland.

Traffic, particularly in goods, from all these areas passed to the East along the E.C.R., and it was only natural that other companies whose trains ran to Peterborough should try to extend their services into East Anglia.

By 1849 the G.N.R had absorbed a company which had been empowered to build a line directly from Peterborough to Wisbech. There it could have gained access to the E.A.R., which would have allowed traffic to reach Dereham independently of the E.C.R. The E.C.R. had itself obtained an Act in 1847 to build a second route towards the North, from Wisbech via Sutton Bridge to Spalding, on the G.N.R., but they had not been able to undertake the work. In 1849 the G.N.R. agreed to abandon its own proposed line to Wisbech, and in return the E.C.R. granted it running powers from Peterborough to Wisbech.

After a time the G.N.R. negotiated a working agreement with the E.A.R. and served notice on the E.C.R. that it intended to make use of the running powers to Wisbech. The first G.N.R. train to Lynn ran on 10th July, 1851, and all went well until it reached Wisbech, where there was a short connecting line put in by the E.C.R. between the two stations; its staff refused to allow the train to pass over it to gain access to the E.A.R. Some waggons chained to the track made the blockage complete.

The matter eventually ended up in the High Court and surprisingly it was the E.C.R. which won the day — because, although the learned judge conceded that the G.N.R. should have been allowed to use the connecting line, the proposed arrangement had no Parliamentary sanction and was therefore illegal.

The G.N.R. position was untenable and the E.A.R. was worked by the E.C.R. as from 1st January, 1852. Of course, this arrangement also had to be approved by Parliament but, as so often happened, the authorising Act came later. It did not receive the Royal Assent until 17th June that year, but it applied retrospectively.

Away in Suffolk, J.C. Cobbold must have been quick to realise that he had powerful potential allies in the G.N.R. boardroom, not least Edmund Denison, the chairman, who had master-minded the whole E.A.R. debacle. In fact, he had done it without the approval of even his own shareholders and was under attack as a result, but he weathered the storm. Both Cobbold and Denison were Members of Parliament and both had personal and family links with the legal profession. Neither had any love for the E.C.R.

That company's Act of 17th June, 1852, contained some far-reaching provisions. The E.C.R. was obliged to carry traffic to or from the E.U.R. over the Norfolk Railway from Norwich to Dereham, and thence over the E.A.R. to Lynn or Wisbech. Any dispute arising from this could be referred to arbitration at the behest of the E.U.R. and the resultant findings would be binding on the E.C.R., although running powers were specifically excluded. But more importantly, the Act provided that *any company*,

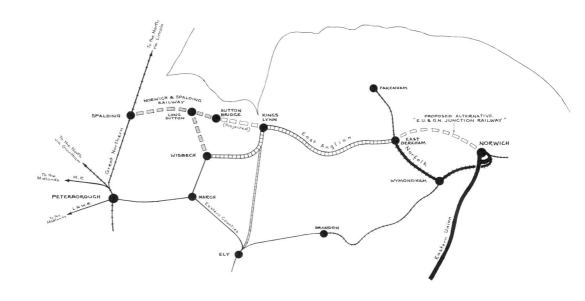

J.C. COBBOLD'S PROPOSED ROUTE TO THE NORTH 1851-2

existing then or in the future, which might be authorised to build a line from the G.N.R. to Wisbech or King's Lynn was to have running powers over the E.A.R. system to Dereham, "so as to communicate with the railways beyond Dereham".

Even during the brief alliance between the E.A.R. and the G.N.R., when the courts were considering the legality of the blocked line at Wisbech, Cobbold had endeavoured to promote yet another line from Norwich to Dereham — the Eastern Union and Great Northern Junction Railway — but the judgment had frustrated the scheme.

Now he had another chance, and in the autumn of 1852 the Norwich and Spalding Railway was promoted, with Bruff as engineer and J.C. Cobbold's name at the head of the list of provisional directors. Two of his colleagues on the E.U.R. board, W.W. Hawkins and E.S. Cayley, also featured in the list, as did Charles Locock Webb, one of the E.U.R. auditors; the other directors came from the locality.

In spite of its grandiose title, the N.&S.R. sought power only to build a line from Spalding to Sutton Bridge, by way of Holbeach and Long Sutton, with "a line diverging from Long Sutton direct to the East Anglian Railways station at Wisbeach." The prospectus mentioned the running powers that would be granted automatically to Dereham, "and authority will be sought by the Bill to extend such running powers to Norwich". The Parliamentary plans of the line show that Bruff had also surveyed the route for a direct line to Lynn from Sutton Bridge, but as this would involve a costly viaduct across the estuary of the Great Ouse it was not pursued.

The Bill received the Royal Assent on 4th August, 1853. J.C. Cobbold did not become the company's chairman. Great difficulty was experienced in raising the authorised capital of £170,000; not until 1858 was any of the line opened, and then only as far as Holbeach, worked by the G.N.R. The powers to build the connecting line to Wisbech having lapsed, they were never revived. Construction continued slowly, and trains began to run to Sutton Bridge in 1862.

A few days later the E.U.R. system became part of the Great Eastern Railway; so far as Cobbold and his colleagues from East Anglia were concerned the primary reason for the line had long ceased to be relevant. After other amalgamations, the Norwich and Spalding line eventually became part of the Midland and Great Northern Joint Railway in 1893. Bruff laid out no other railway so far from his home territory.

The principal preoccupation of Bruff and the E.U.R. board during the summer and autumn of 1851 was to negotiate a revised traffic agreement with the E.C.R. Ever since February, 1850, all receipts for traffic between London and Norwich had been divided into two equal portions. The E.C.R. took one portion, as representing that over the route by way of Cambridge, while the other portion was divided between the two companies in the ratio of the route mileage which each owned, by way of Colchester. The E.U.R. held the view that if the Colchester route was organised equitably it would attract more than half the traffic, since it was a shorter journey. The E.C.R., not unnaturally, wished to attract as much traffic as possible to the Cambridge route and keep all proceeds.

The talks, often necessarily postponed by the absence of one of the participants, dragged on. In December, 1851, the E.U.R. gave notice that it wished the dispute to be referred to arbitration, in accordance with the provisions of its recent Act. There were further delays while the E.C.R. looked for an arbitrator (there were to be three, with one acting as umpire) and then further quibbles over terms of reference.

Before the arbitrators had even met, a letter from Bishopsgate arrived at Ipswich saying that the E.C.R. board had decided to terminate the old agreement, temporarily extended for the past fifteen months, forthwith. Or rather, the accounts for the past half-year had been made up a fortnight previously (even the letter had been a week in the post!) and that was to be that. Henceforth

The Ipswich Steam Navigation Company's Orwell *leaving Ipswich in 1840; an aquatint by E. Duncan after W. J. Huggins.*

Frank Hussey

only the traffic actually passing through Colchester would be divided, according to the rules of the Railway Clearing House, as from 5th July, 1852.

The directors immediately authorised Cobbold and Bruff to act as they thought best; they arranged what the press had urged them to over two years before — a steamer service to London. The service began on 2nd August, with the Ipswich Steam Navigation Company's vessel *Orwell* sailing to Blackwall, where passengers boarded a train of the London and Blackwall Railway for Fenchurch Street. A thrice-weekly service was offered, and the inclusive fare from Norwich or Bury St Edmunds was 10s. first class and saloon cabin, or 6s. 3d. third class and fore cabin. The corresponding fares by rail throughout, via Colchester, were 20s. 6d. or 8s. 3d.

Two companies between them had operated five sailings a week in summer between Ipswich and London, before the railway arrived; but the I.S.N. Company had managed to continue ever since, offering two sailings each way per week. For several years the London terminal had been at Blackwall. Steamer advertisements rarely alluded to arrival time, but the journey could normally be accomplished in about seven hours in good weather. Although the railway had undoubtedly reduced the number of passengers travelling by sea, the steamer offered several advantages to those who were not in a hurry. Apart from low fares, the facility to stretch one's legs, and a real stove to sit by on chilly days (for first class travellers, at least), there were a buffet and toilet facilities at a time when such amenities were unknown on trains.

Under the combined rail/steamer arrangements, the traveller

from Norwich faced a ten-hour journey to the capital, but the advertisements cheered him with the promise that the "sea passage" did not exceed four hours (presumably the time occupied by sailing down the Orwell and up the Thames, from some unspecified point, was excluded). The boat train left Norwich Victoria at 7 a.m., fifteen minutes before the one which would connect with the E.C.R. at Colchester and get passengers to Bishopsgate shortly before 1 p.m. Norwich people, of course, also had the choice of travelling to London in three and a half hours via Cambridge, and having a reasonable length of time in the capital before returning the same day.

The service by sea seems to have prospered, but the *Orwell* steamer was due to be laid up as usual for the winter, and Bruff looked about for a vessel to replace her. He purchased the *Pearl*, a wooden paddler of 80 registered tons, from Milford Haven in October, 1852, and financed the deal by mortgaging her for £800 to a merchant in that port, probably her former owner. In December he purchased the iron paddler *Orion*, of 128 registered tons, from Goole. Oddly enough, she had been built at Ipswich in 1841, and had shared the London traffic with the *Orwell* until 1845, before the railway came, when she was sold to Fleetwood owners.

Both ships were managed by the Ipswich Steam Navigation Company, and the inclusive fares were boldly cut by about twenty per cent. Four sailings a week were offered, with passengers being landed and embarked at Blackwall, and goods at Chamberlain's Wharf, Southwark, where the E.U.R. set up an office for the purpose.

The Steam Navigation company went into liquidation early in 1853, and the E.U.R. purchased its ships *Orwell* and *River Queen*. As with the other vessels, the directors must have financed the deal from their own resources, and the new pair were re-registered as owned by Alfred Cobbold, who already owned other ships and was a younger brother of the chairman. Neither ship was mortgaged.

The *Orwell* returned to service in April, and the frequency of the sailings was increased to five each week. Shortly afterwards the *Prince Albert*, another iron paddle steamer, was acquired in Bruff's name, and a daily service down from London was inaugurated. There was no sailing in the reverse direction on Saturdays.

For a short time, the service was advertised under the title of "The Eastern Union Steam Navigation Company" but this name was quickly dropped, presumably to avoid calling attention to the fact that the railway company was only empowered to raise steam on land. Bruff was now the legal owner of no fewer than six ships which, with Alfred Cobbold's, sailed under the suitably vague title of "The New Steam Navigation Company".

Even David Waddington was forced to admit that the ships constituted a threat to his company. The E.C.R. retaliated by establishing goods and parcels offices in Ipswich, the very citadel of the E.U.R., with road waggons plying to and from their station at Colchester. According to one account, some of these waggons were first brought to Ipswich by rail! Goods and parcels consigned down the line from Bishopsgate and other E.C.R. stations were intercepted at Colchester, labels were altered or replaced, and the items continued their journey by road.

J.C. Cobbold later related how a friend once invited him to partake of some champagne which had just arrived from London, but when the hamper was opened it was found to contain bottles of castor oil, due to the label having been changed. No doubt even this case on its own would have been sufficient to precipitate the advertisement which appeared in the local press, requesting people sending goods to E.U.R. territory to forward them, with the addresses of consignees, "to the care of the Station Master at Ipswich".

Meanwhile, the arbitrators nominated by the two railway companies had begun their deliberations. The E.C.R. had first chosen Robert Stephenson as their nominee, but he was found to be away in Egypt and when he returned he refused to act. G.P. Bidder was then approached, but he was about to visit Sweden (one wonders whether Waddington knew about all this), but at last he returned and met Charles Locock Webb, the E.U.R. nominee, who was a barrister. To act as their umpire the pair chose I.K. Brunel who, it will be remembered, had acted in a similar capacity over the price to be paid for the incomplete line from Colchester to Ardleigh.

Eventually, in April, 1853, the arbitrators announced their award, which was to the effect that the E.U.R. was entitled to have, among other things, reasonable connections for their trains at Colchester. The company immediately announced that they would run an "Express or Quick" train, for first and second class passengers only, to London on 18th April. Connections would leave Norwich at 8.15 a.m. and Bury at 8.40 a.m.; the combined train would leave Ipswich at 9.30 and arrive at Colchester at 9.55, "from whence the Eastern Counties Company are ordered to forward the said train in an hour and a half to London". The fares would be as usual and the train would run daily; it was hoped there would be a similar train down in the evening. The advertisement ended on a less confident note:

Passengers will arrive in ample time at Colchester to proceed by the ordinary train which leaves Colchester at 10.25, in case the E.C.R. decline to forward such train on to London in accordance with the Arbitrators' Award.

And that was precisely what happened. When the train arrived at Colchester, red flags were flying where the tracks of the two railways met. As soon as the train had stopped, an official of the

The descendant of the E.C.R. road waggons; a G.E.R. delivery van in Ipswich about 1910.

E.U.R., apparently closely followed by a reporter from the *Ipswich Journal*, alighted and confronted the local manager of the E.C.R. He asked if the passengers were to be forwarded so as to reach Bishopsgate in an hour and a half, and received the reply, "Only by the 10.25" (This was the usual slow train, which did not arrive in London until 12.50.) The train was backed into a bay and the passengers, who numbered about twenty, stepped out. It was recorded that they did not appear to be surprised, and E.U.R. staff asked them for their names and addresses, as witnesses to what had happened.

In June the E.U.R. applied in the High Court for an injunction compelling the E.C.R. to abide by the arbitrators' award, that an express should be run once a day in each direction between London and Colchester, with traffic to or from the E.U.R., in one and a half hours. The defendants claimed that speed was not within the arbitrators' terms of reference, but judgment was given for the plaintiffs. However, it seems that J.C. Cobbold and his colleagues never obtained their ninety-minute express to or from London; other events intervened.

As long before as 1849, before their Norwich Extension was even complete, the E.U.R. board had first proposed a lease of their system to the E.C.R. as a way out of their financial difficulties and had sought Parliamentary authority for such a move. But the Bishopsgate shareholders, who were unhappy with their takeover of the Norfolk Railway, had refused to countenance any further involvement of this kind, and the E.U.R had thereupon deleted the offending clauses from their Bill. A later proposal for joint working was also rejected by the E.C.R. proprietors in 1851, and since then Cobbold and his colleagues had striven to make their own way.

There was a steady increase in traffic but working expenses also rose, from about fifty per cent in 1850 to a crippling sixty per cent and more in 1853. The creditors' stock had aroused the hostility of the company's own preference shareholders. The situation was desperate, in spite of the Micawberish note upon which the directors' half-yearly reports invariably ended. The final blow was the failure to gain any satisfaction from the arbitrators' award.

As 1853 drew to a close, talks took place between Brassey and Waddington and, as the E.C.R. working of the Norfolk Railway was due to be re-negotiated in any case in 1855, a new arrangement was worked out between the three boards. Brassey, as the contractor who had built the E.U.R and had been paid mostly in E.U.R. stock, was probably considered by the E.U.R. board the most suitable person to negotiate on their behalf. The new arrangement was approved at special meetings of the three companies, all held on 19th December, and the E.C.R. took over all working on 1st January, 1854.

The agreement was implemented with remarkable speed, for it was not even formally signed until 6th February. All receipts were to be pooled, with the E.C.R. taking five-sevenths and the other two companies a seventh each, less forty-six per cent for working expenses. Certain losses which the E.C.R. sustained in working other lines, e.g. the Newmarket and the East Anglian railways, were to be reimbursed before receipts were divided, and also guaranteed dividends to subscribers of capital for building various new lines, such as that to Woodbridge. E.U.R. rolling stock, and the steamships, were to be purchased at a price to be agreed between Bruff and J.V. Gooch, the E.C.R. locomotive superintendent.

These arrangements were legalised by an Act of Parliament dated 7th August, 1854, which included the proviso that a Bill for the complete amalgamation of the three companies, together with the Newmarket and the East Anglian railways, was to be deposited before the end of 1861. This, in due course, led to the formation of the Great Eastern Railway (according to one account, it was originally proposed that the combined system be named "The London and East Coast Railway") and by coincidence that Act received the Royal Assent exactly eight years later, on 7th August, 1862.

The hostility between the E.C.R. and the E.U.R. continued throughout the period of the working agreement. The latter always resented the fact that it received only a seventh of the surplus income although it owned a fifth of the combined route mileage. Nevertheless its profits, which had been only £50,000 in

1853, rose from £79,000 in 1854 to £90,000 in 1856. In 1855 the company was able to declare a modest dividend on its ordinary shares for the first time since it had amalgamated with the Ipswich and Bury Railway.

Thereafter, although traffic continued to increase, its share of the profits did not. Resentment increased when it was discovered that the E.C.R. was withholding certain income for itself and was offsetting certain costs against the combined receipts, instead of meeting them out of its own share. Things were going on which the joint committee of directors did not know about.

In this dispute the Suffolk company and the Norfolk Railway were allies; although in 1859 they jointly won an action against the E.C.R., the matter was not finally resolved for another two years.

When the E.U.R. ceased to work its own traffic, Bruff could report with justifiable pride that there had never been an accident involving compensation claims from passengers or destruction of the company's property. He must have been saddened to see much of the administrative organisation which he had built up dismantled in the early weeks of 1854; he was even technically unemployed for a few months while he worked on the valuation of the stock, for he received no pay.

Mr Boatwright, previously stationmaster at Lowestoft, came to superintend the working of the line from Colchester to Norwich. Before the takeover, Waddington had asked Bruff to carry on in his post and, as soon as he was free to resume his duties, the ex-manager wrote to remind him of the offer. Bruff was reinstated in June, 1854.

The Ipswich locomotive works were downgraded. Mr Hammond, the E.U.R. carriage superintendent, and some of his staff were transferred to Stratford. Just before they went, they joined many of their workmates for a last convivial evening at an Ipswich pub; their colleagues saw them off at the station, singing *God Save The Queen* as the train pulled out to signal the end of a era.

Branches and Associated Lines   13

Hadleigh

THE BRANCH to Hadleigh was originally an independent line, the Eastern Union and Hadleigh Junction Railway. The chairman of the provisional committee of directors, who did much of the work of promoting the company and preparing its Bill for Parliament, was one Rowland Hill; but whether or not he was the originator of penny postage, I do not know.

The company's Act, dated 18th June, 1846, authorised it to raise capital of £75,000 and build a seven-mile line to Hadleigh from a two-way junction in the parish of Bentley. The line was to be single, but the Board of Trade could order the company to double it at any time after it had been open for a year; it could have become part of an important cross-country link, even from the Midlands to Harwich. J.C. Cobbold was elected chairman, and among the other directors were his father, John Cobbold, John Footman, James Allen Ransome and Rowland Hill.

The company was closely bound up with the E.U.R. from the start; the secretary was J.F. Saunders and the engineer was Bruff. A lease had been agreed as early as October, 1845, months before the Hadleigh company received its Act; but, on 26th August, 1846, the two boards of directors agreed that the E.U.R. should purchase the branch outright.

The Hadleigh company, with E.U.R. approval, accepted an offer from George Wythes to construct the line for £51,700, including the supply of the rails.

The work began with a ceremonial cutting of the first sod on 5th September, 1846, near Kate's Hill Farm, Hadleigh. Here the line was to be carried across a tributary of the River Brett with a double culvert under an embankment 50 feet high, at that time said to be the highest in Suffolk or Norfolk. Although it was not reported who actually wielded the spade, Allen Ransome (as he was usually called) made a short speech and, with the autumn afternoon drawing to a close, a party of about forty gentlemen retired to a nearby tent for "an excellent cold dinner". A journalist recorded "one little circumstance" which attracted his attention when Bruff's health was drunk, "the hearty and enthusiastic manner in which the cheer was taken up and responded to by the hundreds who had assembled around the tent" (or did they wish to remind those inside that they were hungry, too?). The party did not break up until "a late hour".

Bruff was for the first time referred to as "Engineer in Chief", but the main line schemes, with surveys and Parliamentary work, occupied him for most of the time. The Hadleigh branch was dealt with by his "oldest assistant", Robert Richardson, with two assistant engineers, Charles Russell and Edward Sheppard, previously at Ipswich tunnel.

Wythes' agent, and maybe partner, was one Joseph Jackson. The construction of the Hadleigh line was divided into two sub-contracts; a Mr Morris carried out the work between Bentley and Raydon Wood, and one J. Alcock was responsible for the shorter length at the Hadleigh end, where the earthworks were comparatively heavy. The work proceeded with little hindrance, apart from the collapse of the Kate's Hill culvert, which was soon repaired.

Bruff prepared a scheme for extending the line to Lavenham but the Bill was abandoned, partly no doubt for financial reasons and partly because the engineer considered it advisable to pass the track under Station Road at Hadleigh, which would have meant the delay of altering the levels of the work in hand.

The purchase deal was sanctioned by an Act of Parliament dated 8th June, 1847, and was effective from the following 20th October.

The formal opening took place on 20th August, 1847, after consecutive meetings of shareholders of the two companies had finally agreed the details of the sale. A special train, hauled by a locomotive named *Hadleigh*, and consisting of "three splendid saloons,[51] two first class and four second class carriages", with a truck for Humfress' band, conveyed the party from Ipswich to Hadleigh. The station buildings at Capel, Raydon and Hadleigh were still under construction, but a triumphal arch and a fusillade of fog signal detonators greeted the train at Capel. At Hadleigh, flags flew and guns fired. The party proceeded to the Town Hall for a dinner, and there was a firework display as the train started on its return journey several hours later.

The line opened for goods traffic on the following day[52] and

The formal opening of the railway at Hadleigh on 20th August, 1847, as depicted in an etching by Henry Davy dated 29th September, 1847. Davy was certainly there—he would never have invented that leaning flagstaff! Note passengers even standing on the roofs of the train.

Mr W. A. B. Jones

Hadleigh station about 1880. The locomotive seems to be a T7 0-4-2 tank, built at Stratford in the early 1870s and re-boilered by William Adams a few years later; note weatherboards but no roof to protect the engine crew.
Mr W. A. B. Jones

The front page of a contemporary journal bearing an exaggerated illustration of "The Hurricane at Hadleigh Station".

for passengers on 2nd September,[53] with five trains each way on weekdays and three on Sundays.

One mysterious feature of the Hadleigh branch is the Ipswich-facing leg of the junction with the main line, where the empty cutting exists to this day. The report in the *Ipswich Journal* of the opening said, "The train arrived at the Bridge at Bentley at twenty minutes to four, when it left the main line". The now-abandoned cutting is less than 200 yards from this bridge, but at that time the London-facing leg of the junction already extended as a third line of rails to Bentley Station, nearly three-quarters of a mile away, as it did until the branch finally closed. A timetable of 1848 indicates that no passenger trains ran directly between Ipswich and Hadleigh; perhaps they might have done if the branch had been extended to Lavenham and beyond. After a heavy snowfall in January, 1854, one of the major blockages on the Colchester to Ipswich line was reported to be at "Bentley bridge junction". This junction may have been used for goods working, and a few passenger specials, in the early days but the track had certainly been lifted by 1904.

The station at Hadleigh was still incomplete on 16th September, 1847, when an excursion was arranged to take trippers to Ipswich for the annual regatta. The day was marked by a violent gale, and over a hundred people were waiting for the train to arrive when suddenly a wall along the back of the platform collapsed upon them. No one was killed outright; but a woman, after a leg had been amputated some days later, was "not expected to recover". According to one account, sixty-five people were injured, many seriously.

In March, 1850, John Staines, a Hadleigh tailor, sued the E.U.&H.J.R. Company for damages of £500 because of injuries sustained by his wife, Elizabeth. She had run a grocery shop for him, but a fractured pelvis crippled her and the husband was bankrupt.

A bricklayer[54] employed by Alcock on the work was called to explain to the court what had happened. The wall which fell was 14 feet high and 40 feet long, a continuation of the front of the station house, and it was intended to carry a canopy over the platform at the southern end of the station. The final bricks in it had been laid only about four hours before, and it fell just as the train hove in sight and the platform was thronged with intending travellers.

The defence was that the action was against the wrong company — it was the E.U.R., and not the Hadleigh Junction Company, which organised the excursion and had operated the railway from the day it opened. Martin, the E.U.R. traffic superintendent, testified that he had issued the handbills; Henry Ward, the stationmaster, said that he had never been employed by the Hadleigh company, although they had an office at Ipswich station, where he had served previously.

The evidence, as reported in the *Ipswich Journal*, was full of fascinating detail:

Mr Wilkin, of the Ipswich firm of Wright and Wilkin, said that they began the work of building the station, and signed a contract on 7th September, 1847 — with the Hadleigh company — but the work was taken out of their hands because they did not proceed with sufficient speed. (The contract must have been signed after the work began. The newspaper had reported in June that the site

Hadleigh station platform in 1906 as a train headed by one of Holden's 0-6-0 tanks arrives.

R. G. Pratt

of the station was being levelled, and that Wright and Wilkin were believed to be the contractors. They were dismissed speedily, too; nine days after they had formally signed, Alcock's men were on the job!)

Mr Alcock said that the wall was commenced about the beginning of August. He had been paid £300 for building the station.

Frederick Barnes, the architect of the station — "I concluded my articles 16 years ago" — Bruff and his assistant, William Holland, all attested that the wall was properly designed and soundly built. No one blamed the contractor.

After a hearing lasting two full days, judgment was given for the plaintiff, who was awarded £100.

The Stour Valley Line

THE LINE from Marks Tey to Sudbury began its life as a separate concern, the Colchester, Stour Valley, Sudbury and Halstead Railway, promoted in Essex in 1845, with Bruff as engineer. It was to be in two separate portions — a twelve-mile line to Sudbury, with a branch to Halstead from Chappel, and another branch line from the E.U.R., near the Colchester station, to the Hythe. Both sections, with transit over the E.C.R. between them,

An unusual sight on the Hadleigh branch: E4 No 62797, one of Holden's "Intermediates", boasts express headcode as it heads a rail enthusiasts' special across the level crossing by Capel station in the 1950s.

H. N. James

would give direct access to Sudbury for goods brought into Colchester by sea. It was proposed to have a two-way junction at Marks Tey, for trains to or from both Colchester and the direction of London.

The Sudbury line had to cross the narrow valley of the River Colne at Chappel and traverse the Mount Bures ridge, which rose quite steeply above the river on the far side, before dropping down into the Stour valley beyond. To reach the Mount Bures summit, the line was to be carried across the Colne on a timber viaduct about 70 feet high.

In spite of opposition from the E.C.R., who were promoting a rival line to Bures and the Stour valley from Lexden, nearer their Colchester terminus, the Stour Valley company received their Act of Parliament on 26th June, 1846. The share capital was to be £250,000, with power to borrow an additional £83,000. For the first time, one section of the Act specified that "for the greater Convenience and Security of the Public" the company was to erect and permanently maintain either a station or a lodge at all level crossings over public highways.

The chairman of the Stour Valley company was a Mr Thomas L'Estrange Ewen, who seems not to have been a local man; the vice-chairman was William Warwick Hawkins, of Alresford Hall, near Wivenhoe, who was also a director of the E.U.R.

The picturesque gatekeeper's lodge at Church Farm Crossing, Bentley, on the Hadleigh branch. The large windows would have given a good view up and down the line.

Within a few weeks, the Stour Valley directors had provisionally agreed with those of the Ipswich and Bury Railway that the latter company should lease the line, as they were proposing a line of their own from Stowmarket to Sudbury (see Chapter seven). For their part, the Stour Valley were to make their Sudbury line a double one, like the proposed link to Stowmarket. They submitted a Bill to Parliament for authority to raise the necessary extra capital of £100,000, and also to empower them to take over the Stour Navigation.

All the construction work was let in one contract to George Wythes, at a price of just under £190,000; and work began early in August, 1846, on the Hythe branch. Earth for the embankment near Colchester station was brought from works on the E.U.R., probably from Stoke Hill at Ipswich.

Early in 1847, operations began on the Marks Tey to Sudbury line, where Wythes divided the work into sub-contracts under his agent, Joseph Jackson. The cutting at Mount Bures was entrusted to a man named Weston, while the work nearer Sudbury was let to a Mr Brown (probably he who had worked on the E.U.R. at Ardleigh). When he had completed his work on the Hadleigh line, Alcock came to build the Chappel viaduct. Another sub-contractor was Richard Robinson, known as "Whittlesea Dick", whose career

Bruff's viaduct across the Colne valley at Chappel. The foundation stone can be seen beneath the arch on the right.

ended abruptly in June, 1849, when his vehicle collided with another as he drove away from a pub in Bures.

To secure the traffic of West Suffolk, and to exclude possible incursion by rivals into the county, the Stour Valley company promoted Bills for extending their line to Long Melford, Lavenham and Clare; and from Lavenham to Bury St Edmunds. These applications were successful and both received the Royal Assent on 8th June, 1847. The Bill for taking over the Stour Navigation, however, was thrown out in April.

Incidentally, Bruff's proposed northward extension of the line did not follow the river round Sudbury, as the railway did later. The line sanctioned in 1847 was to pass under the rising ground to the east of the town in a tunnel. And what a tunnel it would have been; less than 300 yards long, it would have been S-shaped, with reversed curves of only 110 yards radius! There can be no doubt that Bruff intended to perpetuate his memory with some extraordinary tunnelling.

The proposed lease to the Ipswich and Bury company was also sanctioned on 8th June, although the two boards of directors did not agree terms until the very same day. The annual rent was to be five per cent on issued capital of up to £300,000 and an equal division of any further profits. By that time, however, the I.&B.R. was in the process of amalgamating with the E.U.R. and, as with other matters, the proposed lease had to wait until the reconstituted company could approve it.

In the meantime, the Colchester Hythe branch was opened on 1st April, 1847,[55] when "a powerful engine" traversed the line to take ten waggons, with 200 quarters of malt and grain and about 30 tons of coke, up to Colchester station. Some "open carriages" were also brought along and the directors, with Bruff and their guests, accompanied the goods on the journey. The branch remained in use for goods traffic only; the company purchased their own goods waggons and hired locomotives, presumably from the E.U.R. It was decided not to commence passenger traffic until the Sudbury line was opened.[56]

Bruff had originally intended to carry the Sudbury line over the Colne at Chappel on a timber viaduct, using laminated timber arches, probably on brick piers; but the discovery of good brickearth at Mount Bures prompted him to change to brick arches. Such a structure would entail lower maintenance costs.

The foundations of what was to be his most impressive work were commenced in July, 1847; the ground was good gravel, and it was not even necessary to carry the piers on piles. Within a month or so, two million bricks were ready, burnt in clamps.

All through that spring and summer the work on the line had been carried forward. Nearly a third of a million cubic yards of earth had been moved; nearly ten miles of the route was fenced. Most of the permanent way materials were on site, and three miles of track had been laid. By the end of August, the workforce had risen to 606 men, using 106 horses.

Although there had been no ceremonial cutting of the first sod when the work began, a foundation stone for Chappel viaduct was laid with suitable pomp on 14th September, about 10 feet above ground level, in one of the piers between the road and the river bank, where it can still be seen. A "spacious marquee" had been pitched nearby, from whence issued a procession, headed by a band and a party of navvies "in their white frocks and straw hats". They were followed by the "master of the works", whoever he may

The foundation stone on Chappel viaduct. The coins were probably placed in a recess between the two sections. The trowel used by Mr Ewen at the ceremony is now in the National Railway Museum, York.

have been, bearing on a cushion two silver trowels which were to be used by the chairman and vice-chairman of the company to lay the stone. The chief participants mounted a platform and the stone was duly laid; but not before a bottle, containing a newly-minted sovereign and half-sovereign, a shilling, a sixpence and a four-penny piece, had been placed under it. After the speeches and the cheers, about 200 people adjourned to the marquee for refreshment.

If it was unusual for the stone to be laid by two people, what followed was extraordinary; within hours it was discovered that the stone had been lifted again and the coins removed! Detection followed swiftly, too, after a mint half-sovereign had been tendered that night to the barmaid at the *Rose and Crown* in Chappel. Although she undoubtedly handled much cash from navvies, the new coin caught her attention and she at once gave it to the landlady. Perhaps the taproom was already echoing with guffaws of laughter as the story of the theft was recounted. Certainly by the next morning the coin was in the hands of the agent, Jackson, and it was not long before the man who had taken it to the pub, William Coates, or Coote, a bricklayer from Norwich, was arrested. A few weeks later, he appeared before the Quarter Sessions, charged with the theft of £1 11s. 10d., belonging to the Stour Valley Railway Company.

There could be little doubt that Coates had taken the money, although the evidence seems to have been circumstantial. The barmaid knew him, and he had certainly been in attendance on the platform when the bottle was placed in position. Jackson testified that he had "searched the money paid to the men in wages on the previous Saturday, and could not find one sovereign of the present year" (the money was probably given back to him for safe keeping, and kept as ready cash to be dispensed for regular drinking sessions).

The bricklayer did not conduct his own defence. His counsel, "in an ingenious speech, contended that the Company had no property in the money and that there was an entire absence of proof in the moral guilt of the prisoner". The case was dismissed.

Apart from this episode, the work of building the viaduct went smoothly ahead. Bruff's resident engineer on the project was Charles Russell, who may also have been responsible for much of the detailed design.

Eighteen of the piers were erected on mass-concrete foundations, varying in thickness between 3 feet and 12 feet but, due to the good subsoil conditions, the remainder, and the abutments at the extreme ends, needed little more than the removal of topsoil and ordinary brick footings. By February, 1848, the foundations were all complete and the piers were rising across the valley. At the

The former Rose and Crown *public house at Chappel still maintains an association with the viaduct. It was here that one of the stolen coins was tendered.*

185

end of the first twelve months, ten arches had been finished and five more were partially turned. To the inhabitants of the district it must have seemed something like the building of the Pyramids, with the great row of scaffolding-shrouded piers marching across the meadows, the humps of massive timbers up aloft to support the arches, the endless cartloads of materials, and men everywhere. It is a pity that no artist seems to have recorded the scene. By February, 1849, Bruff's *magnum opus* was complete, apart from the parapets. Not the least remarkable thing about it is that it seems to have been built without loss of life. It is now a listed building.

In his Paper to the Institution of Civil Engineers (see Chapter ten), Bruff explained that the viaduct was on a gradient, the Sudbury end being 9 feet 6 inches above the other. Each of the thirty-two arches, horizontal in itself, was $3\frac{1}{2}$ inches higher than its neighbour. The turning of the arches began at the lower end. Although only nine sets of timber centres for supporting the arches were used, the massive beams between the tops of the piers which carried the formwork were put up first from end to end to brace all the piers together.

Even so, "it was found, that though each arch left the centering freely, and preserved its shape perfectly, an almost inappreciable easing of the haunch occurred, on the upper, more than on the lower side. As this was noticed to be the case in each arch in successsion, it appeared to demand attention, and upon careful examination it was found, that a very slight yielding, not amounting to a sixteenth part of an inch, took place, from there not being sufficient weight on the upper side to equalize the pressure of the arching. As soon as this was discovered, all danger was obviated, by the introduction of a few diagonal struts, which were left in the work until the entire arching was completed". The horizontal beams were left in position until after the line was opened.

The brickwork was not as solid as it appeared. Each pier was hollow on either side of the central opening, and the permanent way was carried across the spandrels, between the arches, on five longitudinal vaults supported on walls between the backs of the arches (so far as I know, these voids are still there).

Bruff added that the total cost of the viaduct was £21,000, or £55 per yard of its length, whereas he had estimated that a timber structure would have cost £67 per linear yard.

A number of engineers whose names are now legend took part in the discussion after the lecture. "Mr Brunel" said that it should not be assumed that £55 per yard was a low cost for a viaduct not more than about 60 feet high with very good foundations. He thought that a timber viaduct of the best quality could have been erected on the site for only £27 per linear yard; perhaps, but where are Brunel's timber viaducts today? "Mr Vignoles" also thought the costs at Chappel were high, but Peter W. Barlow,[57] a member of a famous family of engineers, supported Bruff's views on the costs, although he was doubtful of the wisdom of not making the brickwork completely solid. The President of the Institution, the great William Cubitt, merely asked a straight-forward question about Bruff's calculations, and accepted the answer without comment.

Although the Chappel viaduct was built for a double line, the second track was never laid. The late 1840s were hard economic times. Little work was completed on the Halstead branch, and even the London-facing part of the junction at Marks Tey was abandoned. The company was unable to contemplate any work north of Sudbury.

When in June, 1848, the E.U.R. held its first meeting after the practical amalgamation with the I.&B.R., the terms of the proposed lease of the Stour Valley line were firmly rejected; the shareholders were more concerned to secure a share of the traffic to Norwich than that of Sudbury. The two boards of directors were dismayed; the Stour Valley looked like having a railway with no trains, while Cobbold and his colleagues feared that the E.C.R. would seize the opportunity to move in. The negotiations began again, and within a few months it had been agreed that the E.U.R. should pay five per cent merely on the £83,000 which the S.V.R. had borrowed at that rate; the shareholders would receive only three per cent until E.U.R. dividends improved. A single line to Sudbury was to be opened as soon as possible. It was estimated that the annual rent would be about £11,000 and the arrangement was reluctantly accepted by the E.U.R. shareholders in November, 1848, more to protect their own territory than to secure any immediate profit.

All through these uncertainties the work of building the line continued steadily. Cash was short, but Wythes, like many other contractors at that time, agreed to accept payment in the company's stock. In April, 1849, the cutting at Mount Bures was finally completed, the contractor having resorted to the use of gunpowder to blast away the last of the stubborn clay. The earth which was dug out at Cornard, near Sudbury, was good gravel; it was used to ballast the permanent way over much of the line (it would seem, therefore, that the locomotive used to haul the ballast trains was probably taken up the Stour by barge). By mid-May, all the rails were laid and the building of the stations had begun. Brunel would doubtless have approved the timber bridge which carried the line across the Stour at Cornard.

At last, on 30th May,[58] a two-coach directors' special ran all the way to Sudbury, where the party was greeted by a peal of bells. The government inspector came, and J.S. Martin, the E.U.R. traffic superintendent, issued an advertisement that passenger traffic would commence on 2nd July. And so it did, but formal approval from the Board of Trade was received only just in time.[59]

On that day the first train carried an official party from Colchester. The Mayor of Sudbury took his seat at Marks Tey. Bruff was not there — his health had broken down and he was then recuperating abroad — but he was well represented by his assistants. There was Robert Richardson (of fishplate fame) and another "civil engineer" named Chadwick, together with two "engineers" named Scott and Cooke (a Mr Scott was resident engineer on the building of "Halfpenny Pier" at Harwich, while James Cooke, aged 21 and born at Lawford, Essex, was living with Bruff as an "apprentice" at the time of the 1851 Census).

As the train entered the branch line, a hastily-erected triumphal arch was found to have been put up without due regard to the loading gauge; the chimney of the engine struck it, "causing a huge descent of verdant ornament and more solid woodwork". A band played merrily at Bures; and eventually the train reached Sudbury, where a great crowd of people was waiting at the yet-unfinished station. Bells pealed and flags flew. But despite all the "éclat" — not to mention the descent of woodwork — the journey had taken less time than had been expected. When nobody could think of anything else to say at the station, both visitors and hosts had to wander aimlessly round Sudbury for a couple of hours until it was time for the official banquet at the Town Hall.

The E.U.R. worked the line and paid the outgoings, as had been agreed, but the full rent was not paid because there was some delay before Wythes rendered his final account, and until it was received the precise capital cost of the line could not be ascertained. Then Cobbold and his colleagues (some of them on the Stour Valley board) prevaricated, saying that the line to Sudbury had not been formally approved by the E.U.R. — although it had been laid out and constructed by their engineer! It was two years before these points were resolved. They were criticised by the shareholders for involving the company in the Stour Valley line at all, but they feared that the E.C.R. might still step in to use Sudbury as a base from which to reach out towards Norwich. A reduced rent was negotiated, and the E.U.R. applied to Parliament for authority to abrogate the 1848 lease agreement. The Stour Valley shareholders were furious, and the directors with seats on both boards found themselves sitting on a very precarious fence.

Despite opposition from the S.V.R., the E.U.R. won the day and their Act of 1852, which authorised the creditors' stock to pay Brassey, also fixed the Stour Valley rent at £9,500 per annum. The first half-yearly payment would not be due until January, 1853, and all arrears were wiped off the slate. The lease, like that of the Harwich branch, was for 999 years (today, we can only marvel at the sublime faith of the Victorians that the world they were creating would endure). The Stour Valley Company remained as a separate entity until it was absorbed by the G.E.R. in 1898.

Harwich

RARELY can a branch line have been the subject of so many rival schemes and unsuccessful applications to Parliament as that to serve the port of Harwich.

Harwich had been an important packet port since the time of Charles II, with little sailing ships carrying passengers and mails to and from the Continent, but by the second quarter of the nineteenth century its packet owners and captains had become too complacent and too settled in their ways. In 1832 the contract for carrying the mails to Holland and North Germany was lost to steamers sailing from the Thames; two years later the last mail service from the Essex port, to Gothenburg, was transferred to Hull. These were heavy blows to Harwich, but it was obvious that a railway to London would lay the foundations of renewed prosperity.

The first steps were taken in 1836, as soon as the E.C.R. Company was authorised to build its line from London to Yarmouth. In that year, William Hosking brought out a proposal for a line as straight as an arrow from Colchester, and in 1840 an almost identical route was surveyed by a man named R.B. Mosse. Both schemes were apparently called "The Harwich Railway"; the backers of each were reported to be about to introduce a Bill in Parliament, but nothing more was heard, for the E.C.R. was still too far from Colchester for investors to take up shares in a Harwich line.

In 1841 a railway speculator named John Attwood was elected one of the Members of Parliament for Harwich. He laid out several thousands of pounds in bribes and, as an additional inducement for the voters, he announced that if he was successful he would advance £20,000 for a railway to the town. He may indeed have tried to arrive as a candidate with an Act already in his pocket, for

Harwich as it was before the railway arrived, seen in an eighteenth-century print.

189

Mosse's scheme was rumoured to have been promoted by a single individual, but he did not immediately make good his promise after he had been returned to Westminster.

Meanwhile, the E.C.R. was building its line to Colchester and had purchased land as far as Ardleigh. With backing from the company and other promoters in Harwich, Braithwaite, the E.C.R. engineer, surveyed a route for a "Colchester & Harwich Railway", using this land.

Early in 1843, when the trains were about to begin running to Colchester, the Mayor of Harwich convened a meeting at which it was resolved to remind Attwood of his promise, and a deputation called upon the M.P. at his home, Hylands Hall, near Chelmsford. He now had to act, but he was understandably reluctant to stake his political future on Braithwaite's estimates of the cost of a scheme backed by some of his opponents in Harwich. He turned to Joseph Locke, and the resultant "Harwich Railway & Pier" ran on a more northerly course from Ardleigh.

Both schemes were submitted to Parliament but both were thrown out in May, 1844, because it was thought that the traffic would be insufficient. "The original Hosking's line" was represented in opposition to both Bills, but the Commons Committee declined to hear Mr Hosking, "Professor of Engineering and Architecture at King's College", presumably in London.

Attwood had been so confident of success that rails for his line were even on order. He now persuaded the backers of the Colchester and Harwich to join forces with him, and Braithwaite prepared a new "Harwich Railway & Pier" scheme, using part of Locke's design.

Locke himself was now engineer-in-chief to the newly-incorporated E.U.R. Company and, under his guidance, Bruff was surveying the route for a line to Harwich from Manningtree. It will be remembered that Bruff had originally proposed a branch to Shotley, with access to Harwich by ferry, an expedient which seems to have been adopted because of opposition from the owner of Mistley Park to a line along the south side of the Stour estuary; but it was suspected that the Admiralty would oppose the Shotley idea, and so, after Mistley Park had changed hands, a branch from Manningtree became the logical choice. It is said that to conceal the scheme from his rivals Bruff conducted his survey by moonlight.

Bills for Attwood's line and the E.U.R. branch were submitted to Parliament for the 1844/5 session; and Hosking's and Mosse's schemes were, for the first time, entered too. All failed to pass Standing Orders.

The two main contenders repeated their attempts in the following year, with Attwood's line now called "The Harwich & Eastern Counties Junction". This time, however, the E.C.R. did not support him. Their land between Colchester and Ardleigh — the notorious two and a half miles — was required by the E.U.R. for their line to Ipswich. By the agreement of September, 1845 (see Chapter five), the E.C.R. undertook to abandon their own proposal for a direct line from Colchester to Harwich, and to support the new branch from Manningtree. Upon its completion, they would lease and work it, and would be granted running powers over the E.U.R. tracks between Colchester and Manningtree.

In spite of all this, the honours nearly went to Attwood. His Bill passed the Commons but was thrown out in the Lords on 9th June, 1846, because, it was said, their Lordships thought that quite enough railway schemes had been approved for the time being!

At last, in the following year, the E.U.R. were successful, when the Railway Commissioners recommended approval of their Bill. The Manningtree branch was shorter than the H.&E.C.J.R., although the earthworks were heavier; but it had only one level crossing, compared to its rival's sixteen, and it was better placed to serve the Midlands and the North. The Act, dated 22nd July, 1847, authorised the company to raise capital of £200,000 and to lease the line to the E.C.R. upon completion. As with so many projects sanctioned in that summer, the work had to be postponed due to lack of funds, although a token start to the construction was made near Manningtree in October, 1848.

The directors' report to the shareholders in February, 1849, spoke of the urgent necessity of raising more capital to complete the line to Norwich and said that it was proposed to issue shortly a further £200,000 of shares, as they were empowered to do by "an Act obtained in 1847". Although the directors were careful not to say so, this capital was intended by Parliament for the building of the Harwich line.

John Bagshaw, one of the M.P.s for Harwich, objected violently. He was an important landowner and businessman in the town, and he had been an ardent supporter of some of the many schemes to get the benefit of a railway there. He even obtained a court injunction restraining the company from applying this capital to anything except the Harwich line, but there was no legal power in the land to require investors to take up the shares — and they did not.

Cobbold and his colleagues agreed with their opposite numbers on the E.C.R. board to lease the line for 999 years at an annual rent of four and a half per cent of its cost, with a division of any profits above this figure. The powers to build the line expired but were revived by another Act in 1850. The E.C.R. decided that four and a half per cent was too optimistic, and another agreement in 1851 lowered the rent to four per cent. Eventually the capital was raised by lowering the dividend on some six per cent preference stock, about to be issued, to four per cent; and guaranteeing that the accounts of the Harwich branch would be kept separate from the rest of the company's business. This was another provision of the E.U.R. Act of 1852, and must have seemed a welcome change from the apparently endless issues of preference stock, each issue taking precedence over the previous ones.

Meanwhile, the people of Harwich had become tired of waiting for the railway to provide them with a pier. They obtained their own Act in 1851 for carrying out various improvements, including a pier and a quay[60] from the shipyard to King's Head Street.

The engineer was none other than Peter Bruff, who must have been grateful for this commission, for there was "really no paying business in the office".

The driving of the first pile for the pier took place on 2nd June, 1852, and Bruff was one of six dignitaries who laboured at the manually operated piledriver to deliver not one but four blows upon the pile, while the local brass band struck up *Rule Britannia*. The pier was opened in July, 1853; it was known as "Halfpenny Pier" — the due per person on the E.U.R. pier was to have been a penny.

At last, at the end of January, 1853, the construction of the railway began in earnest, with gangs of men working at several points along the route. Bruff had selected Wythes as the contractor years before. At the time of the lease negotiations with the E.C.R.

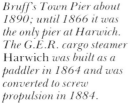

Bruff's Town Pier about 1890; until 1866 it was the only pier at Harwich. The G.E.R. cargo steamer Harwich *was built as a paddler in 1864 and was converted to screw propulsion in 1884.*

in 1851, the E.U.R. engineer had written to David Waddington, the
E.C.R. chairman, to tell him that the original "arrangement" was
that Wythes should complete the line, including the provision of
rails and chairs, for £100,000. Stations and sidings, estimated to
cost a further £16,000, were excluded, but it was hoped that
Wythes would agree to include these in the contract at no extra
charge.

The contractor's site agent was again Joseph Jackson, and
Joseph Alcock, builder of the Chappel viaduct, was one of the
sub-contractors. Mr Smith, the Manningtree surgeon, sent out his
assistant to attend to those injured on the works, as he had when
the original E.U.R. line was being built. The branch was a single
line, and the Ipswich-facing leg of the junction with the main line
(the Manningtree North Curve), although originally included in
the scheme, was not constructed until 1882, when the branch was
doubled.

The first train traversed the line on 29th July, 1854,[61]
carrying a large party of navvies, with Bruff and his assistant
engineer, Francis Leonard, and contractor's representatives on the
footplate. About two miles from the terminus the train stopped to
pick up a band from Harwich, and continued on its way to the
strains of *There's a good time coming, boys.* Upon arrival, "toasts were
dispatched with electric speed", including one to "Charley, the
engine driver". The train was also available that day to carry
workers from the Stratford Works on an excursion to Harwich, but

most of them preferred to continue on to Ipswich and take a steamer down the Orwell.

Major Wynne inspected the branch for the Board of Trade on 4th August and it opened for traffic on the 15th,[62] at such short notice that the Mayor and Corporation had only twenty-four hours in which to organise the celebrations.

Hurrah for Harwich — now the Rail
And stately ship with crowded sail
Shall soon bring Harwich trade and wealth
And sick'ning commerce bless with health.

Some optimistic bard had written this long before[63] but, poetic licence apart, it was a steamer service to the Continent that Harwich wanted. There were to be as many disappointments with this as there had been with the railway.

The Harwich and Eastern Counties Steam Packet Company, of which the secretary had been one of the party aboard the steamer *Orwell* for the experimental trip from Ipswich to Rotterdam in 1846, was promoted by the E.C.R. directors; but the scheme was effectively blocked by their shareholders. There was little prospect of success until their railway reached Harwich.

In December, 1851, a public dinner had been held at the *Cups Hotel* in Harwich in honour of a certain Captain Raymond, who was

An 1867 view of the then-new Harwich station from an album of views published by Rock and Company. In the background can be seen St Nicholas's Church and the High Lighthouse, one of a pair of lights erected in 1818.

Mrs Winifred Cooper

194

said to have placed the steamer *Arab* on the Harwich and Rotterdam station. The captain presumably got a free meal, but nothing ensued.

In 1852 the North of Europe Steam Navigation Company was established. This enterprise has become associated exclusively with Samuel Morton Peto, its vice-chairman, but among the promoters were J.C. Cobbold, David Waddington and other railway company directors. It was intended to operate services from Harwich, Lowestoft and Grimsby — in that order, according to the company's prospectus.

To provide better facilities at the Essex port than would be afforded by Bruff's Town Pier ("Halfpenny Pier"), when completed, a "Harwich Dock and Pier Company" was promoted. It was to construct a new pier adjacent to the proposed railway terminus, and a dock to the west of the town. The powers to build such a pier which the Eastern Union company had obtained under its Acts of 1847 and 1850 were to be superseded. The company's directors, however, were well represented among the promoters, with J.C. Cobbold and his father, and W.W. Hawkins and Thomas Brassey. David Waddington was another subscriber.

This dock company was the first of several to be proposed over the next fifty years or so; unlike those which followed, it even

The original station at Harwich. It stood close to the quayside and was demolished about 1864 to make way for cattle pens and sidings ready for the G.E.R. services from the company's adjacent Continental Pier.

R. G. Pratt

obtained an Act of Parliament, dated 20th August, 1853. Little seems to have followed. As soon as the railway was opened, the E.C.R. negotiated the purchase of the Town Pier from Harwich Corporation.

The N.E.S.N. Company ran an experimental crossing to Antwerp with its new steamer *Aquila* on 16th September, 1854, but the venture was unsuccessful and the ensuing weekly service was cancelled early in the following year.

In spite of this, the E.C.R. chartered the *Aquila* and another vessel, the *Cygnus*, and began a three times weekly service to Antwerp on 2nd May, 1855. It was no more successful — only eleven passengers were carried in the first week, and after two months the losses amounted to £2,400. For this, and other reasons, Waddington came under bitter attack from the company's shareholders, and the service ceased in the spring of 1856.

In the following year yet another attempt was made to bring a steamer service to Harwich. A "London, Harwich and Continental Steam Packet Company" was promoted to operate a twice-weekly service to Rotterdam. Waddington, no longer on the E.C.R. board but an M.P. for Harwich, was among the backers, together with John Bagshaw, his colleague at Westminster, and Mr Walters, the then chairman of the E.C.R. A vessel named the *London* was

A rare photograph of an E.C.R. waggon, on the quay at Harwich. It was probably taken in 1859, and is a detail from a negative by John Wiggin, an Ipswich chemist and early photographer.

Mr Nicholas Wiggin

advertised to begin sailing on 1st July, but a fortnight later the company was being wound up.

Shortly afterwards, the *London* was again advertised to begin sailing to both Rotterdam and Antwerp; and in June, 1858, a meeting was held in Harwich to launch yet another company, operating the *London* with another steamer, the *Brighton*, on a service to Rotterdam. Nothing more seems to have happened.

Eventually, the Great Eastern Railway established viable services in 1863 and subsequent years, but that is another story.

Woodbridge

WITH the early prospect of rail travel from Ipswich to the capital, it was only natural that the people of Woodbridge, a mere eight miles away, should think that their town ought also to have a railway station.

A meeting was called on 10th June, 1846, at which Cornelius Welton, a land agent and surveyor from Wickham Market, produced plans of a line passing through Ashbocking and Clopton, from where a branch would run to Framlingham. He felt sure the scheme would be opposed in Woodbridge; a more direct line was wanted. Although no copy of this plan survives, it would appear that it was a long-outdated proposal to branch from the original E.C.R. line from Ipswich to Norwich, via Ashbocking, projected away back in 1834. A Woodbridge Committee was set up to explore ways and means.

In November, 1846, Bills were deposited in Parliament for two alternative Woodbridge branches, by the E.U.R. and the I.&B.R. respectively. Both were drawn up by Bruff. The E.U.R. proposed a line passing across Ipswich from the site of the present station, under St Matthew's Street, and then in a curving tunnel, over 1,000 yards long, under Christchurch Park and so to Woodbridge by way of Kesgrave and Martlesham. The I.&B.R.'s proposal approximated to the line that was in fact constructed later.

Ipswich Corporation considered which scheme it should support, but the members were not long in doubt. The tunnel would pass exactly beneath the Wilderness Pond in the park; the springs which fed the pond were one source of the town's water supply, and they would certainly have to be diverted. J.C. Cobbold — himself a town councillor — was asked to explain the extraordinary proposal, and his answer was that both his companies put forward schemes "for reasons which existed at one time", so that one might perhaps succeed, but the Christchurch tunnel had by then been abandoned because of the water supply problem (it is difficult to imagine that Bruff ever seriously considered the idea).

The I.&B.R.'s Bill received the Royal Assent on 9th July, 1847, authorising the raising of £200,000 in new shares, in addition to the usual borrowing powers. However, the state of the money market prevented a start being made, although some land was acquired before the company's powers lapsed in 1850.

Railway building in East Suffolk was revived by Samuel Morton Peto, who lived at Somerleyton. He had important interests in Lowestoft and wished to improve the rail links of the town, but the Norfolk Railway, of which he was then chairman, had been taken over by the E.C.R. and Lowestoft traffic was taken the long way round through Cambridge, rather than by the shorter E.U.R. route. The story of Peto's efforts to provide a shorter route between Lowestoft and London is so closely bound up with that of Bruff's line to Woodbridge that we must consider the two together.

In 1851 an independent company, the Halesworth, Beccles and Haddiscoe Railway, had been incorporated, with Peto and Edward Betts, his partner and brother-in-law, prominent among the subscribers; the Norfolk Railway then secured an Act to enter into a working arrangement for the new line. By 1853 construction was in hand and Peto was engaged in promoting a larger concern, the East Suffolk Railway, to continue to Woodbridge, where it would link up with the E.U.R.

The alignment of Bruff's proposed line was amended to permit the end-on junction, and the E.U.R. obtained renewed powers to build the Woodbridge line by an Act dated 16th June, 1854. The revenue of the line, less forty-six per cent for working expenses by the E.C.R., was reserved for holders of "Woodbridge shares", but the Act entitled the E.C.R. to redeem these shares for four per cent preference stock, and they did so.

The E.S.R. Company was incorporated on 3rd July, 1854, taking over the powers of the H.B.&H.R. George Berkeley, the designer of Fenchurch Street Station, was the engineer; and his relationship with Peto must have been somewhat odd, as the latter had obtained the company's Act at his own expense, and no one could doubt that he was going to build the line.

Peto and his associates expected that the E.C.R. would work their new line as a logical extension of the arrangement by which it was to work the H.B.&H.R. on behalf of the N.R.; it would also, of course, work the Woodbridge branch since it had recently taken over the E.U.R. Waddington, the E.C.R. chairman, was agreeable but his shareholders were divided and argued the matter in a series of stormy meetings. "The proceedings soon afterwards terminated after the usual uproar", according to a press report of one. Waddington was at that time under bitter attack for many reasons.

The E.S.R. decided to press ahead on their own. Lord Stradbroke was invited to become chairman and several extra figures, including J.C. Cobbold, were co-opted on to the board. Meetings were held in the towns along the route to raise support. Peto offered to lease the line at six per cent of cost for fourteen

years, and with Brassey and Betts contracted to build it for £10,000 per mile, including the purchase of land.

Peto was also largely instrumental in promoting two other companies, the Yarmouth and Haddiscoe and the Lowestoft and Beccles, both incorporated in 1856 and amalgamated with the E.S.R. by an Act of 1858. He even promoted another line from the E.U.R at Colchester to Pitsea, on the London, Tilbury and Southend, of which he was also lessee; but the Bill was withdrawn after its second reading when the E.C.R. board agreed in May, 1857, to work the E.S.R.

The E.U.R. negotiated a contract with Alexander Ogilvie, Brassey's partner, to construct a double line from Ipswich for £144,000, and Brassey was thus involved with different partners in the work on either side of Woodbridge. Work began on both contracts in the spring of 1856.

Investors were slow to take up the Woodbridge shares and the work was not pressed forward rapidly. As had happened before, puritanical locals closely watched the behaviour of the newcomers who were disturbing their rustic peace. A Playford resident wrote to the *Ipswich Journal* complaining of work on the railway for two successive Sundays. Ogilvie's agent, John Boys, replied that the men did not usually work on the Sabbath, but it was sometimes

One of Holden's "Intermediate" 2-4-0s heads a train over the timber bridge built by Bruff to carry the Woodbridge branch across the Gipping at Ipswich. This photograph was taken by the author's father in 1898.

199

The view from the footbridge at Woodbridge, looking towards Lowestoft. The further level crossing was the scene of the extraordinary building operation to block the construction of the East Suffolk Railway. The E.U.R. ended at the nearer crossing.

necessary when the temporary rails had to be moved. "Otherwise", as he quaintly put it, "it would result in the throwing out of employment a great number of men and horses, and filling the beer-houses with the former" (no one ever suggested that the horses got in the pubs!).

Initially it was hoped that both contracts would be complete after about a year, but completion dates were progressively postponed. Gradually it became apparent that the E.U.R. part of the line was lagging behind. In May, 1858, Bruff was maintaining that the branch would be finished by the following September; but even J.C. Cobbold was forced to admit, at an E.S.R. meeting, that he did not share this view — the works were very heavy.

At that time the construction of the station at Woodbridge had started, and a river wall across the head of the town dock was ready to carry the line to the end-on junction point at the adjacent level crossing.

In June, 1858, a bizarre episode nearly caused a considerable delay in the joining of the two railways. A lane which crosses to the tide mill by another level crossing nearby was recorded by Cornelius Welton (who reappeared as land agent for the E.S.R.) as a public highway — and indeed it led to an ancient ferry. Everyone was amazed, therefore, when the navvies had reached within sight of the place, to see men building "a shed" right in the path of the railway! The "shed" was probably only a wall, as otherwise traffic to the mill and the adjacent wharves would have been obstructed. The owner claimed it was private land — and the company's powers to buy it compulsorily had expired! Fortunately the company had a

Bill then going through Parliament, and a clause was hurriedly inserted to overcome the obstruction.

The story was explained in the Lords' Committee.[64] George Manby, a Woodbridge merchant and shipowner, owned the land on one side of the lane, and John Cobbold was the landowner on the other side. The company served notice on both, as owners of the soil under the roadway, but Manby claimed it was all his and asked £350 for it. Welton ignored this as absurd and did not immediately pursue the matter further, but to make his point Manby then sold the strip to a Robert Cobbold,[65] who owned land on the other side of the river. Although he was related to J.C. Cobbold, Robert was bitterly opposed to the railway and began his building.

Parliament thought he acted unreasonably and in the Act dated 23rd July, 1858, gave the company compulsory powers until 1st September to buy the plot. Incidentally, the first locomotive to reach Woodbridge arrived along the E.S.R. on 12th July; it is unlikely that it reached the station.

Some indication of the reason for the delay in completing the E.U.R. part of the line was given at the company's half-yearly meeting in August, 1858. The directors' report mentioned difficulties at Rushmere and Playford, and Bruff spoke of the need to acquire additional land for embankments.

The line there follows the valley of the little River Fynn, which includes a swampy area known as Playford Mere. The railway, as constructed, passes the Mere nearly 100 yards further away than Bruff originally intended. The Parliamentary plans which were prepared in 1846, and again in 1853, both show the road which descends into the valley to the village of Playford crossing the railway at a level crossing; but due to the re-alignment towards higher ground there is now, and apparently always has been, an overline bridge. Oddly enough, until a few years ago a cottage exactly like a gate-keeper's lodge stood close beside the line next to this bridge, although the cutting just beyond the arch shows no sign of diversion.

The mysterious "level crossing gatekeeper's lodge" at Playford, now demolished. Note the bricked-up doorway; was the railway intended to have passed the other side?

In December, 1858, the *Ipswich Journal* reported:

We believe that an arrangement has been made by which a short temporary single line and bridge are to be constructed over Mr Biddell's land in the vicinity of Playford Mere, in order that the immense wooden viaduct may not be used for the present.

It would seem that Bruff decided at the outset that the line would have to be constructed further from the Mere than shown on the Parliamentary plans, with the viaduct across the lowest land. It was now necessary to replace this viaduct with a solid embankment which could be topped up as required — hence the need for extra land, both to stand it on and from which to "borrow" soil. There is evidence of borrow pits at the Bealings end of the

A summer scene at Woodbridge about the turn of the century, with a Holden "Intermediate" 2-4-0 about to pull away under the timber footbridge.
Suffolk Photographic Survey, Suffolk Record Office

embankment. By 3rd March, 1859, the work was sufficiently complete for the first train to traverse the line with materials for the telegraph, although many men were said to be still working at Rushmere and Playford. Heavy rain in the following winter, after the line had been opened, caused further subsidence, and the buttressing of the embankments with extra earth can still be seen today.

In April the line was reported to be ready for the government inspection, but nothing happened, although Captain Tyler had inspected the East Suffolk company's line on 4th March. Peto wrote to Bruff urging him to request the inspector to attend, while Woodbridge people were suggesting that the E.S.R. should open to provide traffic via Norwich. It was even said that Peto should start a steamer service from the Deben to London. Eventually Captain Tyler viewed the E.U.R. Woodbridge line on 2nd May and it opened, with the E.S.R., on 1st June, 1859. The final blow was that no timetables were available at Woodbridge!

Completion of this line marked the end of new construction for the E.U.R.; like the Harwich branch, it was worked from the outset by the E.C.R.

The Waveney Valley Line

THE Waveney Valley Railway Company, although nominally independent, was more closely connected with the E.U.R. than the Stour Valley, but no part of its line opened for traffic until the parent system had lost its separate identity. Five of its six directors, under Samuel Bignold as chairman, were also members of the E.U.R. board, the secretary was Edmund Ayres and the engineer was Bruff.

When the company was first promoted in 1850 it advertised its intention to introduce a Bill to construct a line from Tivetshall to Bungay, from there to Beccles, from Bungay to Halesworth and from Bungay "to the Lowestoft Railway at Raveningham". These ambitious hopes had to be severely pruned and the W.V.R. Company was incorporated by an Act dated 3rd July, 1851, with powers to raise capital of £80,000 and within four years to build a railway from Tivetshall to Bungay only. The Act authorised the making of arrangements for working the line with the E.U.R., and a second Act, obtained in 1853, sanctioned the extension from Bungay to Beccles.

Investing members of the public declined to take up the shares, and the story of the company is one of a series of Acts to extend the time for completing the work.

Nothing seems to have happened until December, 1853, when a local committee was set up in Harleston. A contract was let for constructing the line only as far as that town, and it opened for traffic on 1st December, 1855. Landowners on the route were asked to accept paid-up shares in payment, or to rent the neccesary land to the company for a term of years. Eventually the line was opened to Bungay on 2nd November, 1860. It was originally intended that the E.U.R. should work the line for fifty per cent of receipts, but when the time came for the trains to run this duty was taken over by the E.C.R., which demanded seventy-five per cent of receipts — and even retained the balance to settle a disputed debt!

Between Bungay and Beccles the offer of cheaper land on the Norfolk side of the river led the company to abandon its originally proposed route on the Suffolk side. The Bill for the new route, however, was thrown out in the Lords in June, 1858, on the representations of hostile landowners, who claimed that the company had no capital available for the works, having been unable to issue a single share, the powers to reach even Bungay were about to expire, and the whole line was completely unremunerative. But the Bill went through in 1859.

The dispute with the E.C.R over the working arrangements dragged on for several years, with mounting discontent over the service provided. At last the W.V.R. directors gave notice that they intended to work the line themselves as from 15th September,

Bruff's "temporary" timber station building at Bungay, built in 1860, being demolished in 1933. The brick replacement was to be required for barely twenty years.
Lens of Sutton

1860; the E.C.R. promptly offered to reduce its charge to fifty per cent of receipts, but this offer was refused.

Construction of the final section to Beccles began at about the same time, and on it Bruff employed his eldest son, William, as his assistant. Incidentally, while the contract was in progress, William married Louisa, the daughter of Edmund Ayres. Traffic through to Beccles began on 2nd March, 1863, whereupon the W.V.R. was immediately purchased by the G.E.R., as had been provided for in that company's 1862 Act of Incorporation.

*   *   *

The final surveys for new lines carried out by Peter Bruff in his capacity as engineer of the E.U.R. were in 1853 for a link line from Forncett to Wymondham and a branch to Eye from Mellis. Not surprisingly, nothing happened with either at that time, but the Wymondham line was constructed by the G.E.R. in 1881. The Eye branch became a separate line, the Mellis and Eye, incorporated in 1865 with William Bruff as engineer; opened two years later, it was worked by the G.E.R. until it was absorbed in 1898.

Epilogue 14

AFTER taking a leading part in the negotiations relating to the working of the E.U.R. which marked the end of the company's independent existence, Bruff entered the service of the E.C.R., at first as engineer and superintendent of the Eastern Union section; after November, 1854, he assumed responsibility for the whole system.

He was shocked by the condition in which he found the bridges and permanent way on the Cambridge line, although his predecessor, a Mr Ashcroft, had reported that the line was in good repair only a few months before departing to the South Eastern Railway. The new engineer submitted a full report to the directors in February, 1855, saying that expenditure of at least £150,000 would be required. Ashcroft denied this, but the board commissioned an independent report from John Hawkshaw which confirmed Bruff's opinion. In fact, over the next two years more than £263,000 was laid out on major replacements, while expenditure on routine maintenance was also increased.

At this time the E.C.R. Company was in a state of turmoil. Waddington was under bitter attack by the shareholders, not only for seeking to involve the company with the East Suffolk Railway but also over losses incurred with chartered steamers between Harwich and Rotterdam. Now came the news that vast expenditure was required to put the railway to rights. A committee of shareholders was appointed to investigate all aspects of the company's activities.

The city fathers of Norwich, who had decided to investigate the train services to the city in response to many complaints that the fastest trains ran on the longer Cambridge route, were deeply concerned by Bruff's revelations. The Mayor was requested to take up the question of safety with the Board of Trade, and as a result Lieutenant-Colonel Wynne (as he then was) was detailed to carry out an inspection. His report, dated 3rd January, 1856, was an appalling catalogue of rotting timber bridges and sleepers, so that "I am of opinion that the public cannot travel over the railway between London, Cambridge and Norwich without incurring serious risk".

The company replied to the Board of Trade with Bruff's comments that repairs and replacements by a large workforce had been in hand for many months, although the line had never been closed to traffic. Braithwaite, the first engineer of the E.C.R., wrote to *The Times* pointing out that on the Colchester line not one of the 350 bridges was then built of timber. Cambridge Town Council petitioned the company to serve their town by way of Hitchin and the G.N.R., and passed a vote of thanks to Norwich. Ipswich Town Council, noting that the Colchester line was apparently safe and expecting an increase in the number of trains to be routed through their town, appointed a committee to press the company for a new station.

While he was struggling to put the Cambridge line to rights, Bruff was accused of criminal negligence over the matter by the *Railway Times*. He sought a High Court injunction against the paper, presumably to silence it quickly, but the application was unsuccessful.

Unlike other E.U.R. staff, he did not immediately pass on to the E.C.R. payroll. His claims for expenses, even at that stage, were being ignored. He was involved with the struggling W.V.R., and also with the Woodbridge line. In the circumstances it is not surprising that he suffered a stroke. When he returned to his duties in November, 1856, after an absence of several months, Waddington had resigned and Bruff found himself at odds with the new board of directors over policies adopted in his absence. He resigned from the company's service in March, 1857.

He later sued the E.C.R. for the salary which he should have received as engineer of the E.U.R., during the period immediately after the takeover, and won a negotiated settlement. He had been retained by the E.U.R. at a nominal salary to watch over its interests during the lease period, and after the company finally disappeared into the G.E.R. in 1862 he successfully sued his old employers for a share in a redundancy fund set up for former employees who were not re-employed. The company claimed that he was a consultant and not an employee, but the court directed that the engineer should be one of the four beneficiaries. The £5,000 fund was applied to the purchase of annuities in the proportion of their salaries in August, 1862.*

Soon after leaving the E.C.R. Bruff embarked on several speculations in seaside land development. In 1855 he had bought land at Walton-on-the-Naze, then a small village with a reputation as a select watering place with a pier at which steamers called on their passages between Ipswich and London. He laid out the Tendring Hundred Railway, incorporated in 1859 with W.W. Hawkins as its chairman, which extended from the Stour Valley Railway branch at Colchester Hythe. By the time the line was opened to Walton in 1867 he had provided the resort with an hotel, an entertainments hall and a gasworks, besides housing.

In the meantime, too, he purchased a large area of then-empty land at Clacton and Frinton. Eventually he disposed of much of it for development by others, but he himself was responsible for the erection of the Royal Hotel at Clacton (1872) and the pier (1873), together with laying out the railway to connect the growing town to the T.H.R. at Thorpe-le-Soken. The independent Clacton-on-Sea

Apart from the Tendring Hundred lines, Bruff was little involved with railways after the formation of the G.E.R., although

*Bruff testified that his age at the time was 51.

he did lay out the Bury St Edmunds and Thetford Railway, an independent concern which was authorised in 1865. Great difficulty was experienced in raising capital and the line was not opened until 1876.

After 1862 the Eastern Union itself became only a small part of the Great Eastern system. Its later history has been chronicled elsewhere.

We have seen that Bruff was concerned in a proposal to improve the port facilities at Colchester as early as 1842, and he maintained an interest in harbours throughout his career. The Colchester Channel Commissioners promoted a scheme for a dock designed by Bruff in 1845, but the Act obtained in 1847, although authorising paving and lighting work in the town, restricted navigation powers to improving the existing channel of the river. Parliament rejected the proposed dock on the grounds that it would be fronted mostly by private land, and the revenue to be raised from it should not be linked to the revenue derived from rates levied on the town.

A model of a proposed harbour of refuge at Aldeburgh, to Bruff's design, was shown at the Great Exhibition in 1851, and a Bill to authorise its construction was introduced into Parliament shortly afterwards. This Bill also failed because of intended methods of administration and finance, but the scheme did bring its designer into contact with Newson Garrett, one of the proposers and a well-known local resident whose place of business was at Snape Maltings.[66] They were later involved together in land development schemes in the town, and in 1860 Bruff's eldest daughter, Elizabeth, married Garrett's son, Lieutenant Newson Garrett of the Bengal Artillery.

Harwich was the principal haven of refuge on this part of the East Coast, and it had served this purpose for centuries. But by the middle of the nineteenth century Landguard Point was moving steadily southwards and closing off the entrance, due to the removal of vast quantities of septaria stone from outcrops nearby for manufacturing the so-called "Roman cement". These outcrops had served a vital purpose in the conservation of the harbour by acting as natural groynes.

Following urgent representations the Admiralty had investigated the problem and, recognising that the harbour was of national importance, they began to take remedial measures in 1846. Over the next ten years some works were carried out, but to little avail, and their Lordships then declined to advance any more funds.

As neither Harwich nor Ipswich had the means to tackle the task, eventually, in 1863, the Harwich Harbour Conservancy Board was set up. Bruff was appointed the board's first engineer and he held the position for thirty-two years, although like that of most officials at that time in local public service, it was only a part-time job. It was over twenty years, due to the very limited resources available, before the extension of Landguard Point was effectively halted.

At the time of his death, Bruff was credited with "opening the way for the creation of modern Parkeston ... a public service which has never perhaps been adequately recognised", but even those who wrote his obituary tributes can have had no conception of the Haven Ports of our own time.

Bruff also supplied the town of Harwich with gas and water, the latter being a protracted quest which occupied him for over thirty years before a satisfactory supply was obtained from Mistley. The water from his Tendring Hundred Waterworks Company at last arrived in Harwich in 1887, and was therefore known as Jubilee Water.

Earlier, he had been involved in the waterworks at Colchester and the sewerage of Ipswich. He was also engineer and one of the promoters of the Ipswich Tramways Company which operated horse trams during the last two decades of the century until the undertaking was purchased by the Town Council in 1901.

In his later years, Bruff confined his activities to the Harwich Harbour Conservancy Board, with which he remained as a consultant after he had relinquished the post of engineer, and to presiding as chairman over the Tendring Hundred Waterworks Company. He did, however, embark upon a novel and uncharacteristic business venture about 1885 when he purchased the ailing Coalport China Works, far away in Shropshire. His youngest son Charles, home on leave from India in 1889, visited the place and immediately resigned from his post as an engineer in government service to become managing director of a new Coalport China Company, under his father's nominal presidency. Charles Bruff, later joined on the board by his brother-in-law, Major Garrett, led the Coalport Works into a new era of prosperity and became a father-figure to the whole local community. The company, however, was unable to weather the recession after the Great War and the works were sold in 1924, closing down soon afterwards.

Peter Bruff died at Handford Lodge, Ipswich, on 24th February, 1900. The news was published in a local newspaper as "an announcement which might well have been expected years ago, seeing that Mr Bruff had outlived all his contemporaries and passed far beyond 'the allotted span'." He was then the Father of the Institution of Civil Engineers, to which he had been elected nearly sixty years before. He was buried in Ipswich Cemetery, where his redoubtable wife was laid beside him seven years later.

His Eastern Union Railway is his principal monument. The main line, from Colchester to Norwich, is now being electrified to serve what is perhaps the most rapidly expanding region of the country. Even today, almost the entire route mileage (with the exception of the line to Hadleigh) still carries passenger traffic.

Notes & References

1. Palmer later constructed the Wet Dock at Ipswich.
2. Dr Chevallier was the maternal grandfather of Lord Kitchener.
3. The stipulation about the gauge was very necessary. At that time the E.C.R. was laid to a gauge of five feet, although converted to standard gauge in the autumn of 1844.
4. Better remembered as Colonel Pasley, who demolished the sunken wreck of H.M.S. *Royal George* at Spithead.
5. Company's notice dated 29th May, in *Ipswich Journal*, 30th May, 1846.
6. The late H.F. Hilton, in his 1946 booklet on the E.U.R., named these as *Colchester* and *Ipswich*. I have been unable to find any contemporary account which gave this information.
7. A crack opened in the wall when the slip occurred in the tunnel.
8. As 5 above; also, inter alia, *Ipswich Journal*, 20th June, 1846.
9. Hughes was Liberal M.P. for the Borough of Caernarvon from 1837, with one short break, until his death in 1882.
10. The tunnel was hailed locally as the first curved one. But according to Whishaw (1842), tunnels on a radius of a mile were already in use at Groveley Hill, near Bromsgrove, on the Birmingham and Gloucester Railway; and at Callander, near Falkirk, on the Edinburgh and Glasgow. Both are longer than the Ipswich tunnel. In 1842 "slightly curved" tunnels were also to be found at Bristol, Kensal Green and Preston.
11. Humfress had a music shop in the town; the band would have been an important part of his business. Most of the performers were probably young, like today's pop musicians. Humfress himself died at Calcutta in 1860, having attained the position of "Bandmaster General of H.M. Forces in India"; he was then only thirty-four.
12. This picture has appeared in at least two books, with the caption that it shows the northern portal. Both the curvature of the rails and the direction of the light indicate that the southern entrance is portrayed.
13. *Suffolk Chronicle*, 5th December; *Bury Post*, 2nd December, 1846.
14. *Ipswich Journal*, 26th December; *Bury Post*, 30th December, 1846.
15. The line was not opened through to Yarmouth until the Trowse swing bridge was completed in the following December.
16. George Parker Bidder (1806–1878) was renowned for his powers of rapid mental arithmetic, which often enabled him to demolish the claims of rival advocates in the cut-and-thrust of cross-examination before Parliamentary Committees. His services were consequently in great demand. Later, as chairman of the Norfolk Railway Company, he was the staunch ally of J.C. Cobbold in the disputes with the E.C.R. after that company had taken over both their railways. He was one of the first directors of the G.E.R. in 1862.
17. The Railway Commissioners were a special body set up in November, 1846, to handle the railway functions of the Board of Trade. The Board resumed its jurisdiction in October, 1851.
18. This spade, complete with verifying silver plate, turned up about 1913 in an Ipswich second-hand shop. It was bought by A.J. Hill, Locomotive Superintendent of the G.E.R., and presented to the

Board Room Museum at Liverpool Street. It is now in the collection at the National Railway Museum, York.

19. William Shalders was a pump maker of Bank Plain, Norwich.
20. E.S. Cayley was a nephew of Sir George Cayley, the aviation pioneer.
21. Directors' report to half-yearly general meeting, 25th August, 1848.
22. Crushed blast furnace slag did not supplant gravel ballast on the G.E.R. until 1900.
23. *Norwich Mercury* and *Ipswich Journal*, 2nd June, 1849.
24. Company's notice dated 23rd May, in *Ipswich Journal*, 26th May, 1849.
25. Company's notice dated 29th June, in *Ipswich Journal*, 30th June, 1849.
26. Several farms and houses in Tharston have names commemorating Harvey's service in the Peninsular War, e.g. Picton Farm, Ciudad Rodrigo and Vittoria.
27. Company's notice dated 30th November, in *Ipswich Journal*, 1st December, 1849.
28. Company's notice dated 5th December, in *Ipswich Journal*, 8th December, 1849.
29. Board of Trade's intention, reported to the directors, 20th August, and *Ipswich Journal*, 30th August, 1851.
30. *Ipswich Journal*, 30th August, 1851.
31. *Ipswich Journal*, 27th September, 1851.
32. Many railways, e.g. G.W.R. and E.C.R., maintained their permanent way by contract.
33. When the E.C.R. invited tenders for removing manure from their stables at Bury in 1860, it was stated that the horses there numbered from thirty-seven to forty-five.
34. It is now the third. The original second bridge, carrying a private road to Thurston House, was demolished a few years ago.
35. In 1972 I could find neither of the stationmasters' graves.
36. Early railways were often laid with some variation from the so-called "standard gauge". The York and North Midland gauge was 4 foot 8½ inches where stone sleepers were used, and 4 foot 9 inches where the sleepers were of timber, both kinds being used according to the nature of the ground. The Hull and Selby was laid to a gauge of 4 foot 9 inches "to give more play to the flanges of the wheels".
37. 24th November, 1849.
38. Hitherto, buffers had been of leather, stuffed with horsehair and girt with metal bands to prevent them bursting on impact.
39. Wealthy passengers often preferred to travel in their own horse-drawn carriages, conveyed on these special trucks, while the horses accompanied their owners on the same train—an arrangement analogous to modern "moto-rail" travel. First-class fares were usually charged, apart from the freight charges involved.
40. A similar system was adopted on the Bristol and Exeter Railway in 1854—precisely because luggage was not carried on the roofs, according to the report of an Inspecting Officer of the Board of Trade. A cord available to passengers, by being led along above the windows on one side, was generally introduced after 1868. Its invention is attributed to T.E. Harrison of the North Eastern Railway.
41. James Ransome (1782–1849) was the son of Robert (1753–1830), who founded the firm. (James) Allen Ransome (1806–1875), referred to in these pages, was James' son.

42. Minutes of Proceedings I.C.E., vol xvi, pp 226 et seq.
43. Minutes of Proceedings I.C.E., vol ix, pp 287 et seq.
44. G.E.R. Magazine, vol 2 (1912), pp 248 et seq., reviewing fifty years of progress after the company's incorporation.
45. A fuller account of his work is given in his obituary in the *East Anglian Daily Times*, 7th December 1898.
46. This bridge would have been of timber. A steel replacement was removed in 1984, preparatory for the electrification works, and acquired by the preserved North Norfolk Railway.
47. The line from Ipswich to Bury St Edmunds has always been "down" as far as Haughley Junction. Thenceforth it is the "up" line.
48. The track layout is shown on the Parliamentary plans of the E.U.&G.N. Junction Railway (see Chapter twelve), Plan No 361 in the Norfolk and Norwich Record Office.
49. The ordinary second class fare from Ipswich to Colchester was 2s. 6d. (12½p) single.
50. The E.A.R. also included the Ely and Huntingdon Railway.
51. Nothing more splendid than a first class carriage ever featured in the company's stock lists. Presumably these were E.C.R. smoking saloons, borrowed for the occasion.
52. *Ipswich Journal*, 28th August, 1847.
53. Evidence from J.S. Martin in the case John Staines v. E.U.&H.J.R. (q.v.), reported in *Ipswich Journal*, 6th April, 1850.
54. Walter Kingsbury of Boxford. Kingsburys had been building in Boxford since the sixteenth century, and the firm existed into the 1980s.
55. Both the *Ipswich Journal* and the *Suffolk Chronicle*, Saturday 3rd April, 1847, stated that this event took place "on Thursday".
56. Engineer's report to company's general meeting, August, 1847.
57. P.W. Barlow invented the tube tunnel, lined with cast-iron segments.
58. *Ipswich Journal*, 2nd June, 1849.
59. *Suffolk Chronicle*, 7th July, 1849.
60. The building of the quay necessitated the removal of the last of the old hulks which had been sunk as breakwaters to shelter the former Navy Yard. One of these was the former H.M.S. *Glatton*, commanded by Captain William Bligh at the Battle of Copenhagen in 1801.
61. One modern account states that this event took place on 4th August, but the *Ipswich Journal*, Saturday 5th August, 1854, reported it as having been "on Saturday".
62. Directors' report to E.U.R. general meeting, August, 1854.
63. *Essex Standard*, 3rd April, 1846.
64. Parliamentary Plans and Book of Reference (150/2/5.76 in the Suffolk County Record Office, Ipswich Branch); *Ipswich Journal*, 12th June and 10th July, 1858, and The East Suffolk Railway Companies Amalgamation Act, 1858.
65. Robert Knipe Cobbold owned Methersgate Hall, Sutton. Rails and trucks brought home from Peto and Brassey's Crimean Railway were reported (*Ipswich Journal*, 29th November, 1856) as being landed there for him from a barge. The equipment was probably for use in his unsuccessful attempt to reclaim land from the foreshore; the incomplete banks survive as "The Tips".
66. Garrett was the father of Elizabeth Garrett Anderson. His maltings are now the home of the Aldeburgh Festival.

Bibliography

Among the many books consulted for background information were:

Ahrons, E. L. *The British Steam Railway Locomotive, 1825–1925*. 1927, reprinted Ian Allan, London, 1969.

Anon. *A Word or Two about EU*. 1860.

Clark, D. K. *Railway Machinery*. 1855.

Gordon, D. I. *A Regional History of the Railways of Great Britain: Vol 5: The Eastern Counties*. David & Charles, Newton Abbot, 1968.

Helps, A. *The Life and Labours of Mr Brassey*. 1872.

Hughes, B. Carlyon. *The History of Harwich Harbour*. Harwich Harbour Conservancy Board, 1939.

James, Leslie. *A Chronology of the Construction of Britain's Railways, 1778–1855*. Ian Allan, London, 1983.

Lewin, H. G. *The Railway Mania and its Aftermath, 1845–1852*. 1936, reprinted David & Charles, Newton Abbot, 1968.

MacDermot, E. T. *History of the Great Western Railway*. G.W.R. Company, London; vol i, 1927, vol ii, 1931.

Malster, Robert. *Lowestoft—East Coast Port*. Terence Dalton, Lavenham, 1982.

Marshall, John. *A Biographical Dictionary of Railway Engineers*. David & Charles, Newton Abbot, 1978.

Sandström, Gösta E. *The History of Tunnelling*. Barrie & Rockliff, London, 1963.

Simmons, Jack. *The Railways of Britain*. Routledge & Kegan Paul, London, 1961.

Tomlinson, W. W. *The North Eastern Railway: its Rise and Development*. 1915, reprinted David & Charles, Newton Abbot, 1969.

Whishaw, F. *The Railways of Great Britain and Ireland*. 2nd ed. 1842, reprinted David & Charles, Newton Abbot, 1969.

Williams, F. S. *Our Iron Roads*. 1852, 1883.

Wrottesley, A. J. *The Great Northern Railway*. Batsford, London, 1979.

and also:

Report from the Select Committee on Railway Labourers. Printed by order of the House of Commons, 28th July, 1846: Reports, Committees (9) 1846, 13.

Donations to the Robert Sallis Relief Fund

(see Chapter five)

Organised by Joseph Young—"considering that I am a stranger in Ipswich, I succeeded far beyond my expectations."

Alexander Ogilvie	£5 0 0	Brassey's partner and agent.
Joseph Young	£1 0 0	At Ipswich tunnel. E.U.R. clerk by 1851?
John Hawley	10 0	Sub-contractor for Ipswich tunnel.
William Hornick	6 0	Probably a sub-contractor.
Robert Page	5 0	
Samuel Hawley	10 0	Sub-contractor for Ipswich tunnel.
Solomon Durden	10 0	
Harry Hawkes	5 0	
Elijah Thomas	5 0	
"Curley"	5 0	Probably a navvy.
Thomas Firth	10 0	
M. O'Connell	5 0	
George Franklin	2 6	
Patrick Ogilvie	10 0	Later, agent on Norwich line. Probably Alexander Ogilvie's son.
Workmen at Tunnel	£1 0 0	
William Martin	3 0	
James Piper	£1 0 0	
Samuel Girling	2 6	
Collected by		
William Hornick	£1 11 0	
J.R. & A. Ransome	£5 0 0	Partners in Ransomes of Ipswich.
Thomas Readshaw	10 0	
Harmer & Ransome	5 0	
Messrs T. & W. Evans	£2 0 0	Sub-contractors, later on Norwich line.
John West	£1 0 0	Sub-contractor of Wythes', later on the Harwich line?
George Schulen	5 0	
By Morris & Bellis	£1 17 6	Sub-contractors at Ardleigh. Morris worked on the Hadleigh branch later. (Bless him!)
2nd by William Hornick	£2 5 0	
Rev. Stephen Croft	10 0	Rector of St Mary Stoke, Ipswich. The tunnel was in his parish.
Benjamin Quadling	2 6	Of the Ipswich rolling-stock firm?
"A Friend"	£1 0 0	
John Douglas and men	£2 11 6	Sub-contractor at Stowmarket; later on the Norwich line.
By the Rev. S. Croft	£1 10 0	
James Martin	£1 0 6	
Thomas Jefferies	5 0	
G. Baker and Son	10 0	Beer merchants at Elmswell?

J. Brown and four friends	£2 14 0	The sub-contractor on E.U.R. at Ardleigh?
Henry Beacom	2 6	
George Brassey	10 0	A relative of Thomas Brassey?
John Thomas Ward	10 0	A farmer at Sproughton. The railway went through his land.
James Luff	10 0	
Henry King	2 6	
James Thorndike	£1 0 0	Of Ipswich? He had a brickyard in what is now Rectory Road, near the tunnel, for which he may have supplied bricks.
John Ranson	2 6	
Cooper & Noble	10 0	Smiths and spring-makers at Ipswich.
John Fisher	5 6	Sub-contractor for brickwork at Ipswich tunnel.
J.B. Smyth Esq	5 0	Landowner near Ipswich tunnel.
George Sillitoe	£2 10 0	Sub-contractor, later on Norwich line.
Henry Smith	2 6	
Thomas Butcher	10 6	
Peter Arnull	5 0	Later, timekeeper on Woodbridge line contract.
Messrs Hawkins	£3 3 0	
Higgs & George	£1 0 0	
Messrs Dowson	£5 0 0	
"Gentlemen & Workmen at Messrs Ransomes"	£9 2 2	
By North Biggs	£1 2 6	
J. Varden & Son	10 0	
A.T. Cobbold	10 0	The brother of J.C. Cobbold.
Collected at Stowmarket	£2 14 0	
Charles Wallis	£1 0 0	
R. Smith & Co	£1 0 0	
Snell & Bicker	£2 0 0	
Joseph Warden & Son	£2 0 0	
Lloyds, Foster & Co	£1 0 0	Suppliers of turntables.
E.U. & Extension Railway Co.	£10 0 0	
William Barnard	10 0	Builder of Brantham Bridge?
William Downs	2 6	
Alexander & Co	£1 0 0	Bankers at Ipswich and Needham.
Taylor & Jessup	15 0	
Edward, Lord Thurlow	£10 0 0	Of Great Ashfield.
Edward Parry	£1 0 0	Sub-contractor; later on Norwich line.
James Blount	£1 0 0	
Don Mackenzie	£1 1 0	A relative of William Mackenzie?
Robert Jolly	£1 0 0	The wheelwright at Norton?
Rev. James Oakes	10 0	Rector of Tostock and Vicar of Thurston.
"Mrs Grigsby"	10 0	Probably Mrs Anna Grigby, of Drinkstone Park.
William Frost	5 0	

Samuel Frner (sic)	5 0	
J. Langham	5 0	
Robert Wright	10 0	The farmer and/or grocer at Elmswell?
Collected by Mr Glaspoole, himself, and men	£3 18 0	
Mr Booly (?)	10 0	
Mr Biddle	5 0	Probably Arthur Biddell, a valuer who acted for several landowners along the route of the I.&.B.R.
"Collected by (for?) Sallis, J. Lawton, Esq"	£1 0 0	Possibly the Rev Joseph Lawton, Rector of Elmswell. Or perhaps John Lawton, a farmer in the same parish.
William Day	£1 0 0	
Charles Lark	£1 0 0	Sub-contractor near Bury, previously at Bentley.
Ditto's men	18 0	
— Howlett	5 0	Possibly John Howlett, a farmer of Elmswell.
D. Bridges	2 6	Probably Denis Bridges, a farmer of Elmswell (the railway went right through his farmyard).
Collected by James Holt	£5 0 0	Foreman bricklayer at Ipswich tunnel.
	£117 5 8d	

Published in the *Suffolk Chronicle*, 9th May, 1846.

Locomotives of the Eastern Union Railway

E.U.R. No.	Name	E.C.R. No.	Delivery Date	Builders	Builders' No.	Type	Dia of driving wheels
1	Colchester	260, later 2600	May 1846	Sharp Brothers, Manchester	346	2-2-2	5′ 0″
2	Ipswich	261	,,	,,	347	,,	,,
3	City of Norwich	262, later 2620	,,	,,	349	,,	,,
4	Bury St Edmunds	263	October 1846	,,	368?	,,	5′ 6″
5	Orwell	264, later 2640	,,	,,	369?	,,	,,
6	Stour	265	,,	,,	370?	,,	,,
7		205	Winter 1846/7	Stothert & Slaughter, Bristol	—	,,	5′ 0″
8		206	,,	,,	—	,,	,,
9	} One was Essex?, the other perhaps Suffolk?	207	,,	,,	—	0-4-2	,,
10		208	,,	,,	—	,,	,,
11		273	,,	R. & W. Hawthorn, Newcastle	471	2-2-2	6′ 0″
12		274, later 271	,,	,,	472	,,	,,
13		275, later 272	,,	,,	473	,,	,,
14		266	December 1846	Sharp Brothers, Manchester	389?	,,	5′ 6″
15		267, later 2670	,,	,,	390?	,,	,,
16		268	March 1847	,,	406?	,,	,,
17		269	,,	,,	407?	,,	,,
18		270	Spring 1849	,,	*	,,	,,
19		271, later 116	,,	,,	*	,,	,,

Dia of carrying wheels	Cylinders dia × stroke	Boiler dia × length of barrel	Boiler tubes no. × dia (Total heating surface)	Total weight	Remarks
3′ 6″	15″ × 20″	3′ 6″ × 10′ 0″	147 × 1¾″ ext. (767.9 sq ft)	18T 12cwt	Diverted from Blackburn & Preston Rly. Rebuilt May, 1869. Scrapped Dec, 1879.
,,	,,	,,	,,	,,	Diverted from Blackburn & Preston Rly. Rebuilt Apl, 1864. Scrapped Oct, 1874.
,,	,,	,,	,,	,,	Diverted from Blackburn & Preston Rly. Rebuilt May, 1863. Scrapped Dec, 1879.
,,	,,	,,	,,	,,	Rebuilt July, 1862. Scrapped Jan, 1873.
,,	,,	,,	,,	,,	Rebuilt June, 1868. Scrapped Aug, 1877.
,,	,,	,,	,,	,,	Rebuilt Dec, 1865. Scrapped Mar, 1874.
,,	15″ × 22″	— × 10′ 6″	—	34T 9cwt (after rebld)	Rebuilt as 2-4-0 by makers, 1852. Scrapped about 1860.
,,	,,	,,	—	,,	Rebuilt as 2-4-0 by makers, 1852. Scrapped June, 1867.
,,	,,	,,	—	—	Scrapped before June, 1867.
,,	,,	,,	—	—	Scrapped before June, 1867.
,,	15″ × 21″	3′ 7″ × 11′ 6″	120 × 2″ int.	20T 6cwt	Ordered by Ipswich & Bury Rly.
,,	,,	,,	,,	,,	Ordered by Ipswich & Bury Rly.
,,	,,	,,	,,	,,	Ordered by Ipswich & Bury Rly.
,,	15″ × 20″	3′ 6″ × 10′ 0″	147 × 1¾″ ext. (767.9 sq ft)	18T 12cwt	Ordered by Ipswich & Bury Rly. Rebuilt Dec, 1862. Scrapped July, 1875.
,,	,,	,,	,,	,,	Ordered by Ipswich & Bury Rly. Rebuilt Mar, 1869. Scrapped Aug, 1880.
,,	,,	,,	,,	,,	Ordered by Ipswich & Bury Rly. Rebuilt Apl, 1866. Scrapped Mar, 1874
,,	,,	,,	,,	,,	Ordered by Ipswich & Bury Rly. Rebuilt Sep, 1865. Scraped Mar, 1874
,,	,,	,,	,,	,,	Rebuilt Nov, 1863. Scrapped Feb, 1875.
,,	,,	,,	,,	,,	Never rebuilt. Scrapped June, 1867.

20		209	⎫	Stothert & Slaughter, Bristol	—	,,	5′ 0″
21		210	⎪ Four in Autumn	,,	—	,,	,,
22		211	⎬ of 1848, two earlier	,,	—	0-4-2	,,
23		212	⎪	,,	—	,,	,,
24		213	⎪	,,	—	,,	,,
25		214, later 204	⎭	,,	—	,,	,,
26		272, later 117	Spring 1849	Sharp Brothers, Manchester	*	2-2-2	5′ 6″
27		16	November 1849	,,	*/595	2-2-2WT	5′ 6″
28	Ariel's Girdle	17	1851	Kitson, Thompson & Hewitson, Leeds	270	2-2-0WT	5′ 0″
29		13	February 1854	Sharp Brothers, Manchester	765	2-2-2WT	5′ 0″
30		14	,,	,,	766	,,	,,
31		15	,,	,,	768	,,	,,

*see Notes on Appendix.

Notes on Sources used in Appendix two

As this Appendix may be critically studied by some readers, perhaps some explanation is called for.

Much of the information cannot now be verified from contemporary sources, but is taken from a series of articles on "The Locomotives of the Great Eastern Railway" which appeared in *The Locomotive Magazine* in 1905, viz: the data relating to numbering and weights, the fates of the engines, and all information on Stothert and Slaughter's locomotives and *Ariel's Girdle*. In some respects, the 1905 information differs from that from surviving original sources, in which cases I have used the latter. For example, the magazine gave the stroke of the Hawthorn engines as 20 inches, and the cylinder diameter of the Sharp tank No 27 as 14 inches. They may have been altered to those dimensions later, but I suspect misprints. Many 1905 details of the boilers of the 1854 tank engines are different from those which appear in the original works orders, and of course changes may have been made during the building.

Contemporary newspapers indicate some other engine names: *Hadleigh*, on the inaugural train on the branch (*Ipswich Journal* 21 August, 1847); *Diss*, at the opening of the Norwich line (*Norfolk Chronicle* 10 November, 1849), and *Goliath* (*Norfolk Chronicle* 10 November, 1849), or *Goliah** (*Norwich Mercury* 10 November, 1849), and *Essex*, a Slaughter goods engine (*Norwich Mercury* 21 August, 1847).

My theories concerning the dates of delivery of Nos 4 to 15 are set out in Chapter nine. I have assumed that the company generally numbered its engines in the order of receipt, although it is clear from the minutes of board meetings that four Sharp tender engines were outstanding after all those ordered from Slaughters had been received.

The Builders' numbers are taken from lists prepared by latter-day researchers in the archives of the respective manufacturing firms. These

„	15″ × 22″	— × 10′ 6″	—		34T 9cwt (after rebld)	Rebuilt as 2-4-0 by makers, 1852. Scrapped about 1860.
„	„	„	—		„	Rebuilt as 2-4-0 by makers, 1852. Scrapped Feb, 1868.
„	„	„	—		—	Scrapped June, 1867.
„	„	„	—		—	Scrapped before June, 1867.
„	„	„	—		—	Scrapped before June, 1867.
„	„	„	—		—	Scrapped June, 1867.
„	15″ × 20″	3′ 6″ × 10′ 0″	147 × 1¾″ ext. (767.9 sq ft)		18T 12cwt	Rebuilt Oct, 1865. Scrapped Feb, 1875.
„	15″ × 20″?	„	As above?		—	Undelivered (I.&B.R.?) tender engine converted. Scrapped Feb, 1871.
3′ 0″	9″ × 15″	2′ 6″ × 10′ 6″	83 × 1¾″ ext. (434 sq ft)		—	Rebuilt as 2-4-OT, weighing 10T 15 cwt, in 1868. Scrapped May, 1879.
3′ 6″	14″ × 18″	3′ 6″ × 9′ 6″	120 × 2″ ext. (668.9 sq ft)		19T approx	Scrapped Nov, 1871.
„	„	„	„		„	Scrapped Nov, 1871.
„	„	„	„		„	Scrapped Nov, 1871.

lists are now in the Science Museum at South Kensington. No original lists survive.

In the case of the Sharp engines, the following numbers are listed:–
Works Order No 167 (E.U.R.) 346, 347, 349, 368–72.
Works Order No 170 (I.&B.R.) 467, 468 and four other numbers representing three engines delivered to the London and Brighton, and one to the Lynn and Ely Rly.
A later Works Order, No 172, is for about a dozen engines, including No 388 for the E.U.R. and Nos 389, 390, 406 and 407 for the I.&B.R.

If No 388 is assumed to have been delivered elsewhere, the others fall into a better sequence to agree with known deliveries. The Works Order for the 1849 tank locomotive is endorsed "No 595" (possibly in a contemporary hand) but I believe that this relates only to the *conversion* of an existing engine—otherwise there are more progress numbers than locomotives ordered.

Readers may amuse themselves with their own equally valid speculations.

The modern researcher in the Sharp records (a former employee of the North British Locomotive Co, I understand) included a note that the names of Nos 1 to 6 were respectively: *Ipswich, Bury St Edmunds, Colchester, Diss, Stowmarket* and *Haughley*; and that Works Nos 369 to 371 were delivered to the Lynn and Ely Railway ("per Mr Hilton").

The latter's statement, in his 1946 booklet, that Nos 17, 18, 19 and 26 were originally the I.&B.R.'s Nos 1, 2, 3 and 4 respectively is not acceptable, since the last three had not been delivered by January, 1849, long after the Suffolk companies had amalgamated. Sharp's original orders show clearly that the Bury company had received four of their engines by March, 1847, in pairs as shown.

*This was not necessarily a misprint. The G.W.R. had a goods engine of this name at the time.

APPENDIX THREE

Hawthorns' Patent Expansive Valve Gear for Locomotives

This was patented in 1843, providing variable cut-off of steam in the cylinders without infringing the Stephenson patent on the well-known "link motion". The Hawthorn valve was used in conjunction with the earlier type of gear, in which eccentric rods fitted with Y-shaped "gabs" moved the valve rod to the appropriate position as one eccentric was disengaged and the other engaged for reverse running.

In the Hawthorn gear, the reverse eccentric also oscillated a slotted link, from which a radius rod transmitted the motion to an auxiliary valve. This enclosed the main slide valve, and was rather like an inverted open box with most of the bottom removed. The "top" of the box worked on the same face as the main valve, and there was also steam-tight sliding contact between the back of the main valve and the "bottom" of the box.

By altering the position of the radius rod in the slotted link the driver could vary the stroke of the auxiliary valve, and thus the point at which the steam was cut off.

The auxiliary valve was stationary when not in use, i.e. with the engine in full gear with late cut-off, but the main valve was always in motion and it was found, in practice, that it wore down on the port face until it was out of contact with the auxiliary valve. The whole principle was thus defeated and the use of the gear was abandoned after a few years, but it was at one time extensively used on the North British Railway, for which all the early locomotives were built by Hawthorns.

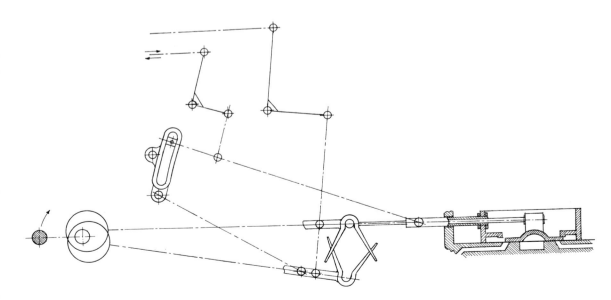

APPENDIX FOUR

"A Return of All Lathes, etc, at Ipswich Station" (1856)

No 1.   Double wheel Lathe suitable for turning Wheels up to 7ft dia. Made by Sharp Bros. Delivered August 1847. Cost £700-0-0.

No 2.   Vertical Drilling Machine, made by Sharp Bros, delivered August 1847. Cost £35-0-0.

No 3.   Slide Lathe, 10in centres 12ft bed, made by Buckton, Leeds, June 1852. Cost £83-0-0.

No 4.   Shaping and Planing Machine, 14in stroke, Smith & Co, Leeds, September 1851. Cost £75-0-0.

No 5.   Back Gear Lathe, 8½in centres 7ft bed, Turner & Co, Ipswich, May 1850. Cost £25-0-0.

No 6.   Small portable Punching and Shearing Machine, Standford & Owen, May 1850. Cost £15-0-0.

No 7.   Hand Lathe, 6in centre 6ft bed, E.U. Company, 1851. Cost £12-0-0.

"A Return Showing Tools at Norwich Station, 20th June 1856", included the following items "removed from Ipswich to Norwich after the amalgamation":

1 No.   5ft Double wheel Lathe, made for the E.U.R., Sharp Bros, Makers. £430-0-0.

1 No.   Self-acting Slide Lathe with bed 11ft long. Headstocks 12″ crs, self-acting surfacing motion and change wheels for screw-cutting complete. Sharp Bros, Makers. £264-0-0.

1 No.   10in hand geared Lathe, bed 12ft long with slide rest. Sharp Bros, Makers. £85-0-0.

1 No.   6in hand Lathe—a small foot lathe made for the E.U. Company. Maker not known. £15-0-0.

1 No.   Portable Machine for boring the Cylinders of Locomotive Engines in their places. Made for the E.U. Company; Maker, Sharp.

1 No.   Iron Saw Bench & Frames with Circular Saw.

Both lists are in a miscellaneous collection of papers, formerly belonging to J. V. Gooch (locomotive superintendent of the E.C.R., 1850–56), and now in the P.R.O.

APPENDIX FIVE

Insurance Valuation of Stations, Buildings, etc

Bruff's recommendations to the E.U.R. Board, 19th March 1849.
(P.R.O. RAIL 187/17)

Colchester Station, Platforms, Engine and Carriage Shed	£1000
Ardleigh Station, Platform, Goods Shed and Dwelling	£1500
Manningtree Station, Platform, Goods Shed and Dwelling	£1500
Cattawade Wharf and Warehouse, Turntable and Machinery	£1500
Bentley Station, Platforms, Dwellings, Shed and Bridge	£1800
Capel Station, Dwelling, Platforms, Goods and Coal Warehouse	£500
Raydon Station, Dwelling, Platforms, Goods and Coal Warehouse	£500
Hadleigh Station, Dwelling, Carriage Shed, Goods and Coals	£1500
Ipswich Station, Carriage Shed and Shops, Platforms, etc	£3000
Ipswich Engine Shed and Shops, Stores and Smithies	£1500
Ipswich Goods Shed	£1500
Bramford Station, Platforms and Clerk's Residence	£1000
Claydon Station, Platforms and Residence	£300
Needham Station, Platforms, Goods and Coal Stores, and Residences	£1500
Stowmarket Station, Platforms, Residences, Goods Shed and Bridge	£2500
Haughley Station, Platforms, Goods Shed and Residences	£1000
Elmswell Station, Platforms, Goods and Coal Sheds	£1000
Thurston Station, Platforms, Goods and Coal Sheds and Residences	£1500
Bury Station, Carriage and Goods Sheds and Residences	£3000
Finningham Station, Platforms and Goods Shed	£300
Flint Wharf Warehouse (Ipswich)	£700
Total	£28,600

Note on Appendix five

The valuations for Capel, Raydon and particularly Claydon, are lower than might be expected, as the surviving station houses appear to be the originals (Capel was demolished in recent years). Finningham on the other hand, was only a temporary structure, apparently with no residence.

The Haughley station referred to seems to have been the original one (the Junction station was not brought into use until July, 1849, and there is no mention of the bridge with which the station was provided from the outset). The goods shed was probably one of the buildings which can still be seen between the railway and the site of the cottage; there is no visible evidence that this short-lived station ever had a siding.

The Eastern Union at first insured its buildings with the now-defunct Suffolk and General Society, but was dissatisfied with the settlement of its claim after the fire at Colchester (see page 157). The business was then transferred to the Norwich Union, on the recommendation of Samuel Bignold.

Steamships associated with the Eastern Union Railway

River Steamers

Name: *Railway*
Built: Ditchburn & Mare, Blackwall, 1842.
Tonnage: 258 G.R.T.
Type: Paddle
Dimensions: 145 feet × 19 feet × 10 feet.
Remarks: Owned by London & Blackwall Rly Co.
              Sailed between Ipswich and Harwich for a few months in the summer of 1850 with agreed division of receipts.

Name: *Atalanta*
Built: Deptford 1841
Tonnage: 60 G.R.T.
Type: Paddle; iron built. She had no masts.
Dimensions: 91.6 feet × 14.4 feet × 6.8 feet.
Remarks: Purchased by Bruff from London owners, 1850.
              Sold to E.C.R., July 1854, by which time she had been lengthened by 9 feet.
              Broken up 1873.

Name: *Cardinal Wolsey*
Built: Bedlington Ironworks, Northumberland, 1845.
Tonnage: 57 G.R.T.
Type: Paddle; iron built. She had no masts.
Dimensions: 104 feet × 11.9 feet × 6.8 feet.
Remarks: Purchased by Bruff from London owners, 1850.
              Sold to E.C.R., June 1854.
              Sold to Middlesbrough owner, 1863.

Name: *Prince*
Built: Harvey & Son, Ipswich, 1852.
Tonnage: 72 G.R.T.
Type: Paddle; wooden built.
Dimensions: 108 feet × 13.3 feet × 7.1 feet.
Remarks: Built for Bruff.
              Sold to E.C.R., June 1854.
              Broken up, 1869.

Name: *River Queen*
Built: Ditchburn & Mare, Blackwall, 1839.
Tonnage: 67 G.R.T.
Type: Paddle; iron built.
Dimensions: 98.3 feet × 13.2 feet × 6.5 feet
Remarks: Built for Ipswich Steam Navigation Co.
               Sailed between Ipswich and Harwich in arrangement with E.U.R., 1849.
               Sold to Alfred Cobbold, May 1853, when I.S.N. Co liquidated.
               Laid up at Ipswich; broken up 1861.

Coastal Steamers

Name: *Pearl*
Built: Blackwall, 1835.
Tonnage: 137 G.R.T.
Type: Paddle; wooden built.
Dimensions: 138.5 feet × 15.5 feet × 8.3 feet.
Remarks: Purchased by Bruff from Milford Haven, 1852.
               Sold to E.C.R., June 1854.

Name: *Orion*
Built: Read & Page, Ipswich, 1841.
Tonnage: 222 G.R.T.
Type: Paddle; iron built.
Dimensions: 160.1 feet × 21.5 feet × 9.6 feet
Remarks: Sailed between Ipswich and London, under ownership of her builders, her engine builders (Lloyd & Easter of London) and Alexanders, the Ipswich bankers, until sold to Fleetwood, 1845.
               Purchased by Bruff from Goole owners, 1852.
               Sold to E.C.R., July 1854.

Name: *Prince Albert*
Built: Walker-on-Tyne, 1842.
Tonnage: 202 G.R.T.
Type: Paddle; iron built.
Dimensions: 154.3 feet × 18.5 feet × 10.3 feet
Remarks: Purchased by Bruff from London owners, 1853.
               Sold to E.C.R., July 1854.

Name: *Orwell*
Built: Ditchburn & Mare, Blackwall, 1839.
tonnage: 335 (Registered under the old pre-1836 rules; her 'New Measurement' tonnage would have been about 220 gross).
Type: Paddle; iron built.
Dimensions: 144 feet × 21.2 feet × 9.7 feet.
Remarks: Built for Ipswich Steam Navigation Co.
               Sold to Alfred Cobbold, May 1853, when I.S.N. Co liquidated.
               Sold to E.C.R., June 1854, who re-sold her in 1857.

Index

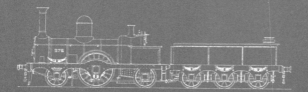

E.C.R.

TO CAMBRIDGE

THU

BURY ST
EDMUNDS

SUDBURY

COLCHESTER, STOUR VALLEY,
SUDBURY & HALSTEAD RAILWAY →

BURES

CHAPPEL

MARKS TEY

E.C.R.

TO CHELMSFORD